Understanding
Mathematics:
From Counting to Calculus

Keith Kressin

For ordering information visit our web site at: *www.understandingmath.info*

Multi-order discounts are available.

Understanding Mathematics: From Counting to Calculus

© 1997 by Keith Kressin

Printed in the United States of America

Library of Congress Catalog Card Number: 97-93143

ISBN 978-0-9657300-1-3

ACKNOWLEDGMENTS

The following students, families, teachers and working professionals have reviewed the first edition of this math text. I would like to thank them for their valuable comments and suggestions.

The Bergerson family

Dale K. Dykema, *Covenant Home Curriculum*

Eric Gnoska, Electrical Engineering Student

Bernadette Halloran, Elementary School Teacher

Jeff Herrle, *Hewlett-Packard*

Aaron Kueck, High School Student

George and Inge Liebl, Retired School Teachers

Also, special thanks to my brother Bob and wife Janet. Not only have they spent many hours proofreading the text, but also they have endured the countless hours I have spent during its writing.

CONTENTS

1   Introduction   **1**

    1-1   Why Anyone Needs This Math Book   *1*
    1-2   What This Book Provides   *1*
    1-3   The Layout of This Text   *2*
    1-4   Who Would Benefit from This Book   *3*
    1-5   Why Buy One Book that Contains 12 Years of Mathematics?   *3*
    1-6   This Math is Really Used in Practice   *4*
    1-7   What the Reader Should Already Know   *4*

Part I - Elementary Mathematics

2   Numbers   **5**

    2-1   The Definition of a Number   *5*
    2-2   Numbers are Universal   *6*
    2-3   Counting   *6*
    2-4   Naming Digits   *8*
    2-5   Decimals   *9*
    2-6   Common Symbols   *13*
    2-7   Summary of Numbers   *14*

3   Addition and Subtraction   **15**

    3-1   Explaining Addition   *15*
    3-2   Addition of Single Digit Integers   *15*
    3-3   Commutative Law of Addition   *16*
    3-4   Understanding Variables   *17*
    3-5   Associative Law of Addition   *19*
    3-6   Explaining Subtraction   *20*
    3-7   Subtraction of Single Digit Integers   *20*
    3-8   Absolute Values   *22*
    3-9   Addition and Subtraction are Complementary   *23*
    3-10   Addition of Multi-Digit Integers   *24*
    3-11   Separating Multi-Digit Numbers for Addition   *26*
    3-12   Adding Decimals   *27*
    3-13   Subtraction of Multi-Digit Integers   *29*
    3-14   Subtraction Resulting in Negative Answers   *31*
    3-15   Subtracting Decimals   *32*
    3-16   Summary of Addition and Subtraction   *33*

4 **Multiplication and Division** **34**

4-1 Explaining Multiplication *34*
4-2 Operators for Multiplication *35*
4-3 Multiplication of Single Digit Integers *36*
4-4 Commutative Law of Multiplication *37*
4-5 Associative Law of Multiplication *39*
4-6 Distributive Law of Multiplication *39*
4-7 Variations of the Distributive Law of Multiplication *41*
4-8 Multiplication of Multi-Digit Integers *42*
4-9 Separating Multi-Digit Numbers for Multiplication *45*
4-10 Explaining Division *49*
4-11 Division of Single Digit Integers *50*
4-12 Division of Multi-Digit Numbers *52*
4-13 Separating Multi-Digit Numbers for Division *57*
4-14 Division with Remainders *58*
4-15 Multiplying Decimals *63*
4-16 Dividing Decimals *66*
4-17 Rounding and Truncation *69*
4-18 A Pause for Congrats! *70*

5 **Fractions** **72**

5-1 Defining Fractions *72*
5-2 Reading Fractions *73*
5-3 Types of Fractions *74*
5-4 Converting Fractions to Decimals *74*
5-5 Converting Decimals to Fractions *75*
5-6 Multiplying Fractions *76*
5-7 Making Different but Equal Fractions *76*
5-8 Simplifying Fractions with Factorization and Cancellation *77*
5-9 Prime Numbers *80*
5-10 Prime Factorization *80*
5-11 Reducing Fractions to Lowest Terms *83*
5-12 Lowest Common Denominators (LCD) *85*
5-13 Adding and Subtracting Fractions *90*
5-14 Conversion of Mixed Numbers *93*
5-15 Dividing Fractions *95*
5-16 Summary of Fractions *97*

6 **Percentages** **99**

6-1 Defining Percentages *99*
6-2 Operations using Percentages *100*
6-3 Finding the Percentage of a Number *102*
6-4 Percentages Shortcuts *106*
6-5 Mean, Median, and Mode *107*
6-6 Summary of Percentages *108*

7   Negative Numbers   **109**

7-1   Defining Negative Numbers   *109*
7-2   Negative Numbers are Necessary   *109*
7-3   Addition and Subtraction with Negative Numbers   *110*
7-4   Multiplying and Dividing Negative Numbers   *112*
7-5   Performing Operations with More than 3 Numbers   *114*
7-6   Summary of Negative Number Operations   *115*

8   Exponents   **116**

8-1   Defining Exponents   *116*
8-2   Multiplying with Positive Exponents   *118*
8-3   Using Negative Exponents   *121*
8-4   More Rules for Using Exponents   *123*
8-5   Summary of Exponential Rules   *125*
8-6   Fractional Exponents   *125*
8-7   Scientific and Exponential Notation   *129*
8-8   Summary of Exponents   *132*

9   Pre-Algebra   **133**

9-1   Review of the Past and Goals for the Future   *133*
9-2   Definitions for Algebra   *134*
9-3   Operations with Variables   *135*
9-4   Order of Operations   *136*
9-5   Summary   *139*

Part II - Intermediate Mathematics

10   Solving One Algebraic Equation   **141**

10-1   Introduction   *141*
10-2   Algebraic Definitions   *141*
10-3   Two Basic Methods for Solving An Algebraic Equation   *143*
10-4   Isolating the Variable   *144*
10-5   Factorization of Quadratic Equations by Inspection   *150*
10-6   Factorization Using the Quadratic Formula   *157*
10-7   Factorization of Higher Order Polynomials   *161*
10-8   Reducing an Algebraic Expression to Lowest Terms   *164*
10-9   Reducing Algebraic Equations Containing Absolute Values   *169*
10-10   Summary   *171*

11   Solving a System of Equations   172

11-1   Introduction   *172*
11-2   Substitution of Equations   *174*
11-3   Elimination of Variables   *177*
11-4   Using Matrices   *179*
11-5   Solving Systems with Matrix Reduction   *183*
11-6   Solving Systems with Cramer's Rule   *186*
11-7   Summary   *190*

12   Word Problems   192

12-1   Introduction   *192*
12-2   Steps to Solving Any Word Problem   *193*
12-3   Word Problem Examples   *193*
12-4   Summary   *199*

13   Functions   200

13-1   Introduction   *200*
13-2   Explaining Functions   *201*
13-3   Dependent and Independent Variables   *202*
13-4   Examples Using Functions   *203*
13-5   Inverse Functions   *204*
13-6   Summary   *206*

14   Graphing   207

14-1   Introduction   *207*
14-2   Plotting Points on the Cartesian Coordinate System   *208*
14-3   Plotting Linear Equations   *210*
14-4   Plotting Systems of Linear Equations   *216*
14-5   Plotting Quadratic Equations   *218*
14-6   Plotting Polynomials of Higher Degrees   *220*
14-7   Plotting Polynomials with Multiple Variables   *221*
14-8   Summary of Graphing   *223*

15   Geometry   225

15-1   Introduction   *225*
15-2   Lines and Angles   *226*
15-3   Triangles   *231*
15-4   Congruent Triangles   *233*
15-5   Polygons   *237*
15-6   Circles   *238*
15-7   Summary   *239*

16   Measurement of Geometric Figures   240

16-1   Introduction   *240*
16-2   Lengths, Perimeters and Areas of Polygons   *240*
16-3   Circle Measurements   *243*
16-4   Volumes and Surface Areas   *245*
16-5   Summary   *248*

17   Trigonometry   249

17-1   Introduction   *249*
17-2   Trigonometric Functions   *250*
17-3   Commonly Used Triangles   *256*
17-4   Oblique Triangle Relationships   *257*
17-5   Trigonometry and Graphing   *258*
17-6   Plotting Sine and Cosine Values   *261*
17-7   Using Radians   *261*
17-8   Summary   *262*

Part III - Advanced Mathematics

18   Logarithms   264

18-1   Introduction   *264*
18-2   Understanding Logarithms   *264*
18-3   Calculating Logarithms   *268*
18-4   Uses of Logarithms   *270*
18-5   Finding the Natural Logarithm   *271*
18-6   Summary   *274*

19   Complex Numbers   276

19-1   Introduction   *276*
19-2   Defining Imaginary Numbers   *276*
19-3   Adding and Subtracting Imaginary Numbers   *280*
19-4   Complex = Real + Imaginary   *281*
19-5   Graphing Complex Numbers   *283*
19-6   Summary   *285*

20   Finding Geometry Using Algebra   287

20-1   Introduction   *287*
20-2   Finding Geometry with Complex Exponents   *287*
20-3   Using Complex Exponents   *292*
20-4   Summary   *294*

21   Introducing Calculus   **295**

21-1   What More is There to Learn?   *295*
21-2   An Essential Introduction to Calculus   *296*
21-3   Summary of the Introduction   *300*

22   The Derivative   **301**

22-1   Introduction   *301*
22-2   Development of the Derivative Using Limits   *301*
22-3   Usefulness of the Derivative   *305*
22-4   Finding the Derivative of a Function   *307*
22-5   Derivatives of Special Functions   *310*
22-6   The Chain Rule   *311*
22-7   L'Hopital's Rule   *312*
22-8   Maxima and Minima   *313*
22-9   Newton's Method   *316*
22-10   Summary of Derivatives   *319*

23   The Integral   **320**

23-1   Introduction   *320*
23-2   Development of the Integral Using Limits   *321*
23-3   Finding the Integral from the Derivative   *323*
23-4   Solving Integrals   *325*
23-5   Summary of Integrals   *328*

24   A Final Word on Mathematics   **329**

24-1   How Computers and Calculators Understand Math   *329*
24-2   Continued Learning   *330*
24-3   Now What?   *330*

Appendix A: Trigonometric Identities   **331**

Appendix B: Table of Trigonometric Functions   **333**

Index   **337**

Introduction

1-1   Why Anyone Needs This Math Book

Math is arguably the most important school subject for success in today's society. Most people are taught mathematics from the time they learn to talk through high school. To some mathematics comes easy, but to others it is extremely difficult. Obviously, people have different abilities. However, math books, math teachers, real-world applications, and a variety of other factors often affect one's perspective on the subject of mathematics. This is a subject which is often either loved or hated. If the subject is hated, it is not math, but the failure to understand the math that gives considerable frustration to the student.

The process of understanding math should not be frustrating and difficult. Mathematics (including Algebra) can be clearly understood with some effort and practice. The goal of this book is for the reader to obtain a clear understanding of mathematics, from counting to Calculus.

1-2   What This Book Provides

Following this book step-by-step will lead from counting to a brief introduction of Calculus, hence the book's title. Therefore, this one text covers all of the math fundamentals normally taught from first grade to college. It is most directly written as a supplement to existing math texts. Therefore, a student could use this book along with his own math text for additional explanation and clarity. However, this book can also stand independently with no outside references.

Concepts and real-world applications are emphasized. This book is not intended to be rigorous. This means that you will not be given detailed proofs or complicated math theory.

This book was written to be read as simply as possible. You won't be given cute stories, long histories, or complex scenarios. The author will be making no effort to impress you with his vocabulary, but will give popular mathematical notation. There will be no leaps of faith in moving from one topic to the next. Each topic will build on the previous topic, creating a smooth flow of mathematical progress.

There are many math help books available. However, the extreme mathematical details and lack of explanation contained in most math books often cloud understanding. Even a thorough review of "made simple" math books reveals that math is not made simple, but is merely abbreviated. Shortening explanation of material is not the answer. Rather, expanding explanation is necessary.

Some math help books only consist of examples. These books are useful for solving particular book problems, but they fail to explain the basic theories and concepts of math which are required to solve real-world problems and to establish a foundation for further learning. Examples are wonderful, and many are given herein. However, without understanding concepts, an infinite number of examples will not prepare the student for the future, or help him understand why problems are solved in a certain manner.

In this text, the examples will make sure that you are on the right track. The formulas will ensure that you are always prepared. But most importantly, math will be explained. The answer to *"Why do I have to do it like that"* will be answered along with the usual *"How do I do it."* This will enable the reader to remember what needs to be done to solve a variety of problems. It will also provide an overall outline of math from the very basics to advanced techniques.

A section on using calculators or computers is not included. These are wonderful and necessary tools, but the goal of this text is to provide understanding. The use of these devices, without a firm math foundation, reduces intuition and the important ability to determine if an answer is reasonable. Even today, standardized tests such as the SAT, ACT, or GMAT do not allow the use of calculators. There is good reason for this policy.

Many examples and detailed answers are provided throughout each chapter. However, there is not a list of problems for the reader to work on his own at the end of each chapter. Numerous problems (and solutions) require much valuable space and can be found in almost every other math book.

Some of the final chapters of this text contain concepts which are seldom explained in any standard math book. Specifically, chapters 18 through 20 provide some of the key derivations which tie different mathematical disciplines together. In addition to practicality, these chapters demonstrate a glimpse at some of the amazing (and even beautiful) qualities of mathematics.

1-3   The Layout of This Text

This text is divided into three parts. Part I (chapters 2 through 9) consists of mathematics normally taught in grade school and are math essentials for everyone. Part II (chapters 10 through 17) consists of mathematics normally taught at the high school level including a thorough coverage of Algebra, the essentials of Geometry, and basic Trigonometry. Part III (chapters 18 through 24) consists of advanced Algebra and an introduction to Calculus.

STEP-BY-STEP boxes give the recipe for solving standard problems.

Bold type highlights important definitions.

Pictures are used to emphasize important concepts and support surrounding text.

Introductions and summaries are provided to keep the reader aware of topics already learned and explain goals for future learning. Notepads are also included at the end of every chapter. Notepad topics include math laws, important definitions, and topics presented in the chapter. The reader may use these notepads to ensure that all important concepts have been reviewed and are understood.

An index is provided for easy reference and encourages the reader to learn a definition in its appropriate context.

1-4   Who Would Benefit from This Book

This book would be especially helpful as a supplemental guide for parents who are home-schooling their children.

However, it does not matter if you are a motivated grade school student, a curious high school student, a struggling non-technical graduate student (or "poet"), a working professional, or a parent attempting to help his child with mathematics. All would greatly benefit from this text.

A motivated grade school student could use this book to reach levels of mathematics normally only obtained in college. An early head start in mathematics will certainly yield dividends in the future. Early starts in mathematics are a common thread with many successful people, from billionaire Bill Gates to Nobel Prize winning physicist Richard Feynman. This fact was a great motivation for the writing of this text.

1-5   Why Buy One Book that Contains 12 Years of Mathematics?

As already stated, this book is divided into three parts. You may wonder why three separate texts are not available rather than one. Does a parent with a fourth grader really need a book that contains Calculus? Does a graduate student need a book that shows how to add and multiply?

Listed below are a few of the benefits of including so much math in one text.

1. It eliminates the need to assume any prior level of mathematical understanding.

2. It ensures that the reader has a complete overview and understanding of mathematical concepts. No concepts are missed in the reader's educational development.

3. One book is very efficient, eliminating unnecessary repetition of explanation.

4. Concepts that the reader already knows well (e.g. numbers) may be explained from a new perspective.

5. A step-by-step methodical progression may be made to give the reader a solid mathematical framework. The importance of this point is represented by the pyramid on the cover.

6. If a new concept is encountered in an advanced class (e.g. matrices in junior high), the reader does not have to find a new supplemental text that contains the subject.

Finally, the price of this one text is comparable to other math help books which cover far less material. The goal of this text is not for the author to make money. The goal is to help readers understand math.

1-6   This Math is Really Used in Practice

Students often hear that "advanced" math is hardly used anyway, so they should not be concerned with learning it. This statement could not be farther from the truth.

Actuaries use complex statistics to determine insurance rates. Physicists use mathematical models to develop nuclear energy. Engineers use math to build all types of electronics, including computers and communications equipment. Math is used to predict the stock market, calculate weather trends, control automobiles, distribute electricity, design roads and determine marketing strategies. Techniques to perform all of these tasks and more, rest on the fundamentals of math which are presented.

Math fundamentals are tested on college entrance exams such as the SAT and ACT. Furthermore, graduate entrance exams such as the GRE and GMAT also test math skills. The math tested on these and other standard entrance exams is explained in this text.

1-7   What the Reader Should Already Know

Every book assumes the reader already knows something about the book's subject. This book assumes that the reader has a basic understanding of the definition of a number, and has already seen addition, subtraction, and basic multiplication and division. However, each of these topics will be explained thoroughly. With parental guidance, students as young as the third or fourth grade may benefit from this text. Unlike most math texts, math concepts do not become increasingly difficult with each ensuing chapter. However, each chapter assumes that previous material is clearly understood.

If the reader already knows much of the material presented, it would still be most beneficial to start at the beginning of the book and confidently read until the area of new material. It is very likely that the reader will obtain a different perspective on even the most basic mathematics.

Now, onto learning...

Numbers

2-1   The Definition of a Number

You probably already understand numbers. However, this chapter may provide a new perspective on already familiar definitions. New perspectives will help you understand math more thoroughly. Many definitions are given, and it is assumed that the reader already has a basic understanding of most of them. If all of these definitions were new, it would take a long time to finish this chapter alone.

A **number** is a symbol used to represent a collection of things. These symbols obey certain rules when they are combined with each other to make new symbols. The theory that explains the rules of combining these symbols is called **mathematics**.

The definition of a number presented above usually works well, but be careful. Sometimes, there are mathematical symbols which are not easy to visualize as a collection of things. To give a very basic example, below are three basketballs.

You most likely could imagine three basketballs without the help of the figure. However, can you now draw or even imagine -1 (or "negative one") basketballs? No, since a negative basketball by itself does not make any sense and is therefore impossible to imagine. The best way to visualize a negative basketball is to think of it as one less basketball than we originally had. Therefore, a combination of three basketballs, and a negative basketball can be visualized as two basketballs (mathematically, 3 - 1 = 2).

Maybe this example confused you since you thought you already completely understood numbers. Maybe for you this was an overly simplified example. Maybe you didn't even understand the point of this short discussion since negative numbers have not yet been explained. The point is that *numbers are simply symbols*. Usually numbers represent something that can be pictured in your mind. However, this is not always true. When a symbol cannot be linked to something physical, we usually try to make up an interpretation that can be pictured physically. In this example, one can think of a negative basketball as one basketball fewer than the number of basketballs that originally existed.

Remember that math merely manipulates symbols according to certain rules. If those symbols can be represented by physical objects, then we have an additional crutch for understanding.

Unfortunately, sometimes it is impossible to even imagine a picture that represents the math symbols. When this occurs (and it will), you must simply perform the calculation based on the rules of mathematics and believe the answer. Sometimes mathematical answers will surprise you by providing answers which differ from intuition.

2-2   Numbers are Universal

Some people know English, while others know Spanish. Thankfully, everyone in the world uses the same numbers. The symbol for the number five has the same meaning to you as to a Japanese student. Numbers are universal. So, if you can speak in mathematical terms, you can speak in any language.

2-3   Counting

The symbols that are called numbers can all be placed in order on a line. A horizontal line with ordered numbers is called a **number line**. The numbers on the number line are all placed in a special order. The higher or greater valued numbers are placed furthest right. A number line is given below, with tick marks (|) indicating positions on the number line. Sometimes points are used rather than tick marks to show where numbers exist on the number line, but they serve the same purpose.

Tick marks are placed at equal distances apart to indicate that the numbers differ by the same amount. Looking at the number line given, you should see that the distance from 0 to 2 is twice the distance from 2 to 3.

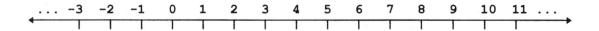

The ' . . . ' is an **ellipsis** and shows that the numbers on the number line could be extended forever. This is also the reason for the arrows on both ends of the number line. An arrow on a line indicates that the line continues in the indicated direction. Since the paper is only a limited size, we can only draw a section of the number line.

The farther a number is to the right on the number line, the **greater** the value of the number. Any number to the left of another number has a **lesser** value. Two numbers that are located at the same point on the number line are called **equal**.

Ask someone to count and he would probably begin 1, 2, 3, 4, 5, and so forth until you told him to stop. These "counting numbers" are all to the right of zero on the number line. Every number with a value greater than zero is called a **positive number**. All positive counting numbers along with the number 0 are defined as **whole numbers**.

One can also count in reverse order, to obtain numbers less than zero (i.e. -1, -2, -3...). All of the numbers less than 0 are called **negative numbers**, and look exactly like the positive numbers except a dash (-) is placed in front of them to indicate the number is less than zero. The dash is actually a negative sign (or "minus sign") so -2 is read aloud as "negative two" or "minus two". You should see that -3 and 3 are the same distance away from 0 on the number line. They are merely in different directions from zero. The group of all of the negative counting numbers, and 0, and all of the positive counting numbers are called **integers**.

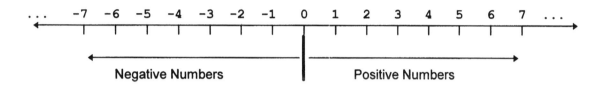

Examples of Number Types	
Integers :	3, 4, -14, 20
Positive Integers:	1, 6, 20, 25
Whole Numbers:	0, 1, 20, 25
Negative Integers:	-1, -20, -25, -32

The numbers that we normally use in mathematics are based on 10 symbols (symbols: 0, 1, 2, 3, 4, 5, 6, 7, 8, and 9). The system based on these ten symbols is called the **decimal system**. To represent a value greater than 9, two symbols must be used such as 10. To represent a value greater than 99, three symbols (100) are required. The term **digit** indicates how many symbols are used to represent one value.

Examples of Multi-Digit Numbers	
One Digit Numbers:	1, 2, 3, 8, 9
Two Digit Numbers:	10, 15, 62, 75
Three Digit Numbers:	120, 265, 320, 989

Numbers don't stop or end with any value. Someone can always name a greater or lesser value than any given number. Therefore, mathematicians use the term **infinity** for the highest of numbers. Infinity isn't a specific number. Any specific number named would be less than infinity. Infinity is the value you would approach, but never reach, if you continued to count increasingly greater numbers, forever. Infinity is represented by the symbol: ∞. Both negative and positive infinity exist. Infinity may not sound practical, but it is often used in advanced mathematics (which will be explained much later).

2-4   Naming Digits

The ability to read numbers aloud is important. A specific number's name depends on both the number of digits and the value of each digit. Each digit has a name or **place** based on its position, regardless of the value of the digit.

Below is a specific 15-digit number with the names of each place listed. The names only depend on the position of the digit, not on the value of the digit. Every three digits are separated by a comma. This is standard in math since commas separate the names of 3-digit sets such as thousands, millions, billions, and trillions. Commas make a large number easier to read.

The names of numerical digits continue to change as digits are added for greater numbers. But, you will seldom see a number containing more than 15 digits with each digit written out as shown below. Numbers greater than 999 trillion are usually written in a different form or **notation**. (See **Scientific and Exponential Notation** in section **8-7** if you are curious.)

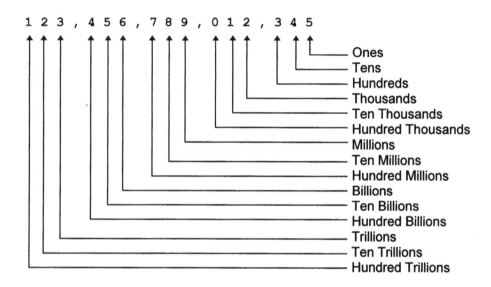

In the above number there are 5 ones, 4 tens, 3 hundreds, 2 thousands, etc...

Example - Reading Multi-Digit Numbers

1 2 3 , 4 5 6 , 7 8 9 , 0 1 2 , 3 4 5

is read aloud

"one hundred twenty-three trillion,
four hundred fifty-six billion,
seven hundred eighty-nine million,
twelve thousand,
three hundred forty-five"

Reading numbers aloud does take practice. However, it is important that you be able to pronounce any number. This book will not explain how to read integer numbers aloud, since it assumes you already know how. However, a few examples are provided.

Example - Reading Multi-Digit Numbers

5   is read "five"
15   is read "fifteen"
1,200   is read "twelve hundred" or "one thousand two hundred"
62,345   is read "sixty-two thousand three hundred forty-five"

The digit farthest to the right in any number is the **least significant digit**. The digit farthest to the left in any number is the **most significant digit**. These definitions should make sense. If you had $2301 in the bank, the two is very significant. However, the one matters least among the digits.

2-5   Decimals

So far, integers have been the only type of numbers presented. To move one space right on the number line, you must increase the value of the integer by one. However, sometimes integers are not descriptive enough. If you started with one whole watermelon and ate part of the watermelon for dessert how many watermelons are left? The answer must be somewhere on the number line between zero and one. We need to use numbers that are more descriptive than integers. A number located in between integers on the number line is called a **decimal number** or simply a **decimal**.

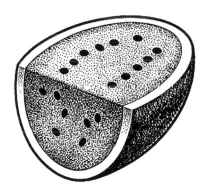

We can see from our previous number line that the number 2 is exactly between the integers 1 and 3. But, what number is exactly between 1 and 2? Let's make another number line, and place tick marks exactly in between the integers. Question marks show that we are not yet sure what these numbers should be.

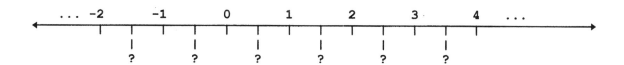

To make greater valued numbers, we added digits to the left of the one's place. We can obtain decimal numbers by adding digits to the right of the one's place. A **decimal point** (.) separates digits in the one's place with digits to the right of the one's place. By using the decimal point, we can define the numbers in between integers.

Symbols 0 through 9 remain the only symbols used. Places to the right of the decimal place also have names, so that decimals can be pronounced. There are no commas ever placed to the right of the decimal point to separate sets of digits.

Note the similarity in the names of numbers left of the decimal point and numbers right of the decimal point. For example the tens place changes to tenths, and the hundreds place changes to hundredths. There is no 'oneths' place. The reason for this should become clear in chapter 5.

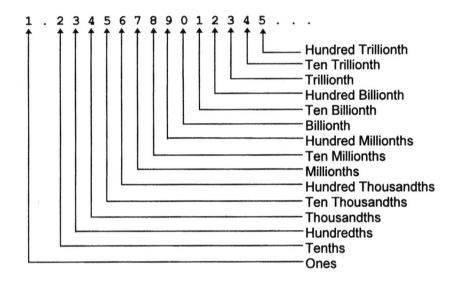

Examples - Pronouncing Decimal Numbers

.1	is read "one tenth"
.5	is read "five tenths"
.01	is read "one one hundredth" or simply "one hundredth"
.05	is read "five hundredths"
3.18	is read "three **and** eighteen one hundredths"
152.365	is read "one hundred fifty-two and three hundred sixty-five thousandths

---

The word **and** is pronounced to separate the digits which are left and right of the decimal point. To pronounce the decimal, read the number as if it were an integer, and then add the name of the least significant digit.

As you may have guessed, pronouncing long decimals may get confusing (not to mention annoying). A short-cut pronunciation is to simply say "point" where the decimal point exist, and then pronounce every digit.

Example - Pronouncing Decimal Numbers

Read out loud the following number.

21 . 2 3 4 5 6 7 8 9 0 1 2 3 4

Answer: "twenty-one point two three four five six seven eight nine zero one two three four"

Let's practice counting with integers and decimals.

Example - Counting

Count from 0 to 10 by integers: 0 1 2 3 4 5 6 7 8 9 10

Count from 0 to 1 by tenths: 0 .1 .2 .3 .4 .5 .6 .7 .8 .9 1.0

Count from 0 to .1 by hundredths: 0 .01 .02 .03 .04 .05 .06 .07 .08 .09 .10

An integer written without a decimal point means that every digit to the right of the decimal point equals zero.   Therefore, 5 and 5.0 and 5.000 would all be placed at the same position on the number line.   These numbers are all equal.

When counting by tenths, it is assumed that every digit to the right of the tenths place is zero. Therefore, 1.1 and 1.10 and 1.1000 all occupy the same position on the number line and are all equal numbers.

Generally, if any digit to the right of the decimal point is not written, it is assumed to equal zero. The following number sequences are all equal.

0	1	2	3	4	5	...
0.	1.	2.	3.	4.	5.	...
0.0	1.0	2.0	3.0	4.0	5.0	...

Do you agree with the following example?

Example - Comparing Decimal Numbers

Which is greater .14 or .2 ?

Answer: .2

This answer may be determined correct by counting in steps of hundredths.

.14   .15   .16   .17   .18   .19   .20

Remember .20 and .2 and .200000 are all the same values. Adding zeros to the right of the decimal point does not change the value of the number.

We can make a new number line by counting by hundredths rather than ones as we did in the integer number line.

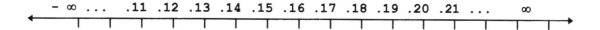

– ∞ ... .11 .12 .13 .14 .15 .16 .17 .18 .19 .20 .21 ... ∞

The number line can be divided into any increment (or step) needed.   In the number line containing only integers, the increment was one.   On the previous number line, the increments are .01.   Soon you'll realize that if you've seen one section of the number line, you've seen them all. The same 10 symbols are always repeated to generate new numbers.

Isn't Every Number Real?

Believe it or not, **imaginary numbers** also exist.

These numbers are not explained until chapter 19.

Any number that may be represented by a point on the number line is called a **real number**.   Therefore, the combination of all decimal numbers and all integers form the set of real numbers.

So, what number is exactly between 1 and 2?   The answer is 1.5.   The number 5 is exactly between 0 and 10.   The number 1.05 is exactly between 0 and 1.10.   Do you see a pattern?   The number lines below may help you.

Some other numbers that are in between 1 and 2 are 1.1, 1.8, and 1.325.   You can name as many numbers as you like in between 1 and 2, since any number of digits can be placed to the right of the decimal point.

There is one more thing to note regarding decimals.   We know that,

$$0.5 = .5$$

Usually, if a number is less than one, the decimal number is written including the zero in the ones place.   The zero indicates that the decimal point wasn't written down accidentally (or is a smudge on the paper).   It also ensures that the decimal point is not overlooked by the reader.

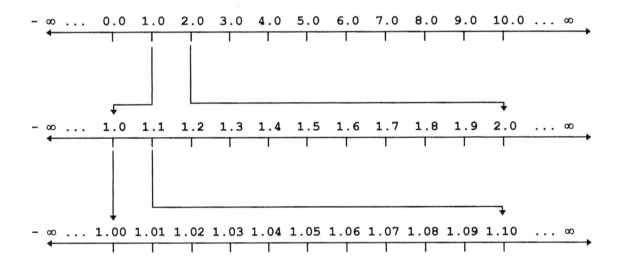

Can you make a number line that starts at 1.00 and finishes at 1.01?

2-6   Common Symbols

Just as symbols 0 through 9 are used to represent values of numbers, other symbols are used to compare numbers. A few of the most common symbols used in math are given in the following table.

Symbol	Description	Examples
=	The equals symbol (or "sign"). The number to the left of the equals sign has the same value as the number to the right of the equals sign.	3 = 3 0.2 = 0.20000 8 = 8 is read "eight equals eight"
≠	The not-equals symbol. The number left of the symbol does not equal the number right of the symbol.	-2 ≠ 2 4 ≠ 2 is read "four does not equal two."
≈	The approximately-equals symbol. The number left of the symbol is close to the value right of the symbol. Using this symbol requires some judgment, since it is not exact.	3.0001 ≈ 3.0000 is valid 3.0001 ≈ 142 is not valid 6 ≈ 6.01 is read "six is approximately equal to six point zero one."
>	The greater than symbol. The number left of the symbol is greater than the number right of the symbol. The open end faces the greater number.	5 > 4 1000.1 > 1000 1 > -2 3 > 2 is read "3 is greater than 2."
<	The less than symbol. The number left of the symbol is less than the number right of the symbol. The closed end faces the lesser valued number.	800 < 1000 2.99999 < 3.000001 8 < 10 is read "8 is less than 10".
≥	The greater than or equal to symbol.	5 ≥ 5 3 ≥ 0
≤	The less than or equal to symbol.	5 ≤ 5 -100 ≤ 0
NOTE:	The open end of the greater or less than sign always faces the greater number, and the closed end always points to the lesser number.	

2-7   Summary of Numbers

Many definitions were given in this chapter, but you need to be familiar with all of them since they are used throughout mathematics. To review, all counting numbers and 0 (e.g. 0, 1, 2, 3, ...) are called whole numbers. All numbers greater than zero are positive, and all numbers less than zero are negative.

Numbers with non-zero digits right of the ones place are called decimal numbers (e.g. 1.1, 2.3, 0.5,), but integers do not have decimal values (e.g. -1, 0, 1, 2, 3). Finally, every number that can be represented as a point on the number line is called a real number. Therefore every integer and every decimal is a real number.

You now know almost everything there is to know about numbers. In the next chapter you will learn about combining and splitting the different types of numbers.

Types of Numbers

Real

Whole

Positive or Negative

Integers or Decimals

Important Definitions

Number

Infinity (∞)

Digits
(Most and Least Significant)

Numerical Places

Greater

Less

Equal

You should be able to...

1.   Read any number aloud

2.   Determine the type of any number (whole, positive, decimal, etc.)

3.   Compare numbers to find which is greater or less

4.   Draw and label a number line containing any number

Addition and Subtraction

3-1 Explaining Addition

Addition is used to combine two or more numbers to produce a new number. If you have 3 apples and your sister has 4 apples, you may want to know the total number of apples that you have together. Finding the total requires addition. You may use addition to calculate how much money you have, total your grocery bill, or determine your bowling score.

Addition is often overlooked, since performing addition is a relatively easy task. However, addition is a mathematical foundation upon which other number manipulations are built. You are encouraged not to skip this chapter, even though you probably already know how to perform addition and subtraction. **At the minimum, please read section 3-11**.

3-2 Addition of Single Digit Integers

In mathematical language, addition is an operation which is performed on numbers. An **operation** is some type of mathematical manipulation of numbers. Addition is represented by the **operator (+)** which is called the **plus** sign or plus operator.

The operation of addition can be performed with the help of the number line. Add two numbers using the following steps:

STEP - BY - STEP
Adding Two Numbers
1. Start on the number line at the first number.
2. Move <u>right</u> on the number line the same number of increments as the second number.
3. The destination reached in step #2 is the answer.

Let's clarify the steps with an example.

<u>Example - Adding Two Numbers</u>
4 + 3 = ?

Step 1: Start at the number 4 on the number line.

Step 2: Move 3 increments right on the number line.

Step 3: The final number reached is 7, which is the answer.

Answer: 7

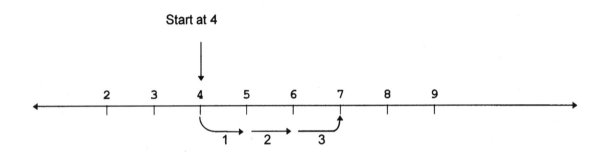

Adding a third or fourth number is not more difficult. Simply add the first two numbers together, and then add any more numbers using the given steps. The steps are valid for adding any valued number, but we will wait until section **3-12** to add decimals. The final example in the box below may look difficult since a negative number is used. However, to find the solution follow the same steps given for adding any two numbers.

You should verify the following examples.

Examples of Addition
3 + 6 = 9
3 + 4 = 7
2 + 1 = 3
4 + 0 = 4
4 + 2 + 1 = 7
1 + 4 + 2 = 7
8 + 0 + 2 = 10
-2 + 3 = 1

3-3   Commutative Law of Addition

Look once again at the steps in performing addition. Note that changing the order of the numbers does not change the answer. That is,

$$4 + 3 = 7$$

and

$$3 + 4 = 7$$

This 'reversal of order' will work when adding <u>any</u> numbers, and thus mathematicians have a rule. The name of this rule is the **Commutative Law of Addition**.

If more than two numbers are added, the Commutative Law of Addition still applies. Numbers can be added in any order, and the answer will always be the same.

<u>Examples - Using the Commutative Law of Addition</u>

$$1 + 2 = 3$$
$$2 + 1 = 3$$

$$3 + 6 + 5 = 14$$
$$3 + 5 + 6 = 14$$

$$2 + 1 + 9 = 12$$
$$9 + 1 + 2 = 12$$

$$8 + 6 + 18 = 32$$
$$18 + 8 + 6 = 32$$

Does the Commutative Law of Addition make sense? Let's think of an example.

If the goal is to find the total number of apples that you and your sister have, the order that the apples are added does not make any difference. You may place your three apples in a bowl, then your sister may place her four apples in the bowl. Counting the total number of apples in the bowl produces the answer seven. Would you get the same answer if your sister put her apples in the bowl first, then you? Of course it would not matter, and the total number of apples is still seven. This is why the Commutative Law of Addition works.

3-4   Understanding Variables

The Commutative Law of Addition tells us that the following math statements are all true.

$$3 + 5 = 5 + 3 \qquad 8.5 + 1.1 = 1.1 + 8.5 \qquad 6 + 20 = 20 + 6$$

We could continue writing true math statements forever since the law is true for any valued numbers. However, it would be very helpful to write a general mathematical statement that would be valid for any number. The Commutative Law of Addition, written with general math symbols, is given in the box below.

Commutative Law of Addition

$$a + b = b + a$$

The letter a can represent <u>any number</u>, as can the letter b. Another word for a letter which represents any number is called a **variable**. Therefore, in this formula a and b are variables. Variables are often used in mathematics and will be used throughout this text.

Variables are very useful. Assume that Mary is two years older than Joe. If Joe is 5 years old, then Mary is 7. If Joe is 9, then Mary is 11. Using variables we can write a general math statement that relates Joe's age to Mary's age. First, you should agree with the following.

Mary's Age = Joe's Age + 2

Now, we may use the letter *J* to represent Joe's Age, and use the letter *M* to represent Mary's age. The general math statement, using variables, is written below.

$$M = J + 2$$

We can use any letter for a variable. In the previous example, we used *J* and *M* since they were the first letters of the children's names.

Verify that you understand the following examples.

Example - Using Variables

Pete's room is always 3 degrees warmer than Bill's room.
Write a general math statement that relates the temperature of Bill's Room to Pete's room.

Let *B* = the temperature of Bill's room
Let *P* = the temperature of Pete's room

Answer: $P = B + 3$

Example - Using Variables

Use the formula $P = B + 3$ from the previous example.
If Bill's room is 90 degrees, what is the temperature of Pete's Room?

That's hot!

$B = 90$ since *B* is the temperature of Bill's room

The temperature of Pete's room = $P = B + 3$

Using the number line, we find that $90 + 3 = 93 = P$

Answer: Pete's room is 93 degrees

3-5   Associative Law of Addition

Math operations should always be performed from left to right. For example to add the three numbers

$$4 + 3 + 2$$

begin with 4 on the number line. Then move 3 increments right on the number line, followed by 2 more increments right. The final point reached on the number line will be the number 9 which is the answer.

$$4 + 3 + 2 = 9$$

Parentheses always indicate an operation which must be performed first. For example,

$$4 + (3 + 2)$$

In this problem, the first addition must be the numbers in parentheses.

$$3 + 2 = 5$$

Then the problem is

$$4 + 5 = 9$$

Based on this rule of parentheses and the Commutative Law of Addition, another useful math law can be developed. Another word for develop in math terminology is **derive**. Let's derive the law using a specific example rather than using variables.

Based on what we already know,

$$4 + 3 + 2 = 9$$

Since the commutative law tells us that numbers added together can be added in any order, the following math statements are true.

$$4 + 3 + 2 = (4 + 3) + 2 = 9$$

$$4 + 2 + 3 = (4 + 2) + 3 = 9$$

$$2 + 4 + 3 = (2 + 4) + 3 = 9$$

$$2 + 3 + 4 = (2 + 3) + 4 = 9$$

Regardless of the number order or parentheses grouping, the answer is always 9.

This leads to the **Associative Law of Addition**.

Associative Law of Addition
$a + (b + c) = (a + b) + c$

This law tells us that any group of numbers can be added first, and the answer will remain the same.   Below is an example which uses numbers instead of variables.

$$6 + (1 + 2) = 6 + 3 = 9$$

and

$$(6 + 1) + 2 = 7 + 2 = 9$$

These laws may not seem important now. However, the commutative and associative laws are very important and should be memorized.

Examples - Using the Associative Law of Addition

$$2 + (5 + 1) = (2 + 5) + 1 = 8$$

$$1 + (1 + 4) + 6 = (1 + 1) + (4 + 6) = 12$$

3-6   Explaining Subtraction

As stated, addition is used to find the combination or total of numbers. **Subtraction** is used to find the difference between numbers. For example, if you and your sister together have 7 apples, and your sister has 4 apples, you may want to know how many apples you have. You know that you have the difference between the total number of apples and the number that your sister has. By experimenting with adding different numbers you could probably find the answer. Let's try.

$$4 + 1 = 5$$
$$4 + 2 = 6$$
$$4 + 3 = 7 \qquad \sqrt{} \;\; yes$$

It was necessary to add 3 to 4 to get 7 total, and therefore 3 was the correct answer. Experimenting with addition could take a long time for a complicated problem. Also, it is necessary to be able to write the difference between numbers using mathematical operators and numbers. Subtraction will meet this requirement.

3-7   Subtraction of Single Digit Integers

Subtraction is represented by the operator (**-**) which is called the **minus** sign. The operation of subtraction can also be performed on the number line with three steps.

STEP - BY - STEP

Subtracting Two Numbers

1. Start on the number line at the first number.
2. Move left on the number line the same number of increments as the second number.
3. The destination reached in step #2 is the answer.

Let's clarify the steps by finding the difference between the total of 7 and the number 4.

<u>Example - Using Subtraction</u>

7 - 4 = ?

Step 1: Start at the number 7 on the number line.

Step 2: Move 4 increments left on the number line.

Step 3: The final number reached is 3, which is the answer.

Answer: 3

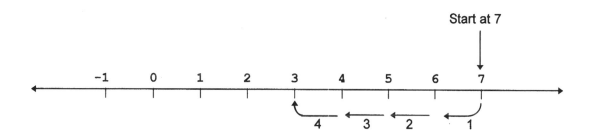

You should verify the following examples. Remember that for addition you must move right on the number line, but for subtraction you move left.

<u>Examples of Subtraction</u>

$$9 - 6 = 3$$
$$7 - 4 = 3$$
$$3 - 1 = 2$$
$$4 - 0 = 4$$
$$4 - 2 - 1 = 1$$
$$7 - 4 - 1 = 2$$
$$10 - 8 - 2 = 0$$
$$3 - 4 = -1$$

With practice, you will begin to memorize all of the different combinations of additions and subtractions for single digit numbers. The number line will no longer be needed to obtain the solution. In the meantime, instead of the number line, you can also conveniently use your 10 fingers. If you have clean feet (or you're by yourself), you can also use your toes.

There is **no** commutative or associative law for subtraction.

$$a - b \neq b - a$$

$$a - (b - c) \neq (a - b) - c$$

3-8   Absolute Values

You can use any numbers to verify that changing the order of numbers subtracted changes the answer. Using the number line, verify the following math statements.

$$5 - 3 = 2$$

but

$$3 - 5 = -2$$

Remember, subtraction finds the difference or 'distance and direction' between numbers. The distance is found by the size of the answer. The direction is found by the sign (positive or negative) of the answer. Looking at the number line below, we see that the distance between the numbers 3 and 5 on the number line is 2.

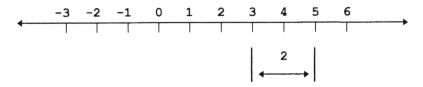

5 - 3 = 2 shows that the difference between 5 and 3 is 2. Furthermore, 5 > 3 as indicated by the positive answer.

3 - 5 = -2 shows that the difference between 5 and 3 is also 2. However, 3 < 5 as indicated by the negative answer.

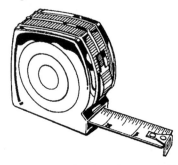

Sometimes, we simply want to know the difference between two numbers, and we do not care about whether the sign of the answer is positive or negative. We just want to know the distance between the numbers on the number line, and distance is always positive. To find the distance of any number from 0 on the number line we use the absolute value symbol.

Absolute Value Symbol

$|\,a\,|$ is the **magnitude** or **absolute value** of any number *a*.

$$|\,a\,| \geq 0$$

The absolute value (or magnitude) of any number must be positive since it represents the distance the number is away from zero on the number line. Verify the following examples.

<u>Examples - Using Absolute Values</u>

$|\,5\,| = 5$	$|\,-5\,| = 5$	$|\,-2.15\,| = 2.15$	$|\,-3\,| > 2$

Using absolute values, the following statement is true. However, there is no official name of this math truth. Does it make sense to you? Following are some examples which verify this statement.

$$|a - b| = |b - a|$$

Examples - Using Subtraction and Absolute Values
$\|4 - 3\| = \|1\| = 1$
$\|3 - 4\| = \|-1\| = 1$
$\|8 - 2\| = \|6\| = 6$
$\|2 - 8\| = \|-6\| = 6$

We may use official math language, and symbols from section **2-6** to state the following. Do all of these statements make sense? There is no need to memorize these rules, since they do not tell you anything that you should not already know based on previous explanations. However, they are a check to make sure you understand variables, numbers, and a few symbols.

$$\text{if } a > b \text{ then } a - b > 0$$

$$\text{if } a < b \text{ then } a - b < 0$$

$$\text{if } a = b \text{ then } a - b = 0$$

3-9   Addition and Subtraction are Complementary

You may recognize the complementary nature of addition and subtraction. This means that addition and subtraction are very much related. In fact, addition and subtraction are almost opposites and are called **inverse operations**. For example:

$$3 + 4 = 7$$
$$7 - 4 = 3$$
$$7 - 3 = 4$$

In general, variables can be used to state that:

$$\text{If}$$
$$a + b = c$$
$$\text{then}$$
$$c - b = a$$
$$c - a = b$$

You should be able to verify these formulas for any numbers a, b, and c on the number line. Therefore, subtraction can 'undo' addition, and addition can 'undo' subtraction. Again, they are inverse operations.

Examples - Using the Inverse Operations of Addition and Subtraction		
$5 - 3 = 2$	$5 - 2 = 3$	$3 + 2 = 5$
$5 - 3 + 3 = 5$	$5 - 2 + 2 = 5$	$3 + 2 - 5 = 0$

3-10   Addition of Multi-Digit Integers

You know how to add and subtract using the number line. This method is valid for numbers of any value. However, adding 152 + 323 + 84 would take quite an effort on a number line. Even with a number line, it would be easy to make a mistake! There is a much better way to add and subtract large numbers, assuming you have already memorized how to add and subtract all single digit number combinations.

We'll begin by showing how to add multi-digit integers. After learning how to add them, we'll answer why we add them as shown.

STEP - BY - STEP

Adding Multi-Digit Numbers

1. Place all numbers to be added in one column. Place the numbers with the most digits on top of the column. Make sure the numerical places of all numbers are aligned. Place a line under the bottom number to be added to separate the question from the answer.

2. Add all numbers in the ones place.

3. Add all numbers in the tens place. Repeat (if necessary), by moving one place left until all places have been added. Use carries as necessary.

Let's clarify the steps with an example.

Example - Adding Multi-Digit Integers

Add 152 + 84 + 323

We'll follow the procedure described in **STEP-BY-STEP**.

Step 1: Writing the problem correctly yields,

$$
\begin{array}{r}
152 \\
323 \\
+\ \ 84 \\
\hline
\end{array}
$$

Remember that the numbers can be added in any order, by the Commutative Law of Addition.

Step 2: It is necessary to add the numbers in the ones column. In this case 2 + 3 + 4 = 9, as we showed earlier.

$$
\begin{array}{r}
152 \\
323 \\
+\ \ 84 \\
\hline
9 \\
\end{array}
$$

Step 3: Move one column to the left, and add that column as before. Adding the digits in the tens place gives 5 + 2 + 8 = 15. Now there's a problem. If 15 is written down, the 1 in the number 15 would interfere when we add the next column.

If a column ever adds to more than 9, the answer will not fit in one numerical place. Therefore, a carry is necessary.

Just write down the digit farthest to the right, and move the other digit(s) to the top of the next column. The digit(s) moved to the next column is called a **carry**.

In this example, write down the 5 and carry the 1.

$$
\begin{array}{r}
1 \quad \longleftarrow \text{ This is the carry} \\
152 \\
323 \\
+ \ 84 \\
\hline
59
\end{array}
$$

Step 3 (con't):   Continuing the pattern given in step #3, move left to the final column to obtain 1 + 1 + 3 = 5, so the final answer is 559.

$$
\begin{array}{r}
1 \\
152 \\
323 \\
+ \ 84 \\
\hline
559
\end{array}
$$

It is necessary to understand why we add numbers this way. The obvious answer is that "it works." However, you need to understand why this method works.

Some questions may be:

- Why start on the right-hand column instead of the left column?
- Why use a carry instead of just writing the number down?
- Why does the carry give the correct answer?

These questions and more will be answered in the next, very important section. However at this point, you should be able to follow the given steps to verify the examples.

Examples - Addition of Multi-Digit Numbers

48 + 180 + 921 = 1149

999 + 1 = 1000

24 + 81 + 120 + 3 = 228

3-11   Separating Multi-Digit Numbers for Addition

The key to math calculations with multi-digit numbers is to separate all of the numbers into numerical places. Following the method for adding multi-digit numbers presented in the previous section, you should be able to verify the following addition is true.

```
      100
       50
  +     2
     ─────
      152
```

This shows that the number 152 can be separated into the addition of three numbers which each only have one non-zero digit. In other words, the number 152 can be separated into the addition of numbers 100, 50 and 2.

$$150 = 100 + 50 + 2$$

Any number may be separated as shown. For example, the number 8,425 is read "eight thousand, four hundred twenty-five". This means that the number is a total of 8 thousands, 4 hundreds, 2 tens and 5 ones.

$$8,425 = 8000 + 400 + 20 + 5$$

Separating numbers like this allows every calculation to be performed on single digits. This technique is used throughout mathematics.

Here is the same problem as shown in the previous section, except each number is separated into individual components. The components in the hundreds, tens, and ones are added together.

```
    152   =   100   +    50   +   2
    323   =   300   +    20   +   3
 +   84   =     0   +    80   +   4
  ─────       ───        ───      ─
    559   =   400   +   150   +   9
```

Now the carry should make more sense. The carry separated 150 into 100 + 50. The digit 5 was correctly placed in the tens column to represent 50. However, a 1 was carried to the hundreds column to represent the 100.

Let's look at the same problem a little differently. We will first add the ones column, then the tens column, then the hundreds column. Then, all of the ones, tens and hundreds will be added together to find the answer.

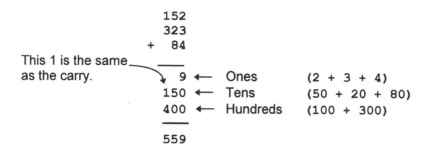

This number separation concept is **very** important. You will often use it to make mathematics much more simple. Note that the carry was actually allowed by rules given in the commutative and associative laws of addition.

You should understand why numbers are aligned in columns. (Answer: to add each numerical place using only single digits.) You should also understand why the numbers are added beginning on the rightmost column. (Answer: in case there are carries which are added to the next column left.)

Usually the numbers with more digits are placed at the top of the column, so that the carry will not cause confusion.

What happens if the numbers are not aligned in proper columns and added? In the example below 840 is added rather than 84, since 84 is placed in the wrong column.

```
   152
   323
 +  84
 ─────
   ???
```

152	=	100	+	50	+	2
323	=	300	+	20	+	3
+ 84	=	800	+	40	+	0
1315		1200		110		5

As you can see, the wrong answer results if numerical places are not aligned properly.

If you do not understand this section, please review. This section was meant to provide understanding of why multi-digit numbers are added as shown in section **3-10**.

3-12 Adding Decimals

Adding decimals is just like adding integers. The only difference is that you must keep track of the position of the decimal point in the answer.

Example - Adding Decimal Numbers

1.52 + 3.23 + 0.84 = ?

Use carries as shown in section **3-10** to find the answer.

```
      1.52
      3.23
  +    .84
      ─────
      5.59
```

Answer: 5.59

Let's look at another example.

<u>Example - Adding Decimal Numbers</u>

0.2 + 0.04 + 1.6 + 18 = ?

Do NOT line up the numbers as shown below, otherwise you will get very confused. You must add the same numerical places together as shown in the previous section. Adding numbers in the ones and tens place together does not make any sense, and will give you the wrong result. Addition of the ones column, then tens column, then hundreds column, etc., is the proper method, unlike that shown here.

```
      .2
      .04
      1.6
      18
      ────
```

To keep all of the digit places correctly aligned, it sometimes helps to insert zeros after the decimal point. The zeros to the right of the decimal used for alignment are called **placeholders**. They do not change the value of the number, but are inserted as a reminder of the proper column's numerical place. The example problem is rewritten using placeholders to properly align each numerical place.

```
       .20
       .04
      1.60
     18.00
     ──────
     19.84
```

<u>Examples - Adding Decimal Numbers</u>

1.5 + 6.8 + 100.001 = 108.301

83.642 + 0.01 + 18.3 + 2001 = 2102.952

4.4 + 6.6 = 11

3-13   Subtraction of Multi-Digit Integers

Subtraction closely follows the ideas used in the addition of integers. Remember that the order of subtraction is important. Unlike addition, a different order will give a different answer. For now we'll assume that the number subtracted is less than the original value so the answer will be positive. We also assume that only one number is subtracted from the other. To subtract additional numbers, repeat the steps for each pair of numbers.

STEP - BY - STEP

Subtracting Two Multi-Digit Numbers

1. Place the two numbers to be subtracted in one column. Place the first number on top of the column. Make sure the numerical places of all numbers are aligned. Place a line under the second number to separate the question from the answer.

2. Subtract numbers in the ones place.

3. Subtract numbers in the tens place. Repeat (if necessary), by moving one place left until all places have been subtracted. Use borrows as necessary.

Let's clarify the steps with an example.

Example - Subtracting Multi-Digit Integers

323 - 152 = ?

Step 1: Write down the numbers and put a line under the bottom number.

$$
\begin{array}{r}
323 \\
-\ 152 \\
\hline
\end{array}
$$

Step 2: Begin on the right-hand column and subtract the single digits. In this case 3 - 2 = 1.

$$
\begin{array}{r}
323 \\
-\ 152 \\
\hline
1
\end{array}
$$

Step 3: Move one column to the left, and subtract. Subtracting in the second column gives

$$2 - 5 = -3$$

To follow the method of addition, we should write down the 3 and carry a negative sign, but this doesn't make any sense. The problem is that there are only 2 tens in 323, which is fewer than the 5 tens in 152.

The solution is to move tens from the hundreds column to the tens column in 323, so that we have enough tens to subtract. In performing addition, we needed to carry numbers into the higher numerical place. We now need to **borrow** numbers from the higher numerical place.

1 ten = 10. 2 tens = 20. 10 tens = 100. We may change the form of the number 323 by moving 10 tens from the hundreds column into the tens column. Therefore, we change the 3 in the hundreds column to a 2, and add 10 to the tens column.

$$
\begin{array}{rll}
300 \ - \ 100 & = & \boxed{2}00 \\
20 \ + \ 100 & = & \boxed{12}0 \\
3 \ + \quad 0 & = & \quad 3 \\ \hline
323 \ + \quad 0 & = & 323
\end{array}
\qquad
\begin{array}{r}
\boxed{2}\ \boxed{12} \\
\cancel{3}\ \cancel{2}\ 3 \\
-\ 1\ 5\ 2 \\ \hline
1
\end{array}
$$

Step 3 (con't): Now the subtraction can be finished to get the desired result.

$$
\begin{array}{r}
2 \quad 12 \\
\cancel{3}\ \cancel{2}\ 3 \\
-\ 1\ 5\ 2 \\ \hline
1\ 7\ 1
\end{array}
$$

Let's think about the borrow that was performed.

By performing the borrow, 323 was transformed into 200 + 120 + 3 (323 = 200 + 120 + 3). This transformation allowed us to subtract correctly. Again, the separation of multi-digit numbers is necessary to complete the operation. 171 is the final answer.

Using the number line, you may calculate 100 - 99 = 1. However, let's perform the operation using methods in this section.

First, looking at the ones column we see that 0 < 9, so we must borrow from the tens place in the number 100. However, there are no tens in the tens column of 100. Therefore, we must borrow from the hundreds place. We'll take 100 and separate it into 9 tens and 10 ones (100 = 90 + 10). We may then complete the operation.

$$
\begin{array}{r}
0 \quad 9 \quad 10 \\
\cancel{1}\ \cancel{0}\ \cancel{0} \\
-\quad 9\ 9 \\ \hline
1
\end{array}
$$

This section has emphasized how and why subtraction works as shown. With practice you will not even think about how subtraction works, since it will seem so simple.

To perform a borrow simply add 10 to current column, and subtract 1 from the next column to the left. If the column to the left is a 0, make that column a 9, and subtract 1 from the next column left.

Hopefully you now understand why subtraction works according to math rules.

Examples - Subtraction of Multi-Digit Numbers

154 - 99 = 55

1000 - 52 = 948

1632 - 1605 = 27

3-14   Subtraction Resulting in Negative Answers

The method of subtraction presented only works for subtracting a smaller number from a larger number.

Subtracting a larger number from a smaller number results in an answer less than zero (or a negative number). Let's see why the method of subtraction presented in section **3-13** does not work for this type of problem.

$$
\begin{array}{rcrcrcrcr}
152 & = & 100 & + & 50 & + & 2 & & 152 \\
-\,323 & = & -\,300 & + & -\,20 & + & -\,3 & & -\,323 \\
\hline
-229 & \neq & -200 & + & 30 & + & -1 & = & -171
\end{array}
$$

The correct answer is -171. Using the methods of section **3-13**, -229 results.

The problem is that additions and subtractions are mixed up, as shown in the separation of the numbers (-200 + 30 - 1). To get the correct answer, *always put the greater valued number on top when doing subtraction.* Then, if you had to reverse the order of the problem, insert a negative on the answer. Using the above examples,

$$323 - 152 = 171$$

$$152 - 323 = -171$$

Remember, subtraction indicates the difference between two numbers. These examples show that the difference between 323 and 152 equals 171. 323 is 171 integer increments on the number line away from 152. As stated earlier,

$$|\,a - b\,| = |\,b - a\,|$$

Using other math symbols and variables, a common definition can be written.

$$\text{if } a > b \text{ then } a - b = |\,b - a\,| > 0$$

$$\text{if } a < b \text{ then } |\,a - b\,| = b - a > 0$$

This math comes in very handy if you spend more money than you have, and you are trying to figure out how much you owe!

<u>Examples - Subtraction Resulting in Negative Numbers</u>

$$180 - 242 = -62$$

$$35 - 1821 = -1786$$

$$99 - 97 - 5 = (99 - 97) - 5 = 2 - 5 = -3$$

3-15   Subtracting Decimals

There is nothing different in subtracting decimals from subtracting integers. The only difference is that you must keep track of the decimal point in the answer. Remember to keep the decimal places aligned just like in addition. Borrows are performed using the same method as borrowing with integers. Therefore, to subtract 1.52 from 3.23:

```
      2 12
      3.2̸ 3
  -   1.5 2
     _____
      1.7 1
```

To subtract 1.52 from 323, the following answer is obtained. (Note that two borrows were made but are not shown.) You should confirm this answer.

```
      323.00
  -     1.52
     _____
      321.48
```

Hopefully, further explanations are not necessary.   However, math does get confusing sometimes, and you need to spend time working on examples. If you do not understand the examples in this section, please reread the earlier sections of the chapter.

<u>Examples - Subtraction with Decimals</u>

$$3.5 - 2.2 = 1.3$$

$$2.2 - 3.5 = -1.3$$

$$184.2 - 45.2 = 139$$

$$0.1 - 100 = -99.9$$

3-16   Summary of Addition and Subtraction

Addition and subtraction are two of the four fundamental math operations. You should now understand how to perform either operation on any integer or decimal number. Addition and subtraction of integers is normally taught in early grade school, so you probably knew how to perform addition and subtraction of integers already. However, you should now also understand why addition and subtraction are performed as shown. The separation of multi-digit numbers and the Commutative and Associative Laws of Addition are the keys to really understanding these two math operations.

Addition and subtraction of decimals is normally taught in the middle grades. However, as shown, performing these operations with decimals is not different from integers. You must simply put the decimal point in the proper column in the answer.

The next chapter demonstrates how to perform the final two fundamental math operations.

Math Laws

Commutative Law of Addition

Associative Law of Addition

Important Definitions

Operator

Variable

Absolute Value (or magnitude)

Inverse Operation

Placeholder

You should be able to ...

1. Add any valued integers or decimals

2. Subtract any valued integer or decimal

3. Find the absolute value of any number

4. Understand variables

5. Understand how carries and borrows work

Multiplication and Division

4-1 Explaining Multiplication

Multiplication is the third mathematical operation presented. Often times it is necessary to add the same numbers together many times. For example,

$$3 + 3 + 3 + 3 + 3 + 3 = ?$$

How can we solve this problem? One solution is to use a number line and move 3 digits to the right for all six threes. The second solution is to align the numbers in a column and add. The third solution requires multiplication.

Multiplication is the repeated addition of a certain number. Multiplication is represented by the operator ($\bullet$) or ($\times$). The example below shows how to use the operator.

Example - Writing Expressions using Multiplication

Write 3 + 3 using the multiplication operator, and find the answer using addition.

Three is added together 2 times, or 3 is multiplied by 2. Therefore,

Answer: $3 + 3 = 3 \bullet 2 = 3 \times 2 = 6$

The answer to any multiplication problem is called the **product**. In the above example, 6 is the product. The example (3 $\bullet$ 2) is read aloud "three times two". *Times* is an appropriate word since 3 is added together 2 times.

Example - Writing Expressions using Multiplication

$$3 + 3 + 3 + 3 = 3 \bullet 4 = 12$$

$$2 + 2 + 2 = 2 \bullet 3 = 6$$

$$18.5 + 18.5 = 18.5 \bullet 2 = 37$$

4-2   Operators for Multiplication

Before continuing with our description of multiplication, there is a need to pause due to the different operators used for multiplication in different texts. This book has chosen to use the operator (•) for multiplication.

Most elementary math books use the operator (×), and computer languages generally use the operator (*) to represent multiplication. No one operator is 'better' than another. However, in advanced mathematics, (*) is sometimes used for another mathematical operator. Furthermore (×) is easily confused with the letter *x*, and the letter *x* is often used as a variable (or an unknown number). Generally the reader can determine the operator in context, but the use of (•) will avoid any confusion, since it is not used elsewhere.

Another way to express multiplication is the use of parentheses. Therefore 3 • 4 also may be written as (3)(4). This form or **convention** will also be used in later chapters. Convention is a fancy math word similar to "form" or "the way of writing something mathematical."

Another convention is used with variables. A variable is generally a single letter or a complete word. If the variable is a single letter, the lack of an operator implies multiplication. For example,

$$a \bullet b = (a)(b) = ab$$

$$5 \bullet a = (5)(a) = 5a$$

$$3 \bullet 4 = (3)(4) = 3(4)$$

This method is used in virtually every math book, and should not cause confusion. Obviously, the lack of an operator cannot be used with numbers.

$$5 \bullet 6 = (5)(6) \neq 56$$

<u>Example - Reading Multiplication</u>

3 • 4   is read aloud " 3 times 4 "

a • *a*   is read aloud " *a* times *a* "

a(*b*)   is read aloud "*a* times *b*"

5*a*   is read aloud "5 times *a*" or simply " 5 *a*"

It almost seems necessary to apologize for this long discussion of mathematical convention, but unfortunately it is unavoidable.

Let's get back to mathematics...

4-3   Multiplication of Single Digit Integers

As in many areas of mathematics, memorization is required. In chapter 3, it was necessary to memorize all of the combinations of adding and subtracting single digit integers. For multiplication, the reader should <u>memorize</u> (at a minimum) all combinations of single digit multiplication. Memorization is hard work. You should repeat each of the number combinations in the table over and over until you can state the answer to any single digit combination with ease.

Usually a grade school student is required to memorize the 'times table' which consists of all combinations of integers 0 through 12. You should realize that each value in the table can be obtained through addition as shown earlier. For example

$$3 \bullet 4 = 3 + 3 + 3 + 3 = 12$$

To use the table, decide which two numbers need to be multiplied. Then use the top row and leftmost column to find the numbers to be multiplied. Follow the corresponding row across and the column down until the answer is reached. As you can see, half of the boxes in the table do not contain any values. The reason for this is given in the next section.

#	•2	•3	•4	•5	•6	•7	•8	•9	•10	•11	•12
1	2	3	4	5	6	7	8	9	10	11	12
2	4	6	8	10	12	14	16	18	20	22	24
3		9	12	15	18	21	24	27	30	33	36
4			16	20	24	28	32	36	40	44	48
5				25	30	35	40	45	50	55	60
6					36	42	48	54	60	66	72
7						49	56	63	70	77	84
8							64	72	80	88	96
9								81	90	99	108
10									100	110	120
11										121	132
12											144

Verify the examples given by using the times table.

<u>Example - Using the Times Table</u>
$6 \bullet 7 = 42$
$3 \bullet 8 = 24$
$12 \bullet 12 = 144$

You may also want to ensure that you can obtain any value given in the table through addition.

Knowing this table requires a lot of memorization, but it is well worth it. Once you memorize these combinations, you will be able to multiply numbers of any value.

There a few definitions or rules which also help in learning multiplication. These are basic math truths, often called **axioms**.

Axioms for Multiplying Any Number times 0 or 1

Let *a* represent any number

Axiom 1: $a \cdot 0 = 0$

Axiom 2: $a \cdot 1 = a$

Do these rules make sense?

1.   Any number times 0 equals 0. So, $1,000,000 \cdot 0 = 0$. Why? If you add zero a million times the answer remains zero. Also, $50 \cdot 0 = 0$ since there are zero fifties.

2.   Multiplying any number by 1 does not change the number. So, $50 \cdot 1 = 50$. This makes sense since there is 50 one time.

Before proceeding, you should be able to answer the following example.

<u>Example - Understanding the Times Table</u>

In roofing a house, you need 6 columns of shingles, and 13 shingles in each column.
How many shingles do you need?

The answer is $6 \cdot 13$. But, $6 \cdot 13$ is not in the table, so how do you solve this?   12 is in the table, so 12 sixes is

$$6 \cdot 12 = 72$$

13 sixes must be six more, or

$$72 + 6 = 78 \quad \text{shingles total}$$

Answer: 78 shingles

If you do not understand the math in this example ($6 \cdot 13$), please reread the section.

4-4   Commutative Law of Multiplication

The times table given in section **4-3** is not completely filled for every combination. This is not a typo, and you need perform no additional work. Just as addition has a commutative law, so multiplication has a commutative law.

Commutative Law of Multiplication

For any numbers *a* and *b*

$$a \cdot b = b \cdot a$$

Therefore, the following examples are true, and the times table provided does list all possible combinations of multiplication for numbers 0 through 12.

Examples - Using The Commutative Law of Multiplication

$$3 \bullet 8 = 8 \bullet 3 = 24$$

$$9 \bullet 2 = 2 \bullet 9 = 18$$

Does the commutative law make sense? $3 \bullet 4$ is the same as adding the number 3 four times or

$$3 + 3 + 3 + 3 = 12$$

However, this is also equal to adding the number 4 three times or

$$4 + 4 + 4 = 12$$

The order of multiplication is not important. Six groups of 9 is the same as nine groups of 6.

Below is a group of quarters.

Assume that the goal is to count the total number of quarters. One method is to simply count the quarters. There are a total of 15 quarters. A faster method is to only count the number of rows and columns, and multiply. There are 5 quarters in each of 3 rows.

$$5 + 5 + 5 = 5 \bullet 3 = 15 \text{ quarters}$$

There are also 3 quarters in each of 5 columns.

$$3 + 3 + 3 + 3 + 3 = 3 \bullet 5 = 15 \text{ quarters}$$

Remember that both addition and multiplication are commutative. This makes sense, since after all, multiplication is simply a shortened form of many additions.

Examples - Using the Commutative Law of Multiplication

$$6 \bullet 2 = 2 \bullet 6$$
$$15 \bullet 32 = 32 \bullet 15$$
$$4.8 \bullet 3.1 \bullet 6 = 6 \bullet 3.1 \bullet 4.8$$

4-5   Associative Law of Multiplication

In chapter 3 we developed the Associative Law of Addition, based on the Commutative Law of Addition. We could also develop an Associative Law for Multiplication, but since the derivation is similar to that in chapter 3, the law is merely stated.

Associative Law of Multiplication

For any numbers a, b, and c

$$a \bullet (b \bullet c) = (a \bullet b) \bullet c$$

Remember that both addition and multiplication are associative.

Examples - Using the Associative Law of Multiplication

$$(16 \bullet 21) \bullet 8 = 16 \bullet (21 \bullet 8)$$

$$1.8 \bullet (14 \bullet 3.5) = (1.8 \bullet 14) \bullet 3.5$$

$$(2 \bullet 11) \bullet 6 \bullet 0.1 = 2 \bullet (11 \bullet 6) \bullet 0.1$$

$$(3 \bullet 2) \bullet 1 = 6 \bullet 1 = 6$$

$$3 \bullet (2 \bullet 1) = 3 \bullet 2 = 6$$

4-6   Distributive Law of Multiplication

The final law of multiplication presented is the distributive law. This law is very important and is a key to understanding more advanced math.

Distributive Law of Multiplication

For any numbers a, b, and c

$$a(b + c) = ab + ac$$

IMPORTANT LAW!

Before moving to further explanation, a few examples are presented.

<u>Examples - Using the Distributive Law of Multiplication</u>

$$4(2 + 3) = 4(5) = 20$$

$$4(2) + 4(3) = 8 + 12 = 20$$

$$4(2 + 3) = 4(2) + 4(3) = 20$$

$$3(6 + 1) = 3(7) = 21$$
or
$$3(6) + 3(1) = 18 + 3 = 21$$

This law is used extensively, so make sure you understand and memorize it. Furthermore, it is necessary to understand why the law is true.

To understand why the distributive law is true, you must:

    1.   Understand the Commutative and Associative Laws of Addition.

    2.   Remember the definition of multiplication.

$5 \bullet 3$ means that the number 5 must be added together three times, or 3 must be added five times.

$$5 \bullet 3 = 5 + 5 + 5 = 15$$

or

$$3 \bullet 5 = 3 + 3 + 3 + 3 + 3 = 15$$

Therefore, $a(b + c)$ means that a must be added together $(b + c)$ times, or $(b + c)$ must be added together a times. This is shown below, where an ellipsis (...) has been used since $(b + c)$ and a are unknown. We don't know how many $+$ operators are needed.

$$a(b + c) = \underbrace{(b + c) + (b + c) + (b + c) + (b + c) \ldots + (b + c)}_{\text{added } a \text{ times}}$$

The Commutative and Associative Laws of Addition allow added numbers to be rearranged and regrouped.

$$\underbrace{(b + c) + (b + c) + (b + c) + (b + c) \ldots + (b + c)}_{\text{added } a \text{ times}} = \underbrace{(b + b + b + b \ldots + b)}_{\text{added } a \text{ times}} + \underbrace{(c + c + c + c \ldots + c)}_{\text{added } a \text{ times}}$$

The values of b and c are each added together a times. Therefore, these terms may be rewritten using multiplication.

$$\underbrace{(b + b + b + b \ldots + b)}_{b \text{ added } a \text{ times}} = a \bullet b = ab$$

$$\underbrace{(c + c + c + c \ldots + c)}_{c \text{ added } a \text{ times}} = a \bullet c = ac$$

By combining the previous math statements, we can prove that the Distributive Law of Multiplication is true.

$$a(b + c) = ab + ac$$

The law has been proven based on previously known math laws. Do you see how important it is to know the basic math laws, even though they may seem obvious? Advanced math is always based upon basic principles.

4-7   Variations of the Distributive Law of Multiplication

The official Distributive Law of Multiplication was stated and proven true in the previous section.

$$a(b + c) = ab + ac$$

However, sometimes a problem's form is close but not exactly the same as the law. For example, look at the problems below.

$$a(b - c) = ?$$
$$a(b + c + d) = ?$$
$$(a + b)(c + d) = ?$$
$$(a + b)(c - d) = ?$$
$$(a + b + c)(d + e + f) = ?$$

Although the distributive law does not exactly match any of the above equations, the basic form of the distributive law may still be used. This could be proven for each specific case if desired by following the methods used in the previous section.

$$a\ (b + c)\ = ab + ac \qquad\qquad a\ (b - c)\ = ab - ac$$

The arrows show which terms are multiplied together. We say that the number *a* is **distributed** to each number in parentheses. Using numbers rather than variables,

$$5(3 - 2) = 5(1) = 5 \qquad \text{or} \qquad 5(3 - 2) = 5(3) - 5(2) = 15 - 10 = 5$$

Distribution may also be applied if there are more than two numbers in parentheses.

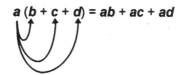

$$a\ (b + c + d) = ab + ac + ad$$

Using numbers rather than variables,

$$3(4 + 1 + 3) = 3(8) = 24 \quad \text{or} \quad 3(4 + 1 + 3) = 3(4) + 3(1) + 3(3) = 12 + 3 + 9 = 24$$

Distribution also works if there are multiple numbers in both parentheses. As shown, both *a* and *b* are distributed.

$$(a + b)\,(c + d) = ac + ad + bc + bd$$

Distribution will be used throughout all of mathematics. There is only one distributive law, but as shown, distribution can be applied to many multiplication problems. A few more examples of distribution are given below. Don't panic when trying to solve the examples. Just apply the distributive law one step at a time.

The last example uses the distributive law, along with the times table in section **4-3**, to multiply a number that is not in the times table (i.e. 15). With practice and memorization of the times table, you could use this method to mentally multiply larger numbers and impress your friends.

<u>Examples - Variations of Distribution</u>

$$a(b - c + d) = ab - ac + ad$$

$$(a + b + c)\,(d + e + f) = ad + ae + af + bd + be + bf + cd + ce + cf$$

$$(a - b)\,(c + d) = ac + ad - bc - bd$$

$$(8)\,(10 + 2) = 80 + 16 = 96$$

$$(12)\,(8) = (10 + 2)\,(10 - 2) = 100 - 20 + 20 - 4 = 96$$

$$(7)(15) = (7)\,(10 + 5) = 70 + 35 = 105$$

4-8   Multiplication of Multi-Digit Integers

It is time to learn how to multiply numbers again, rather than only learning math laws. This section will show how to multiply numbers that are not listed in the times table. The next section will explain how this method of multiplication works.

<u>Example - Multiplication with Multi-Digit Integers</u>

63 students may be seated on each school bus.
Your school uses 42 of these buses every morning.

How many students can all of the buses bring in one morning?

One solution is to use our number line, but that would take a <u>long time</u>. Another way would be to add 63 + 63 + 63 ... + 63 a total of 42 times. The fastest method to obtain the answer requires multiplication.

$$63 \bullet 42 = ?$$

The times table was made by using addition. But, how are numbers multiplied if they are not in the table? Follow the given **STEP-BY-STEP** instructions. For now, we'll assume that only two numbers are multiplied together. If more than two numbers are to be multiplied, multiply them one at a time.

STEP - BY - STEP

Multiplying Two Multi-Digit Numbers

1. Align the integers to be multiplied in a column. Place a line under the bottom number to separate the question from the answer.

2. Multiply the value in the bottom number's ones place with the top number, one digit at a time. Write the answer below the line.

3. Multiply the value in the bottom number's tens place with the top number, one digit at a time. Write the answer below the result from step #2, but shifted one numerical place left.

4. Repeat step #3 for each digit (if necessary), by moving one place left in the bottom number until all places have been multiplied by the top number. Align each product correctly.

5. Draw a line under the last product obtained in step #4. Add all products to obtain the final result.

Let's clarify the instructions with an example.

<u>Example - Multiplying Multi-Digit Numbers</u>

$$63 \bullet 42 = ?$$

Step 1:   Write down the numbers in a column and put a line under the bottom number to separate the answer from the question.

$$\begin{array}{r} 63 \\ 42 \\ \hline \end{array}$$

Step 2:   Multiply the two numbers that are in the ones place together. Here, 3 • 2 equals 6, so write down the 6.

$$\begin{array}{r} 63 \\ 42 \\ \hline 6 \end{array}$$

Step 2 (con't):   Stay with the 2 in the ones place of the bottom number, but now multiply it by the tens place in the top number to get 2 • 6 = 12, and write down the answer.

$$
\begin{array}{r}
63 \\
42 \\
\hline
126
\end{array}
$$

Step 3:   Insert a 0 in the ones column to remind yourself that the next answer must be shifted one place left.

$$
\begin{array}{r}
63 \\
42 \\
\hline
126 \\
0
\end{array}
$$

Step 3 (con't):   Move to digit 4, which is in the tens place in the number 42. Multiply 4 • 3 = 12. Only a single digit may be written in a column, so write the 2 and carry the 1.

$$
\begin{array}{r}
1 \\
63 \\
42 \\
\hline
126 \\
20
\end{array}
$$

Step 3 (con't):   Multiplying the numbers in each tens place yields 4 • 6 = 24; then <u>add</u> the carry.

$$
\begin{array}{r}
1 \\
63 \\
42 \\
\hline
126 \\
2520
\end{array}
$$

Step 4:   There are only two digits so step #4 not necessary.

Step 5:   Place a line under the number 2520, and add 126 + 2520 to get the final answer.

$$
\begin{array}{r}
1 \\
63 \\
42 \\
\hline
126 \\
+\ 2520 \\
\hline
2646
\end{array}
$$

Answer: 2646

So, the final answer is that all of the school buses together can bring 2,646 students to school in the morning.

Whew! Well, this method certainly was faster than using a number line or adding 63 together 42 times. However, multiplication does seem complicated. There are many math books which supply you with months of practice problems using different numbers. However, the procedure presented is used to solve every multiplication problem. It is important to understand why the multiplication was performed as shown. Once you understand why, multiplication will not seem very difficult, assuming the times table is memorized and addition is clearly understood.

IMPORTANT FOR UNDERSTANDING

4-9   Separating Multi-Digit Numbers for Multiplication

As you may have already learned, multiplying any number by 10 shifts the number by one place left.

$$5 \bullet 10 = 50$$
$$12 \bullet 10 = 120$$
$$346 \bullet 10 = 3,460$$

Multiplying any number by 100, shifts the numerical place two digits left.

$$5 \bullet 100 = 500$$
$$12 \bullet 100 = 1,200$$
$$346 \bullet 100 = 34,600$$

Any number multiplied by 1000 is shifted three times and any number multiplied by 10,000 is shifted four times. You may also remember how to multiply by 10, 100, 1000, etc., by simply adding the proper number of zeros to the number being multiplied.

The Associative Law of Multiplication can be used with the above information to help us multiply any numbers that have only one digit that is not zero.

$$5 \bullet 30 = 5 \bullet (3 \bullet 10) = (5 \bullet 3) \bullet 10 = 150$$

$$7 \bullet 80 = (7 \bullet 8) \bullet 10 = 560$$

$$3 \bullet 2000 = 6000$$

As shown for addition in section **3-11**, it is also necessary to separate the multi-digit numbers into numerical places to understand multiplication. To multiply (42)(63) we first separate the numbers as given below.

$$42 = 2 + 40$$
$$63 = 3 + 60$$

Therefore,

$$42 \bullet 63 = (42)(63) = (2 + 40) \ (3 + 60)$$

Using the distributive law from section **4-7**, we can rewrite the problem as shown. As you can see four different multiplications are required. Each result must then be added together to obtain the answer.

Multiplication #:   1   2   3   4

$$(2 + 40)(3 + 60) = (2)(3) + (2)(60) + (40)(3) + (40)(60)$$

Now we will compare the calculation shown in the last section with the calculation required by the Distributive Law of Multiplication. Step #2 from the example in section **4-8** is repeated here.

$$
\begin{array}{r}
63 \\
42 \\
\hline
6
\end{array}
$$

As you can see, 6 is the result of (2)(3). This is the first multiplication required according to the distributive law.

The second part of Step #2 from section **4-8** is repeated below.

$$
\begin{array}{r}
63 \\
42 \\
\hline
126
\end{array}
$$

The second multiplication required according to the distributive law is (2)(60) = 120. In this step we simply multiplied (2)(6) and wrote down the answer of 12 next to the previous answer of 6. However, we actually multiplied (2)(60). As you can see, the result of 1 is in the hundreds column, and 2 is in the tens column.

Step #3 from section **4-8** is repeated below.

$$
\begin{array}{r}
1 \\
63 \\
42 \\
\hline
126 \\
20
\end{array}
$$

The third multiplication required according to the distributive law is (40)(3). As you can see, this multiplication was accomplished in step #3. A 0 was inserted in the ones column to serve as a placeholder, or numerical reminder. This shifted the result of (4)(3) to (40)(3), which was required.

The final multiplication required according to the distributive law is (40)(60). This was also accomplished in step #3 as shown below. $4 \cdot 6 = 24$ and $24 + 1 = 25$.

$$
\begin{array}{r}
1 \\
63 \\
42 \\
\hline
126 \\
2520
\end{array}
$$

Look once again at the result according to the distributive law,

$$(42)(63) = (2 + 40)(3 + 60)$$
$$= (2)(3) + (2)(60) + (40)(3) + (40)(60)$$
$$= (6 + 120) + (120 + 2400)$$
$$= 126 + 2520$$

Step #5 from section **4-8** is repeated. Do you see a similarity with the distributive law?

```
      1
     63
     42
    ----
    126
 + 2520
 -------
   2646
```

126 was added to 2520, and the result of 2646 was obtained. This also was required in the expansion by the distributive law.

As you can see, the method used for multiplication is just application of the distributive law. However, by placing numbers in aligned columns, and using placeholders, we have a 'shortcut' method of applying the law.

To multiply numbers with more than two digits, the same pattern is repeated.

Let's look at an example with two 3-digit numbers.

Example - Multiplying 3-Digit Numbers

What is 246 • 124?

According to the distributive law,

$$(124)(246) = (4 + 20 + 100)(246)$$

The steps for multiplication with placeholders is given below. Note that two 0's were used as placeholders to multiply (100) • (246). Please verify this answer on your own.

```
      246
      124
    -----
      984
     4920
 + 24600
 --------
    30504
```

<u>Example - Multiplication of Multi-Digit Numbers</u>

What is 1024 • 61?

```
     12      ←— these are the carries
   1024
     61
   ——————
   1024
 + 61440
   ——————
   62464
```

If the number with more digits is placed on the bottom, obviously the same answer will result due to the Commutative Law of Multiplication. However, there are more additions to perform.

```
     61
   1024
   ——————
    244
   1220
   00000
 + 61000
   ——————
   62464
```

You should practice multiplication until you are very proficient at it. A good way to test yourself is to get a calculator, multiply two numbers, and see if you can get the same result by hand. You may be wondering, "Hey, if the calculator does multiplication, and a calculator only cost $2, why should I learn how to multiply by hand?"

The most obvious answer at this point is a calculator may not always be available. If a calculator is at hand, the batteries may go dead, or it may be dark whereby the solar cell won't work.

It is often faster to do calculations in your head without any paper. Furthermore, once math gets more advanced you will be multiplying letters (variables) instead of numbers, so the calculator won't help at all.

Standardized tests required for college such as the SAT and ACT do not allow the use of calculators.

Finally, and most importantly, if you completely rely on a calculator to supply the answer you will lose the ability to estimate and understand if your answer to the question is reasonable. Estimating the answer before you even calculate it is a very important ability that comes with much practice and hand calculation.

<u>Examples - Multiplication of Multi-Digit Numbers</u>

111 • 84 = 9,324
12 • 12 = 144
109 • 5687 = 619,883

4-10   Explaining Division

In multiplication a known number is added a certain number of times to yield a total.   In this example 3 is added two times.   The total is found to equal 6, or 3 • 2 = 6.

$$3 • 2 = ?$$
$$3 • 2 = 6$$

However, sometimes the total is known, and it is necessary to determine how many times a number was added to obtain the total.

$$3 • ? = 6$$

In this example, it is necessary to find the number of times 3 was added.   From our experience with multiplication, we can determine that 3 can only equal 6 if 3 was added together two times.

Answer: 3 • 2 = 6

Division is used to find the number of times a value was added to arrive at a known total. Division is the fourth and final fundamental math operation.   Division normally uses the operator   (÷).   Other operators used are (/), (—), and ($\overline{)}$). Therefore, we can write the following equivalent expressions.

$$6 ÷ 3 = 2$$

$$6 / 3 = 2$$

$$\frac{6}{3} = 2$$

$$3\overline{)6}^{\,2}$$

Each one of the expressions above is read aloud "six divided by three equals two". (Note that even the last example is read aloud as such.)   Each division operator is read "divided by." Division is a very appropriate term, since it means "to divide".   In the above example 6 is divided 3 times.   For example, consider a bundle of celery 6 inches long.

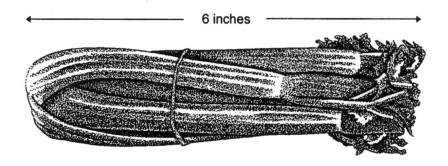

◄—————————— 6 inches ——————————►

Divide the celery into 3 equal length pieces.

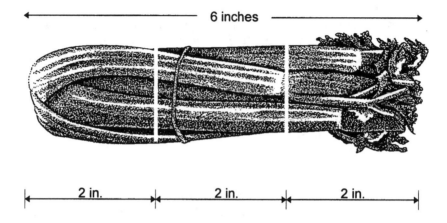

Each of the pieces is two inches long.

$$6 \text{ inches} \div 3 = 2 \text{ inches}$$

The number that is being divided is called the **dividend**. The number that is doing the dividing is called the **divisor**. The answer is the **quotient**.

$$6 \div 3 = 2$$

6 is the <u>dividend</u> since it is being divided.

3 is the <u>divisor</u> since it is dividing another number 3 times.

2 is the <u>quotient</u> since it is the result of the division.

4-11   Division of Single Digit Integers

This section probably should have been titled "Division of Integers which are located in the multiplication times table presented in an earlier section." That title, although more accurate, was lengthy. For this section, we'll merely call all of the numbers in the times table "single digit integers," even though not all of the numbers are of one digit (such as 12).

In section **3-9**, addition and subtraction were demonstrated to have a complementary nature. Multiplication and division also have a complementary nature and are called inverse operations. Division can 'undo' multiplication, and multiplication can 'undo' division. For example,

$$6 \div 2 \bullet 2 = 6$$
$$6 \bullet 3 \div 3 = 6$$

and

$$3 \bullet 2 = 6$$
$$6 \div 2 = 3$$
$$6 \div 3 = 2$$

In general, variables can be used to state that:

If

$$a \bullet b = c$$

then

$$c \div b = a$$
$$c \div a = b$$

Example - Using Division of Numbers in the Times Table

$$36 \div 4 = ?$$

There are several ways to solve this problem.

1. Take a group of 36 objects, maybe 36 marbles. Divide the 36 marbles into four equal sized piles. Then count how many marbles are in one pile to arrive at the answer.

2. Start at 0 on the number line. Then move four places right. Then move another four places right. Continue this pattern until you arrive at 36. Then count the number of times you had to move four places right, which provides the answer.

3. Use multiplication. Try different multipliers of four, until 36 is reached.

$$4 \bullet 1 = 4$$
$$4 \bullet 2 = 8$$
$$4 \bullet 3 = 12 \text{ ...etc.}$$

4. Use the memorized multiplication table. $4 \bullet ? = 36$. Earlier we found that $4 \bullet 9 = 36$.

Answer: 9

Any one of the above methods will solve a division problem, but the last method is most efficient.

Use your knowledge of the times table to verify the following examples.

Example - Division of Numbers in the Times Table

$$56 \div 8 = 7$$
$$8 \div 4 = 2$$
$$81 \div 9 = 9$$
$$30 \div 10 = 3$$

You should also understand division well enough to solve the following example.

Example - Using Division

21 people are taking one van to the zoo.
The van has three equally sized seats.
How many people should sit in each seat.

21 ÷ 3 = 7, so 7 people should sit in each seat

Answer: 7 people

As you may guess, there are no commutative, associative or distributive laws for division.

$$a \div b \neq b \div a$$

$$a \div (b \div c) \neq (a \div b) \div c$$

$$a \div (b + c) \neq (a \div b) + (a \div c)$$

The last math statement may also be rewritten as,

$$\frac{a}{(b+c)} \neq \frac{a}{b} + \frac{a}{c}$$

You may want to choose numbers and verify these statements.

4-12   Division of Multi-Digit Numbers

The 'backwards multiplication' approach is more difficult for numbers not found in the multiplication table. Let's do a multi-digit or **long division** example.

Example - Long Division

Your rich uncle has given your family a total of $39,835 to split evenly
between you and your four cousins.

How much should each of you take?

Division is necessary to solve the problem.

$$5 \cdot ? = 39,835$$

or

$$39,835 \div 5 = ?$$

It is necessary to calculate 39,835 ÷ 5.   As shown previously, there are four ways of writing any division problem.

The four forms are shown below using the numbers in the example problem.

FORM #1   FORM #2   FORM #3   **FORM #4**

$$39,835 \div 5 \; = \; 39,835/5 \; = \; \frac{39,835}{5} \; = \; 5\overline{)39,835}$$

Whenever, it is necessary to perform long division, it is best to use form #4. This form of division is similar to placing numbers in columns to perform multiplication.

Listed are the steps to perform long division of any numbers.

STEP - BY - STEP

Long Division of Any Two Numbers

1. Determine the divisor and dividend and arrange them in the proper form.

2. Determine the correct numerical place and value of the answer's first digit (or most significant digit). This is the largest integer multiplied by the divisor which is less than the dividend.

3. Multiply the answer's first digit by the divisor, and subtract this result from the dividend. Keep all numbers aligned in their proper places.

4. Determine the answer's second digit. Multiply the answer's second digit by the divisor and subtract this result from the result obtained in step #3.

5. Repeat step #4 as necessary for each ensuing digit.

Let's clarify the instructions with an example.

Example - Performing Long Division

$$39,835 \div 5 = ?$$

Step 1: Write the problem in proper long division form. Five is the divisor, and 39,835 is the dividend.

$$5\overline{)39835}$$

Step 2: Determine if the first digit of the answer will be in the ones, tens, hundreds, or greater place. In this example, look at the first digit in the dividend, 3. No single digit integer times five will give a result less than or equal to 3. Therefore, move one digit right in the dividend, to observe the first two digits 39.

There are several single digit integers which, multiplied by five, will yield a result less than or equal to 39. Choose the largest integer which meets this requirement. From the times table 7 is the answer.

```
     7
  _____
5)39835
```

Seven is placed directly above the 9. This implies that the answer has a 7 in the thousands place.

Step 3: Multiply the digit in the answer by the divisor. $7 \cdot 5 = 35$. Subtract this result from dividend. Note that the calculation actually performed is $7000 \cdot 5 = 35,000$ since 7 is in the thousands column.

```
     7
  _____
5)39835
  35000
   4835
```

Note the alignment of all of the numerical places.

Step 4: It is necessary to determine the next digit in the answer. Specifically, what value should be placed in the hundreds place?

Follow the same procedure as step #2. The only difference is that, you must now look at 4835 rather than the dividend to determine the digit. The largest single digit integer multiplied by 5 less than 48 is 9. Actually $5 \cdot 900 = 4500$ which is less than 4835, but we can just say $5 \cdot 9 = 45$ and place this result in the hundreds column.

```
     79
  _____
5)39835
  35000
   4835
   4500
    335
```

Step 5: Repeat step #4 for the next digit. The largest single digit integer multiplied by 5 less than 33 equals 6.

```
     796
  _____
5)39835
  35000
   4835
   4500
    335
    300
     35
```

Step 5 (con't): Repeat step #4, to find the last digit in the answer which equals 7.

$$
\begin{array}{r}
7967 \\
5\overline{)39835} \\
\underline{35000} \\
4835 \\
\underline{4500} \\
335 \\
\underline{300} \\
35 \\
\underline{35} \\
0
\end{array}
$$

The answer is that each of the five family members receives $7,967. To verify the answer, use multiplication.

$$
\begin{array}{r}
7967 \\
5 \\
\hline
39835
\end{array}
$$ √ yes, correct

Answer: $7,967

Let's return to step #5, and choose a wrong digit for the answer to see what happens. Rather than choosing the correct value of 6 for the tens column, let's try 8.

$$
\begin{array}{r}
798 \\
5\overline{)39835} \\
\underline{35000} \\
4835 \\
\underline{4500} \\
335 \\
\underline{400}
\end{array}
$$

(negative result)

As you may see, if too many tens are chosen, the result after subtraction is negative. Subtraction during a long division problem can **never be negative**. A negative result indicates that your value in the answer is too high. In the above problem, there are less than 7980 five's in 39,835.

Let's return to step #4, and choose a value which is too low. Rather than choosing the correct value of 9, use the value 7 in the hundreds place of the answer.

```
        77
    5)39835
      35000
       4835
       3500
       1335
```

A negative answer did not result, so that's good. However, in the next step it is necessary to choose the largest single digit which is less than 133. The best we can do is choose nine.

```
        779
    5)39835
      35000
       4835
       3500
       1335
        450
        885
```

As you can tell, we are now in trouble. No single digit integer times five comes even close to 885. We made a mistake, since there are more than 7799 five's in 39,835. The mistake could be recognized, when we subtracted 4835 from 3500 and obtained 1335. You will begin to recognize these mistakes as you acquire more skill in dividing. After understanding why division is performed in this manner, you will also be able to recognize mistakes more easily.

It is not necessary to use a single digit in the divisor.

Example - Long Division

$38,835 \div 15 = ?$

```
          2589
    15)38835
       30000
        8835
        7500
        1335
        1200
         135
         135
           0
```

Answer: 2589

This problem was more difficult since 15 was not in the times table either. In these problems, more skill is required in choosing the values for the answer. However, with more practice and further understanding, you will find that long division is not extremely difficult.

You should verify these examples. Remember that you may always verify your answer with multiplication.

<u>Examples - Long Division</u>

$1,984 \div 124 = 16$

$1,984 \div 16 = 124$

$9,840 \div 8 = 1,230$

$979,524 \div 1521 = 644$

IMPORTANT FOR UNDERSTANDING!

4-13   Separating Multi-Digit Numbers for Division

It is necessary to understand why division is performed as presented in the previous section. The key to understanding the method of division is the separation of numbers into numerical places. Separation of numbers was the key to addition in section **3-11**. Separation of numbers was also the key to multiplication in section **4-9**.

The following example was presented in the previous section:

$$38,835 \div 15 = ?$$

```
        2589
    15)38835
       30000
        8835
        7500
        1335
        1200
         135
         135
           0
```

The first digit in the answer was a 2 placed in the thousands place. $15 \bullet 2000 = 30000$
The second digit in the answer was a 5 in the hundreds place. $15 \bullet\ 500 =\ 7500$
The third digit in the answer was an 8 in the tens place. $15 \bullet\ 80 =\ 1200$
The final digit in the answer was a 9 in the ones place. $15 \bullet\ 9 =\ 135$

Adding all of intermediate calculations yields the dividend.

$$15 \bullet \underline{2000} = 30000$$
$$15 \bullet \underline{500} = 7500$$
$$15 \bullet \underline{80} = 1200$$
$$15 \bullet \underline{9} = 135$$
$$\overline{38{,}835}$$

Using the distributive law,

$$15 \bullet (2000 + 500 + 80 + 9) = 38{,}835$$

Using the method of division in the previous section applied the separation of numbers. In the above example, it is necessary to first find how many thousands of (15) are in the answer. It is then necessary to find how many hundreds of (15) are in the answer. This process was repeated until it was found that the dividend contained 2,859 fifteen's (i.e. 2859 • 15 = 38,835)

If you understood sections **3-11** and **4-9**, understanding why division is performed as presented should be clear. If it is not clear, please read previous sections before continuing.

4-14   Division with Remainders

So far the division examples have been carefully picked so that the answer is always an integer number. Look once again at the following example.

```
            2589
        15)38835
          30000
           8835
           7500
           1335
           1200
            135
            135
              0
```

After the final digit of 9 was placed in the ones column, subtraction of the remaining dividend resulted in zero.

```
            135
            135
            ───
              0
```

However, what happens if the final subtraction does not result in zero? Look at the following example:

$$38838 \div 15 = ?$$

```
         2589
      ┌─────────
    15)38838
       30000
       ─────
        8838
        7500
        ────
        1338
        1200
        ────
         138
         135
         ───
           3
```

This remaining number, after the final digit in the answer has been determined, is called the **remainder.** All previous division examples had a remainder of zero. However, in the above example, the remainder is 3.

The reason a remainder exists in the above example is that there is no integer multiplied by 15 which equals 38,838. We know that 2589 fifteen's is 38,835, as found in previous examples. We also can easily find that 2590 fifteen's is 38,850 (38,835 + 15 = 38,850, or 2590 • 15 = 38,850). The remainder shows that the answer is slightly more than 2589 but less than 2590.

There are three options to completing the solution to this division problem.

Option #1: Simply state that the solution has a remainder. For the example above, the final solution would be 2589 remainder 3, or 2589 R 3. This is the solution normally used when a student is first learning to divide.

Option #2: Simply state the integer portion of the answer, in addition to whatever remains to be divided. For the above example, the answer is

2589 and 3/15

or

2589 + 3/15

or

2589 3/15

All of these forms are equivalent. You will use this form more often in the next chapter on fractions.

Option #3: Continue dividing. It may look like there are no other numbers to divide. However, remember that you may add zeros past the decimal point of any integer without changing the value of the integer.

```
            2589.2
        _____
    15)38838.0
       30000
       _____
        8838
        7500
       _____
        1338
        1200
       _____
         138
         135
       _____
           3.0
           3.0
        _____
            .0
```

As shown, the answer to this problem is exactly 2589.2. There is no telling how many zeros will be required before the remainder of a division problem will equal zero. In this example only one zero was necessary. The answer can always be completed by assuming that you are close enough (2589 ≈ 2589.2). The type of problem will usually determine how many places after the decimal point are required for an answer which is 'close enough'. Remember to keep all numbers aligned properly.

Let's look at another example.

Example - Division with a Remainder

Your father has promised you and your three brothers $18 total. Each brother must get the exact same amount, or your father will take all of the money back.

How much money should each of you get?

$18 must be split evenly among four people. Therefore, you know that you must divide 18 by 4 to get the correct amount, so perform the division.

```
       4
    4)18
      16
      ___
       2
```

Well, so far you know you get $4 plus a little more since there is a remainder of 2. To continue the calculation, remember that 2 = 2.000 and 18 = 18.000. So, add in whatever number of zeros are needed. Remember to put the decimal point after the ones place in the answer (align the answer with the dividend), and finish dividing.

```
       4.5
   4)18.0
     16.0
      2.0
      2.0
        0
```

Each of you gets 4.5 dollars, or $4.50.

Answer: $4.50

Sometimes the remainder will NEVER reach zero! Also note that the divisor can be greater than the dividend. The answer will then ONLY contain digits to the right of the decimal point. One example with both of these properties is given below.

Example - Remainder Never Reaches Zero

$$1 \div 3 = ?$$

```
       0.33333
   3)1.00000
     0.90000
     0.10000
     0.09000
     0.01000
     0.00900
     0.00100
     0.00090
     0.00010
     0.00009
     0.00001
```

We kept adding zeros after the decimal point, but the remainder never became zero. If this happens, you should stop dividing when you think the answer is close enough to the exact answer.   In this case, 0.333 may be close enough. Computers usually will show up to 8 or 16 places after the decimal. Any more than 16 places right of the decimal will usually change the number too little for anyone to care.

The division problem is again shown without all of the zeros. Do you see that if you keep numbers aligned with the answer that it is not necessary to write down every placeholder, or even every decimal point? This is the method that you will probably want to use when dividing.

```
      0.33333
   3)1.00000
      0.9
      ___
       .10
       .09
       ___
        .010
        .009
        ____
           10
            9
           __
           10
            9
           __
            1
```

To be exact, put a bar over the repeating digits in an ever-repeating decimal. This is standard math notation. Therefore, we may draw a bar over one 3 to indicate that the value of 3 continues for all ensuing digits.

$$1 \div 3 = 0.3333\overline{3}$$

Another example you may want to try is:

$$17 \div 12 = 1.4166\overline{6}$$

You should verify that you can obtain the following results.

Examples - Division with Decimal Results
$12 \div 5 = 2.4$
$164 \div 18 = 9.11\overline{1}$
$1019 \div 51 \approx 19.98$
$5 \div 7 = .\overline{714285}$

When one integer is divided by another integer, the result is a **rational number**. (Section **8-6** defines irrational numbers.) A rational number may be an integer or decimal, as shown in previous examples. A rational number which is a decimal that never ends (such as $1 \div 3$), will always be a **repeating decimal**.

4-15   Multiplying Decimals

As shown in section **4-9**, the number 10 and multiples of 10 (i.e. 100, 1000, 10,000, etc.) are very convenient. Multiplication by 10 simply shifts the decimal point of a number one digit to the right to make the answer 10 times larger. Multiplication by 100 simply shifts the decimal point two digits to the right.

```
0.3 • 10   =    3      (decimal point shifted once right)
0.3 • 100  =   30      (decimal point shifted twice right)
3   • 10   =   30      (decimal point shifted once right)
3   • 100  =  300      (decimal point shifted twice right)
3   • 1000 = 3000      (decimal point shifted three times right)
```

A division by 10 simply shifts the decimal point of a number one place to the left.

```
600 ÷ 10   = 60        (decimal point shifted once left)
600 ÷ 100  =  6        (decimal point shifted twice left)
 60 ÷ 10   =  6        (decimal point shifted once left)
 60 ÷ 100  =  0.6      (decimal point shifted twice left)
  6 ÷ 10   =  0.6      (decimal point shifted once left)
  6 ÷ 100  =  0.06     (decimal point shifted twice left)
```

This information is helpful when multiplying and dividing decimals.

Multiplying decimals is more than just a decimal alignment as in addition and subtraction. Look at the following examples, although you are not expected to understand the decimal point alignment yet.

Example - Multiplying Decimals

6.3 • 4.2

```
   6.3
   4.2
  ─────
  1.26
 25.20
 ─────
 26.46
```

Answer: 26.46

Example - Multiplying Decimals

63.1 • 42

$$
\begin{array}{r}
63.1 \\
42 \\
\hline
126.2 \\
2524.0 \\
\hline
2650.2
\end{array}
$$

Answer: 2650.2

Inserting decimal points with placeholders is confusing for some, and is taught in slightly different ways. The following **STEP-BY-STEP** box shows the method usually given in school.

STEP - BY - STEP

Multiplying Two Decimal Numbers

1.   Shift the decimal point of the numbers to be multiplied to the <u>right</u> a total of *R* times to obtain integers. *R* is the sum of the shifts of both numbers.

2.   Multiply the integers.

3.   Shift the decimal point of the answer a total of *R* times to the <u>left.</u>

In the **STEP-BY-STEP** instructions, *R* is a variable. Let's clarify with an example.

Example - Multiplying Decimals

$6.3 \bullet 4.2 = ?$

Step 1: Make the numbers integers by shifting the decimal point.

$6.3 \longrightarrow 63$ requires one shift of the decimal point right.
$4.2 \longrightarrow 42$ requires one shift of the decimal point right.

$R = 1 + 1 = 2$ shifts total

Step 2: Multiply the integers.

$$
\begin{array}{r}
63 \\
42 \\
\hline
126 \\
+ \; 2520 \\
\hline
2646
\end{array}
$$

Step 3: Shift the decimal point in the answer $R = 2$ places left.

$$2646.0$$

2 shifts left

Answer: 26.46

This method is simple, but why does it work? To completely understand why this method works, it is necessary to understand fractions which are explained in chapter 5. However, you may be able to determine why multiplication of decimals works as described in **STEP-BY-STEP** with the steps given below.

At this point you may not understand how to proceed from step #2 to step #3. However, once fractions are explained (in chapter 5), this method should become clear.

The computation actually performed was:

Step 1:	6.3 • 4.2		Original numbers
Step 2:	$\dfrac{63}{10}$ • $\dfrac{42}{10}$		Two right shifts, numbers put in form of division
Step 3:	$\dfrac{(63 \cdot 42)}{(10 \cdot 10)}$		Change of Multiplication order (allowed per, commutative law)
Step 4:	$\dfrac{2646}{100}$		Multiplication
Step 5:	26.46		Answer by division in previous step

To perform multiplication with decimal numbers, first each decimal is multiplied by a certain number of tens until it is an integer. The integers are multiplied, and then divided by the same number of tens. Since $10 \div 10$, $100 \div 100$, and $1000 \div 1000$, are all equal to one, and since

$$a \cdot 1 = a$$

the problem is not changed. Multiplying, and later dividing by the same number makes the problem of multiplying decimals easier.

Use the method of multiplying decimals to verify the following examples.

Examples - Multiplying Decimals

$0.63 \bullet 42 = 26.46$

$0.63 \bullet 0.42 = 0.2646$

$125.5 \bullet 1.6 = 200.8$

$14.6 \bullet 74 = 1080.4$

$18.5 \bullet 6 = 111.0 = 111$

A NEW WAY OF THINKING?

Think for a moment about multiplication. $4 \bullet 5$ means that the number 4 is added five times. This is simple to understand. However, now we may have problems such as $4 \bullet 0.5$. Does this mean that 4 is added a total of 0.5 times? This is more difficult to understand, even though the calculation of $4 \bullet 0.5$ is not much more difficult than $4 \bullet 5$.

You may think of $4 \bullet 0.5$ as a part of 4. $4 \bullet 0 = 0$ and $4 \bullet 1 = 4$. Therefore $4 \bullet 0.5$ must be between 0 and 4. $4 \bullet 0.1$ must equal a smaller part of 4 than $4 \bullet 0.5$. This idea is expanded upon in chapter 6.

This discussion may be a little confusing. However, when you understand how to perform the math, it often helps to stop and reflect on what the math is doing. Many learn how to perform math calculations, but few stop and think to understand the math. Understanding provides many new insights.

4-16   Dividing Decimals

At this point, you should understand decimals and understand how to multiply, add, and subtract them. You should also know how to divide integers which result in either integer or decimal answers.

If the dividend contains a decimal, divide as presented previously. However, remember to keep the decimal point aligned.

Example - Division with a Decimal Dividend

$38.838 \div 15 = ?$

```
          2.5892
     15)38.8380
        30.0000
         8.8380
         7.5000
         1.3380
         1.2000
          .1380
          .1350
          .0030
          .0030
              0
```

As stated previously, if numbers are aligned properly, it is only necessary to pay attention to the decimal point in the answer. You may simply ignore the decimal point when subtracting the dividend. For example,

```
          2.5892
     15)38.838
        30.000
         8838
         7500
         1338
         1200
          138
          135
           30
           30
            0
```

Verify the following examples.

Examples - Division with a Decimal Dividend
$8.4 \div 2 = 4.2$
$369.6 \div 16 = 23.1$
$1518.435 \div 123 = 12.345$

There is only one more type of division problem encountered. The divisor may be a decimal number. This problem may be solved with the following steps.

STEP - BY - STEP

Division with a Decimal Divisor

1. Shift the divisor **R** places to the right to make the divisor an integer.

2. Shift the dividend **R** places to the right.

3. Calculate the division using the modified divisor and dividend.

Let's clarify with an example.

Example - Division with a Decimal Divisor

It is Thanksgiving and your mother wants to know how many people she can feed with turkey. You know that each one of your family members normally eats 1.5 pounds of Turkey. (You're big eaters!) You also know that the biggest turkey that can fit in the oven is 27 pounds.

How many people will be full?

$$1.5\overline{)27} = ?$$

Step 1: Remove the decimal from the divisor. In this example, one shift is required, or *R* = 1.

$$1.5 \rightarrow 15$$

Step 2: Shift the dividend *R* = 1 place to the right.

$$27.0 \rightarrow 270$$

Step 3: Calculate the division using the modified divisor and dividend.

```
        18
   15)270
      15
      120
      120
        0
```

Answer: 18 people will be full

The reason for this method is similar to the reason for the method of multiplying decimals. By shifting both the divisor and dividend, the problem is actually multiplied by 1. This will become more clear after the chapter on fractions.

For now, you should verify the following examples.

Examples - Division

$120 \div 10 = 12$
$12 \div 1 = 12$
$1.2 \div 0.1 = 12$

$355.1 \div 21.2 = 16.75$
$35.51 \div 2.12 = 16.75$

$100 \div 33.3 = 3.00\overline{3003}$

4-17 Rounding and Truncation

A number's accuracy can be determined by the numerical place of its least significant digit.

If someone asked "How many inches tall are you?", you may measure yourself and reply 60 inches. (Inches are represented by ".") This answer may be close, but with a better ruler you may find yourself to be 63" tall. Therefore, 63" is more accurate than 60". The doctor may find that you are really 63.4" tall, so this measurement is still more accurate.

Many times someone is satisfied with a number that is 'close enough.' (But don't tell that to your math teacher.) For example, your home may be about 1600 miles from Disneyland. After weeks of measurement with a ruler and map, you may find that your home is actually 1613.5 miles from Disneyland. However, your initial approximation of 1600 is probably close enough even though 1613.5 is more accurate.

On the other hand, after much tedious measuring you may find that your home is exactly 1600 miles away. To indicate that 1600 is not an approximation, but an accurate measurement, you could write that your home is 1600.0 miles away. The decimal in this circumstance shows that you paid attention to the number of miles, all the way down to the tenths place.

It is impossible to increase the accuracy of a number by looking at it. However, it is possible to decrease the accuracy of any number. There are two ways of decreasing the accuracy of a number.

The first method is truncation. Truncation is performed only on numbers containing decimals. To truncate a number, first decide the final decimal place you would like to keep. Then remove all digits to the right of that place.

Examples - Truncation

Number	Truncated Number	
3.25	3.2	(truncate to tenths place)
5.62222	5.62	(truncated to hundredths place)
24.89999	24.899	(truncated to thousandths place)
45	45	(cannot truncate an integer)

Therefore, to **truncate** a decimal is to remove unwanted decimal places. Truncate literally means "to shorten by cutting off."

The second method of accuracy reduction is rounding. Rounding may be performed on any number -- integer or decimal. To **round** a number, decide the numerical place of accuracy. Then, look to the digit right of the chosen numerical place of accuracy. If that digit is less than 5, remove that digit and all digits to the right. If the digit is greater than 5, add 1 to your numerical place of accuracy and remove all digits to the right.

Does that sound confusing? Some examples will help clarify. Sometimes examples make much more sense than a long explanation.

To summarize, rounding is choosing the number closest to the desired place of accuracy. Truncating is cutting off all decimal digits to the right of the chosen place of accuracy.

	Examples - Rounded Numbers	
Number	**Rounded Number**	
24.89999	24.9	(rounded to tenths place)
24.89999	25	(rounded to ones place)
24.89999	20	(rounded to tens place)
5.500000	6	(rounded to ones place)
5.504000	5.50	(rounded to hundredths place)
5.505000	5.51	(rounded to hundredths place
5.499999	5	(rounded to ones place)
1603	1600	(rounded to tens place)
1649	1600	(rounded to hundreds place)
1651	1700	(rounded to hundreds place)

When is truncation or rounding used? There are many cases, but the most obvious is in dealing with money. The lowest form of money is a penny ($0.01). Therefore, accuracy of money should only extend to the hundredths place. $5.256 doesn't make much sense, but $5.25 or $5.26 is clear.

4-18 A Pause for Congrats!

If you've made it this far, and thoroughly understand all of the concepts, you should be thankful and deserve to be congratulated! Maybe it's time to go outside and have some fun.

We have covered the four major math operations. All four operations will be utilized throughout your entire math education and daily life. All of mathematics is developed from these fundamental operators. We now move on to expanding our knowledge of these operators and numbers in general.

Remember, all that we have learned started with the operation of addition. After addition, it was necessary to 'undo' addition, so the inverse operator of subtraction was developed. Repeated addition of the same number became tedious, so multiplication was developed. Finally, multiplication also needed an inverse operation. This need was met with division.

The chapters to follow will only make sense if you understand what has been taught previously. If you don't understand some of the following material please reread earlier sections. Sections **3-11**, **4-9**, and **4-14** are especially important since they explain *why* math is performed as shown. If you have understood everything clearly, you are well on your way to becoming a math expert.

Math Laws

Commutative Law
of Multiplication

Associative Law
of Multiplication

Distributive Law
of Multiplication

Important Definitions

Product

Distribute

Dividend

Divisor

Quotient

Long Division

Remainder

Rational Number

Truncate

Round

You should be able to ...

1. Multiply any two numbers (integers or decimals)

2. Apply the Distributive Law of Multiplication

3. Understand how multiplication works

4. Divide any two numbers (integers or decimals)

5. Understand how division works

6. Round or Truncate a number to a given accuracy

Fractions

5-1 Defining Fractions

In previous chapters, only integers and decimals have been used. However, some objects are better described with a number written in a form different than an integer or decimal. For example, assume you have one pizza cut into two slices. You then eat one slice. How many whole pizzas are left? Fewer than one pizza remains. Greater than zero pizza remains. So how much pizza is left? We know there is one slice, but how many pizzas?

We can calculate how much pizza remains with division. Let's determine the amount remaining by dividing the one remaining slice by the original total of two slices.

$$\frac{1}{2} = ?$$

This calculation isn't difficult if you remember the rules given in chapter four.

$$
\begin{array}{r}
0.5 \\
2\overline{)1.0} \\
\underline{1.0} \\
0
\end{array}
$$

There are 0.5 pizzas remaining. But, few state that "there are five tenths pizza left" or "there are zero point five pizzas left" when only one of two slices remain. You probably already know that "one half" or "half" of the pizza is left, but what is one half? One half is a fraction.

Technically speaking, a **fraction** is a number in the form of $\frac{a}{b}$ where a and b are any valued numbers separated by the familiar division sign. (Actually $b \neq 0$, since division by 0 is not allowed.) The number above the division sign (a) is called the **numerator**. The number written below the division sign (b) is called the **denominator**.

In our pizza example, the fraction one-half is written: $\frac{1}{2}$. This fraction indicates that the amount of pizza remaining is one of a total of two slices. The fraction could also be written as 1/2, using an alternate form of the division sign. A fraction is simply an integer or decimal number, prior to completing the division.

So, we found by division that $\frac{1}{2}$ = 0.5. Therefore, the fraction and decimal would be placed in the exact same place on the number line. A fraction is often used when describing the amount remaining from a total.

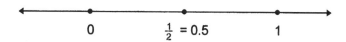

$$0 \qquad \tfrac{1}{2} = 0.5 \qquad 1$$

Examples - Using Fractions

Your mother bakes six cupcakes, and you eat one of them.
What fraction of the original number of cupcakes have you eaten?
What fraction of cupcakes are left for others to eat?

Answer: $\frac{1}{6}$ of the cupcakes have been eaten

$\frac{5}{6}$ of the cupcakes remain to be eaten

5-2   Reading Fractions

Fractions are usually read aloud by first reading the numerator digit, then reading the denominator digit and adding a "ths" sound. So, $\frac{5}{8}$ is read "five eighths", $\frac{23}{67}$ is read "twenty-three sixty-sevenths", and so on. However, there are a few special names for fractions with certain denominators.

A two in the denominator is read "half" or "halves" and a three is read aloud as "third" or "thirds". Therefore $\frac{1}{2}$ is read "one half", and $\frac{7}{2}$ is read "seven halves". Furthermore, $\frac{1}{3}$ is "one third", and $\frac{2}{3}$ is "two thirds".

Another way to read fractions is to use the word "over" to separate the integers in the numerator and denominator. Therefore $\frac{5}{8}$ is also read as "5 over 8" and $\frac{23}{67}$ is read "23 over 67". When using this terminology, the word "over" represents the division bar. 23 is literally written over 67. Verify the following problems using your knowledge of division and reading fractions.

Examples - Fractions to Decimals

three fifths = 0.6

eight thirds = $2.\overline{6}$

25 over 100 = 0.25

$\frac{13}{65} = 0.2$

5-3   Types of Fractions

A fraction may also be defined as a **ratio** of numbers, where a ratio is just the division relationship *a/b*. The values of *a* and *b* can determine the type of the fraction.

1. A **proper fraction** has a value less than one. Therefore, the numerator (*a*) is less than the denominator (*b*) in a proper fraction.

2. An **improper fraction** has a value greater than one. Therefore, the numerator (*a*) is greater than the denominator (*b*) in a proper fraction.

3. A **mixed number** is a number which is a mix of an integer and a fraction. An example is $3\frac{1}{2}$ which is read "three and one half" and is the same as $3 + \frac{1}{2}$. Some answers to division problems in section **4-14** were mixed numbers. Section **5-14** will show how to convert every mixed number into an improper fraction, since improper fractions are easier to use.

5-4   Converting Fractions to Decimals

As explained in the previous section, a decimal is obtained from a fraction by dividing the numerator by the denominator. The division of the fraction is the same as any other division such as $a \div b$. Let's try to find the decimal equivalent of another fraction.

<u>Example - Fraction to Decimal</u>

What decimal is equal to $\frac{1}{16}$? (read aloud as "one sixteenth")

When dividing, remember that as many zeros as necessary can be added to the right of the decimal point past last non-zero digit.

$$
\begin{array}{r}
0.0625 \\
16\overline{)1.0000} \\
\underline{.9600} \\
.0400 \\
\underline{.0320} \\
.0080 \\
\underline{.0080} \\
.0000
\end{array}
$$

Answer: $\frac{1}{16} = 0.0625$

Since you already know how to divide integers and obtain an answer with a decimal from section **4-14**, additional explanation should not be necessary. To convert a fraction to a decimal just divide.

5-5   Converting Decimals to Fractions

The number 0.5 is read "five tenths" as stated in section **2-5** on **Decimals**. But five tenths is also the same as the fraction $\frac{5}{10}$ according to the section on reading fractions (section **5-2**). So, we can now write

$$\frac{5}{10} = 0.5 = \frac{1}{2}$$

These are all equivalent numbers. As you can see, *a decimal is always read aloud as its equivalent fraction*.

Examples - Decimals to Fractions

0.35 = 35 hundredths = $\frac{35}{100}$

0.002 = 2 thousandths = $\frac{2}{1000}$

0.625 = six hundred twenty-five thousandths = 625 over 1000 = $\frac{625}{1000}$

How can two different fractions such as $\frac{5}{10}$ and $\frac{1}{2}$ be equal? Let's go back to thinking about pizzas. Assume you ordered one whole pizza. Would you be eating more pizza if you cut the pizza in two equal slices and ate one slice, or if you cut the pizza in 10 equal slices and ate 5 slices? You would be eating the same amount. In the first situation you would eat one huge slice of pizza, and in the second case you would be eating 5 smaller slices. Either way, once you are finished eating, half of the pizza will be in your belly.

$$\frac{1}{2} = \frac{5}{10} \Rightarrow$$

0.0625 is read aloud as "six hundred twenty-five ten thousandths", or as "point zero six two five." Therefore, using the example calculation of (1 / 16) in section **5-4**,

$$\frac{1}{16} = \frac{625}{10000}$$

It was necessary to divide to find the decimal equivalent of one sixteenth. However, the decimal equivalent of $\frac{625}{10000}$ may be found simply by looking at the fraction.

To summarize, any decimal can easily be written as a fraction after reading aloud the decimal number. The fraction and decimal are equivalent numbers but are written in different forms.

5-6   Multiplying Fractions

There is much to learn regarding fractions. However, learning how to multiply fractions is a necessary first step. As you will see, multiplication is actually the most simple of the four fundamental operations to perform with fractions.

To multiply two fractions simply multiply the numerators together, and multiply the denominators together.

Example - Multiplying Fractions

$$\frac{1}{2} \bullet \frac{9}{8} = \frac{9}{16}$$

$$7 \bullet \frac{3}{4} = \frac{21}{4}$$

(Remember, that $7 = \frac{7}{1}$)

There is no need for further explanation. Multiplying fractions is that simple.

5-7   Making Different but Equal Fractions

In previous sections, you have learned how to convert back and forth between decimals and fractions and how to multiply fractions together. We have also found in section **5-5** that fractions with different denominators may be equal. For example, we learned that,

$$\frac{1}{16} = \frac{625}{10000}$$

The goal of this section is to develop a method for making equal fractions with different denominators. To begin, remember these simple rules from earlier chapters for any number a.

$$a \bullet 1 = a \qquad\qquad \frac{a}{a} = 1$$

Using these rules, we may write the following true math statement.

$$\frac{a}{b} = \left(\frac{a}{b}\right)(1) = \left(\frac{a}{b}\right)\left(\frac{c}{c}\right) = \frac{ac}{bc} = \frac{a}{b}$$

Remember from section **4-2**, ac simply means $a \bullet c$ or $(a)(c)$.

The above math formula shows that a fraction's value remains the same if the numerator and denominator are multiplied (or divided) by the same number. In the above formula, that number was represented by the letter c.

Based on the given formula, we may change 1/2 to 5/10 by multiplying both the numerator and denominator by 5.

$$\frac{1}{2} = \frac{1}{2} \bullet \frac{5}{5} = \frac{5}{10}$$

We can convert $\frac{5}{10}$ into $\frac{1}{2}$ by multiplying the numerator and denominator by $\frac{1}{5}$.

$$\frac{5}{10} \bullet \frac{\frac{1}{5}}{\frac{1}{5}} = \frac{1}{2}$$

or by dividing the numerator and denominator by 5. As you may recognize, multiplying by $\frac{1}{5}$ is the exact same as dividing by 5.

$$\frac{\frac{5}{5}}{\frac{10}{5}} = \frac{1}{2}$$

To summarize, an equivalent fraction can be created by multiplying or dividing the numerator and denominator by the same number.

5-8   Simplifying Fractions with Factorization and Cancellation

**MAKE A NOTE.
FACTORS ARE
IMPORTANT!**

To **factor** an integer is to separate the number into two or more integers, that when multiplied together equal the original number. The separated numbers are called **factors**. You may factor a number using multiplication and division. A number may often be factored into different sets of numbers. The process of finding factors of an integer is called **factorization**. Using your knowledge of multiplication, verify the examples in the box below.

<u>Examples - Factoring Numbers</u>
12 = 2 • 6
12 = 3 • 4
24 = 3 • 8
24 = 4 • 6
24 = 12 • 2
10 = 2 • 5
10 = 10 • 1

In the following equation, the numerator and denominator are both factored, and a common factor of 5 is found in the numerator and denominator. Based on what we learned in the previous section, a factor common to the numerator and denominator may be canceled (since $a \div a = 1$).

$$\frac{5}{10} = \frac{1 \bullet 5}{2 \bullet 5} = \frac{1}{2} \bullet \frac{5}{5} = \frac{1}{2} \bullet 1 = \frac{1}{2}$$

When given a general expression such as $\frac{ac}{bc}$ we can simply **cancel** the c's, to arrive at an equivalent fraction of $\frac{a}{b}$. In the previous example, $c = 5$. This cancellation technique is a very convenient shortcut which is often used when simplifying or multiplying fractions. Verify the following examples using factorization and cancellation.

Examples - Simplifying Fractions with Factorization and Cancellation

$$\frac{6}{20} = \frac{3}{10}$$

$$\frac{8}{28} = \frac{4}{14} = \frac{2}{7}$$

$$\frac{4}{9} \cdot \frac{9}{8} = \frac{4}{1} \cdot \frac{1}{8} = \frac{1}{2}$$

Cancellation of numbers is very useful. However, cancellation may also be applied to units such as miles, feet, and gallons. Let's look at a few examples.

Example - Cancellation of Units

A plane flies 600 miles per hour (mph) for 4 hours.

How far has the plane flown during the 4 hours?

A standard formula from elementary physics tells us that: Rate • Time = Distance

In this example, the rate (or speed) is 600 mph, and the time traveled is 4 hours.

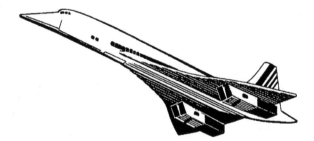

$$\frac{600 \text{ miles}}{1 \text{ hour}} \cdot \frac{4 \text{ hours}}{1} = 2400 \text{ miles}$$

Answer: 2400 miles

Note that the unit of *hours* existed in the numerator and denominator. Therefore, the units of hours were canceled, and units of the resulting answer was simply miles. Prior to any calculation, we knew that distance had to be in miles, not hours. Therefore, we knew before any calculation that the units of hours must somehow cancel so the answer would only contain units of miles.

For hours to cancel, 600 miles/hour had to be <u>multiplied</u> by 4 hours. Any other math operation would have yielded different units. (Note that the word *per* represents division. 600 miles per hour means that 600 miles are traveled for every 1 hour.)

Cancellation of units is extremely helpful when converting between different standards of measurements as the next example shows.

> ### Example - Cancellation of Units
>
> How many meters are in one mile?

By looking at conversion numbers in most math or science books, we can find the following information. However, there is no direct conversion for meters to miles.

$$5280 \text{ feet} = 1 \text{ mile}$$
$$12 \text{ inches} = 1 \text{ foot}$$
$$2.54 \text{ centimeter} = 1 \text{ inch}$$
$$100 \text{ centimeter} = 1 \text{ meter}$$

By knowing that the units of miles must somehow cancel, and only meters must remain, we can make up our own formula.

$$\frac{1 \text{ mile}}{1} \cdot \frac{5280 \text{ feet}}{1 \text{ mile}} \cdot \frac{12 \text{ inches}}{1 \text{ foot}} \cdot \frac{2.54 \text{ cm}}{1 \text{ inch}} \cdot \frac{1 \text{ meter}}{100 \text{ cm}} = 1609.3 \text{ meters}$$

Note that every unit cancels, except meters which is the units of our answer. Remember that units which are the same in the numerator and denominator of a fraction cancel, just like numbers. Anything divided by itself equals one.

Maybe it's time for you to take a break?

The goal of this chapter is first to understand fractions. Then we will use our understanding to add, subtract, and divide fractions. One way to perform each operation is to first convert every fraction to a decimal, and then perform the desired operation as explained in previous chapters.

However, sometimes we should use the fractions in computations. Fractions are more accurate than rounded or truncated decimals (see section **4-17**, **Rounding and Truncation**). Sometimes fractions are even easier to use than decimals since fractions can take advantage of cancellation. Therefore, we need to learn how to directly use fractions to perform operations. Multiplication of fractions has already been shown. However, before we can perform other operations with fractions, we have to talk about a few other topics. The first of these topics is prime numbers.

Hang in there. There is much to be learned before you can perform all four fundamental operations with fractions.

5-9   Prime Numbers

A **prime number** is an integer that produces another integer only when divided by itself or 1. With any other divisor, the result is a non-integer or decimal number.

To determine if a number is prime, divide the number by 2, then 3, then 4, etc., until you reach the number you are attempting to determine prime. If any quotient is an integer, the number is not prime. Let's look at a few examples.

(Note: Actually, if you are trying to determine if the number a is prime, you only need to divide by 2, 3, 4, ... $a/2$ rather than 2, 3, 4, ... a. Try this, and make sure you understand why it is true.)

Example - Prime Numbers

Is 5 a prime number?

$$\frac{5}{2} = 2.5 \qquad \frac{5}{3} = 1.67 \qquad \frac{5}{4} = 1.25$$

Since all of the results are non-integers, 5 is a prime number.

Example - Prime Numbers

Is 6 a prime number?

$$\frac{6}{2} = 3$$

Since the result is an integer, 6 is not a prime number. We did not need to divide six by 3, 4, or 5, since only one integer result is needed to determine that a number is not prime.

Generally, larger numbers require more calculations to determine if prime since more division operations are required. Furthermore, as you continually try greater numbers, fewer and fewer numbers are prime.

One of the ways the government makes secret codes is by figuring out <u>very large</u> prime numbers to use as codes. Even computers would take hundreds of years to calculate whether these huge numbers were prime using the method shown here. Of course, the government has some secret math tricks to find prime numbers. Only the 'rich' mathematicians employed by the government know these tricks. Maybe some day you'll be one of them. Oh well, enough day-dreaming, back to work.

An **even number** is an integer that when divided by 2, produces an integer. So 2, 4, 6, 8, 10, 12, 14, etc., are all even numbers. As you can see, an even number is every other counting number, and is simply 2(1), 2(2), 2(3), etc. Since an even number yields an integer when divided by 2, no even number can be prime. Actually there is one exception. The number 2 is by definition the lowest valued prime number.

An **odd number** is any integer that is not even. This would imply that odd numbers are 1, 3, 5, 7, 9, etc. Obviously odd numbers can be prime.

Listed below are all of the prime numbers less than 100. You should be able to verify that all of these numbers are prime. There are a few shortcuts to figuring out if a number is prime or not. As stated previously, an even number cannot be prime since it can be divided evenly by 2. A number that ends in a 5 or 0 also cannot be prime since such a number can always be evenly divided by 5 or by 10.

All Prime Numbers Less Than 100					
11	2	3	5	7	19
31		13		17	29
41		23		37	59
61		43		47	79
71		53		67	89
		73		97	
		83			

5-10 Prime Factorization

Converting an integer to a multiplication of prime numbers is called **prime factorization**. It is called *prime* since the factors to be determined must be prime. As explained earlier, factorization is the separation of a number into integers that multiplied together produce the original number.

Remember the Commutative and Associative Laws of Multiplication state that numbers may be multiplied in any order, so the order of factors is of no concern. Listed are the steps to prime factorization.

STEP - BY - STEP
Prime Factorization of a Number
1. Obtain two factors of the original number.
2. Continue factorization of numbers until all factors are prime.

There are two ways to obtain factors as required in step #1. The first method is to guess, or use previous experience. The second method is to divide the number by 2. If dividing by 2 does not yield an integer, try 3. Continue until two factors are found. Remember that a number ending in 2, 5 or 0, can easily be factored with the integers 2, 5, and 10, respectively.

It is often convenient to make a factorization tree. A **factorization tree** lists all the factors of the original number. Each branch of the tree can be multiplied horizontally to produce the original number.

As with many topics in mathematics, prime factorization using factorization trees is best explained with a few examples.

Example - Prime Factorization

Find all of the prime factors of 85.

Step 1: Start by placing 85 at the top of the tree. The number ends in a 5, so 85 ÷ 5 must result in an integer. Place the factors as branches on the tree.

Step 2: 17 • 5 = 85. Both 17 and 5 are prime, so prime factorization is complete.

Answer: (5) (17) is the prime factorization of 85.

Let's try another example.

Example - Prime Factorization

Find all of the prime factors of 100.

Step 1: We'll start with 100 at the top of the tree. Since 100 ends in the digit 0, dividing 100 by 10 must result in an integer. (100 ÷ 10 = 10)

Step 2: 10 is not prime either, but can be factored into prime numbers 2 and 5.

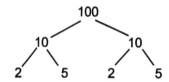

Answer: (2) (5) (2) (5) is the prime factorization of 100.

Example - Prime Factorization

Find all of the prime factors of 156.

Step 1: 156 is an even number. Therefore, it can be divided evenly by 2.

Step 2: Continue Factorization:

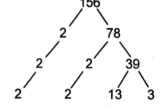

Answer: (2) (2) (13) (3) is the prime factorization of 156.

Remember that each branch of the tree can be multiplied horizontally to arrive at the starting number of 156. (e.g. $2 \bullet 78 = 2 \bullet 2 \bullet 39 = 2 \bullet 2 \bullet 13 \bullet 3 = 156$)

Prime factorization does take practice. However, you should find that it is not too difficult. The goal is to reduce one number into a multiplication of prime numbers. It does not matter which factors start the factorization tree. The bottom row of the tree will always contain the same prime numbers. (Since only one unique set of prime numbers produces the original number.)

Verify the following examples using your knowledge of prime factorization.

Examples - Prime Factorization

$144 = (2)(2)(3)(2)(2)(3)$

$18 = (2)(3)(3)$

$170 = (17)\,(5)\,(2)$

5-11 Reducing Fractions to Lowest Terms

In section **5-8**, we found the following relationship using factorization and cancellation. The fraction $\frac{1}{2}$ has no factors which are the same in the numerator and denominator. There is no fraction, equal to 0.5, which has a smaller valued numerator or denominator than $\frac{1}{2}$.

$$\frac{5}{10} = \frac{1}{2}$$

A fraction of **lowest terms** will have no factor which is the same in the numerator and denominator. Changing a fraction to this form is called **reducing a fraction to lowest terms**.

STEP - BY - STEP

To reduce a fraction to lowest terms

1. Perform prime factorization of the numerator and denominator.

2. Cancel numbers common to the numerator and denominator.

Let's clarify with an example. This section is the application of concepts learned in sections **5-8** and **5-10**, so please review those sections if necessary.

Example - Reducing a Fraction to Lowest Terms

Find an equivalent fraction for 18/45 which is of the lowest terms.

Step 1: Perform prime factorization of the numerator and denominator.

$$18 = (3)\ (3)\ (2)$$
$$45 = (5)\ (3)\ (3)$$

- or -

$$\frac{18}{45} = \frac{3 \bullet 3 \bullet 2}{5 \bullet 3 \bullet 3}$$

Step 2: Two 3's are common in the numerator and denominator, and may be canceled.

$$\frac{18}{45} = \frac{3 \bullet 3 \bullet 2}{5 \bullet 3 \bullet 3} = \frac{3 \bullet \cancel{3} \bullet 2}{5 \bullet \cancel{3} \bullet 3} = \frac{2}{5}$$

Any equal numbers in the numerator and denominator cancel. Therefore, in the above example, a short-cut to reducing the fraction would have been to cancel 9 in the numerator and denominator prior to completing prime factorization.

$$\frac{18}{45} = \frac{9 \bullet 2}{5 \bullet 9} = \frac{\cancel{9} \bullet 2}{5 \bullet \cancel{9}} = \frac{2}{5}$$

To summarize, prime factorization in the numerator and denominator and subsequent cancellation will always result in a fraction of lowest terms. A fraction of lowest terms will have no factor which is the same in the numerator and denominator.

Example - Reducing to Lowest Terms

Reduce the fraction $\frac{57}{90}$ to lowest terms.

Step 1: Perform prime factorization of the numerator and denominator.

$$57 = 3 \bullet 19$$
$$90 = 3 \bullet 3 \bullet 2 \bullet 5$$

Step 2: Cancel terms common to the numerator and denominator.

$$\frac{57}{90} = \frac{3 \bullet 19}{3 \bullet 3 \bullet 2 \bullet 5} = \frac{\cancel{3} \bullet 19}{\cancel{3} \bullet 3 \bullet 2 \bullet 5} = \frac{19}{30}$$

In addition to understanding how to reduce to lowest terms, you should understand why this method works. Remember that canceling common factors does not change the fraction's value since our rule said that

$$\frac{a}{a} = 1$$

and a number is not changed when multiplied or divided by 1.

Verify the following examples.

Examples - Reducing a Fraction to Lowest Terms

34/68 = 1/2

3/100 = 3/100

4/112 = 1/28

21/56 = 3/8

100/1000 = 1/10

12/16 < 7/8

5/16 > 8/32

5-12   Lowest Common Denominators (LCD)

Two fractions must have equal denominators prior to being added or subtracted. Therefore, the goal of this section is to learn how to make two or more different fractions have equal denominators, yet retain their original value. Let's clarify the goal with a quick example.

Example - Finding Common Denominators

Make equivalent fractions for $\frac{1}{4}$ and $\frac{2}{3}$ with

equal (or 'common') denominators.

Through our knowledge of the multiplication table, we find that we can multiply 1/4 by 3/3, and 2/3 by 4/4 in order to obtain equivalent fractions, both having the common denominator of 12.

Answer: $\dfrac{1}{4} \bullet \dfrac{3}{3} = \dfrac{3}{12}$ $\dfrac{2}{3} \bullet \dfrac{4}{4} = \dfrac{8}{12}$

It is necessary to develop a standard method for finding common denominators, rather than merely guessing, or using previous experience.

Common denominators may be found by using prime factorization of each denominator. The goal is to find the 'lowest' or least valued denominator common to both fractions, or the **lowest common denominator (LCD)**. We use the lowest denominator since smaller numbers are generally easier to use than larger numbers.

STEP - BY - STEP

Finding the Lowest Common Denominator (LCD)

1. Perform prime factorization on all denominators.

2. Cancel factors common to at least 2 denominators. Multiply all canceled factors together to produce a number C. If no factors cancel, $C = 1$.

3. Multiply all factors not canceled together to produce the number N. If no factors remain (i.e. all have been canceled), $N = 1$.

4. Multiply $C \bullet N$ to produce the LCD.

Let's clarify with a few examples.

Example - Finding Lowest Common Denominators

20, 30, and 40 are denominators of 3 different fractions. What is the LCD?

Step 1: Prime factorization:

$$20 = (2)\ (5)\ (2)$$
$$30 = (3)\ (5)\ (2)$$
$$40 = (4)\ (5)\ (2)$$

Step 2: (2) and (5) are common to all denominators and may be canceled.

$$20 = (2)\ (\cancel{5})\ (\cancel{2})$$
$$30 = (3)\ (\cancel{5})\ (\cancel{2})$$
$$40 = (2)\ (2)\ (\cancel{5})\ (\cancel{2})$$

(2) remains common to both 20 and 40 and may be canceled.

$$20 = (\cancel{2})\ (\cancel{5})\ (\cancel{2})$$
$$30 = (3)\ (\cancel{5})\ (\cancel{2})$$
$$40 = (2)\ (\cancel{2})\ (\cancel{5})\ (\cancel{2})$$

(2) (5) (2) were canceled.

$$C = 2 \bullet 5 \bullet 2 = 20$$

Step 3: Multiply all numbers not canceled together.

(3) remains from 30, and (2) remains from 40.

$$N = (2)\ (3) = 6$$

Step 4: Multiply $C \bullet N$

$$C \bullet N = (20)\ (6) = 120$$

Answer: 120

Note that the LCD of denominators 2, 3, and 4 is 12.

Another relevant mathematical definition is **least common multiple** (LCM). The LCM of two or more numbers is the smallest number that produces an integer when divided by the given numbers. Therefore, if 2, 3, and 4 are denominators, 12 is the lowest common denominator. Also, 12 is the least common multiple of 2, 3, and 4 since 12/2 = 6, 12/3 = 4, 12/4 = 3.

Finding the LCD of fractions is the same as finding the LCM of the denominators.

Let's continue with a few more examples of LCDs, or LCMs.

<u>Example - Least Common Multiple</u>

Find the LCM of the following numbers: 3, 16, 48

Step 1: Prime factorization:

$$3 = (3)$$
$$16 = (2)\,(2)\,(2)\,(2)$$
$$48 = (2)\,(2)\,(2)\,(2)\,(3)$$

Stop 2: (3) is common to 3 and 48.

$$3 = (3)$$
$$16 = (2)\,(2)\,(2)\,(2)$$
$$48 = (2)\,(2)\,(2)\,(2)\,(3)$$

(2) (2) (2) (2) is common to 16 and 48.

$$3 = (3)$$
$$16 = (2)\,(2)\,(2)\,(2)$$
$$48 = (2)\,(2)\,(2)\,(2)\,(3)$$

(3) (2) (2) (2) (2) have been canceled.

$$C = (3)\,(2)\,(2)\,(2)\,(2) = 48$$

Step 3: All numbers have been canceled so $N = 1$.

Step 4: Multiply $C \bullet N$.

$$C \bullet N = 48 \bullet 1 = 48$$

Answer: 48

ON TO ANOTHER EXAMPLE!

Example - Least Common Multiple

Find the LCM of the following numbers: 3, 15, 20, 36

Step 1: Prime Factorization:

$$3 = (3)$$
$$15 = (3)(5)$$
$$20 = (2)(2)(5)$$
$$36 = (2)(2)(3)(3)$$

Step 2: Cancel (3) from numbers 3, 15, and 36.
Cancel (5) from numbers 15 and 20.
Cancel (2) (2) from numbers 20 and 36.

$$3 = (3)$$
$$15 = (3)(5)$$
$$20 = (2)(2)(5)$$
$$36 = (2)(2)(3)(3)$$

$$C = (3)(5)(2)(2) = 60$$

Step 3: The only factor remaining is (3), so $N = 3$.

Step 4: $C \cdot N = 60 \cdot 3 = 180$

Answer: 180

Verify the following example.

Example - Least Common Multiple

Find the LCM of the following numbers: 3, 15, 20, 35

Answer: 420

Why does the proposed method of finding LCMs or LCDs work? Using the method presented, the LCM is the smallest number which has all of the factors of the given numbers, and therefore cancellation is possible. Let's find the LCM of 3, 15, 20, and 36 using this knowledge.

As shown in step #1 of the previous example,

Factors of 3:	3
Factors of 15:	$3 \cdot 5$
Factors of 20:	$2 \cdot 2 \cdot 5$
Factors of 36:	$3 \cdot 3 \cdot 2 \cdot 2$

By looking at the factorizations, we see:

1.   The LCM must have a 5 since 15 and 20 have a 5.
2.   The LCM must have two 3's since 36 has two 3's.
3.   The LCM must have two 2's since 20 has two 2's.

Therefore, a number with one 5, two 3's, and two 2's will have all of the factors of the given numbers.

$$5 \, (3) \, (3) \, (2) \, (2) = 180 = \text{the LCM of 3, 15, 20, and 36}$$

If you would like, try this method with the earlier examples. It is actually the exact same method as that shown in **STEP- BY-STEP**.

We've determined that 180 is the LCM of 3, 15, 20 and 36. Look at the following division expressions which have been simplified with cancellation. Do you understand why each division problem results in an integer? Each must result in an integer, since 180 is the LCM.

$$\frac{180}{3} = \frac{3 \cdot 3 \cdot 5 \cdot 2 \cdot 2}{3} = \frac{3 \cdot 3 \cdot 5 \cdot 2 \cdot 2}{3} = \frac{60}{1} = 60$$

$$\frac{180}{15} = \frac{3 \cdot 3 \cdot 5 \cdot 2 \cdot 2}{3 \cdot 5} = \frac{3 \cdot 3 \cdot 5 \cdot 2 \cdot 2}{3 \cdot 5} = \frac{12}{1} = 12$$

$$\frac{180}{20} = \frac{3 \cdot 3 \cdot 5 \cdot 2 \cdot 2}{2 \cdot 2 \cdot 5} = \frac{3 \cdot 3 \cdot 5 \cdot 2 \cdot 2}{2 \cdot 2 \cdot 5} = \frac{9}{1} = 9$$

$$\frac{180}{36} = \frac{3 \cdot 3 \cdot 5 \cdot 2 \cdot 2}{3 \cdot 3 \cdot 2 \cdot 2} = \frac{3 \cdot 3 \cdot 5 \cdot 2 \cdot 2}{3 \cdot 3 \cdot 2 \cdot 2} = \frac{5}{1} = 5$$

In the first expression 3, 5, 2, and 2 were the factors contained in 180, but missing from 3. In the second expression 3, 2, and 2 were the factors contained in 180, but missing from 15. Do you see a pattern with these division examples, and our finding the LCM?

The following equations may be written using the above information.

$$3 \cdot 60 = 180$$
$$15 \cdot 12 = 180$$
$$20 \cdot 9 = 180$$
$$36 \cdot 5 = 180$$

With knowledge of the LCD, equivalent fractions with equal denominators may be generated.

<u>Example - Equivalent Fractions Using the LCD</u>

Make equivalent fractions of the following, using the LCD of the fractions.

$$\frac{2}{3}, \frac{7}{15}, \frac{21}{20}, \frac{33}{36}$$

From our previous work, the LCD of 3, 15, 20, and 36 equals 180.

Knowing the LCD, we can directly make equivalent fractions with multiplication of the appropriate 'missing' factors shown above.

Answer:

$$\frac{2}{3}\left(\frac{60}{60}\right) = \frac{120}{180}$$

$$\frac{7}{15}\left(\frac{12}{12}\right) = \frac{84}{180}$$

$$\frac{21}{20}\left(\frac{9}{9}\right) = \frac{189}{180}$$

$$\frac{33}{36}\left(\frac{5}{5}\right) = \frac{165}{180}$$

This section if very important, and much information was presented. It is highly recommended that you reread this section, and try more examples on your own. You should reach a point where you need not follow the **STEP-BY-STEP** directions exactly, and can make equivalent fractions containing the LCD by merely using prime factorization, and looking at the factors.

Our knowledge of making equivalent fractions with a LCD is the last step necessary to understand the addition and subtraction of fractions.

5-13   Adding and Subtracting Fractions

Fractions may only be added or subtracted if the fractions have equal denominators. If the equal denominators are also the LCD, the numbers are usually easier to calculate.

STEP - BY - STEP

To add (or subtract) fractions

1. Make equivalent fractions with common denominators.

2. Add (or subtract) the numerators. The denominator of the answer is equivalent to the common denominator found in step #1.

3. Reduce the result to lowest terms, if necessary.

Let's clarify with an example.

Example - Adding Fractions

You have two pizzas.
One pizza is cut into 10 slices, and 3 are left.
The other pizza is cut into 15 slices and 7 are left.

How many whole pizzas remain?

We already know that one 3/10 of one pizza remains and the other pizza has 7/15 of a pizza left. Therefore, to find the total remaining, we must add $\frac{3}{10} + \frac{7}{15}$.

One solution is to convert each fraction to a decimal, add the decimals, and then convert the answer back to a fraction. Since, 3/10 = 0.3 and 7/15 ≈ 0.46, the answer is approximately 0.77 or 77/100.

However, let's perform the computation using only fractions as described in **STEP-BY-STEP**.

Step 1: Make equivalent fractions with a common denominator.

$$10 = (2)(5)$$
$$15 = (3)(5)$$

The LCD is (2)(3)(5) = 30

Equivalent fractions are:

$$\frac{3}{10} = \left(\frac{3}{10}\right)(1) = \left(\frac{3}{10}\right)\left(\frac{3}{3}\right) = \frac{9}{30}$$

and

$$\frac{7}{15} = \left(\frac{7}{15}\right)(1) = \left(\frac{7}{15}\right)\left(\frac{2}{2}\right) = \frac{14}{30}$$

Step 2: Add the fractions, keeping the denominator the same.

$$\frac{9}{30} + \frac{14}{30} = \frac{23}{30}$$

Step 3: The LCD was used, so the answer is already in lowest terms.

Answer: $\frac{23}{30}$ pizza remains.

To add or subtract fractions, the topics of prime factorization, fractions in lowest terms, equivalent fractions, multiplication of fractions, and lowest common denominators all need to be understood. Then, adding or subtracting numerators is simple.

Here are a few more examples, so you can test what you have learned. Make sure you can prove that the following are true, and understand how the equations were obtained.

Examples - Adding Fractions

$$\frac{3}{8} + \frac{1}{16} = \frac{6}{16} + \frac{1}{16} = \frac{7}{16}$$

$$\frac{4}{34} + \frac{12}{17} = \frac{4}{34} + \frac{24}{34} = \frac{28}{34} = \frac{14}{17}$$

$$\frac{2}{9} + \frac{7}{8} = \frac{16}{72} + \frac{63}{72} = \frac{79}{72}$$

$$\frac{1}{4} + \frac{15}{20} = \frac{1}{4} + \frac{3}{4} = \frac{4}{4} = 1$$

The last example was a little tricky. The fraction $\frac{15}{20}$ was first reduced to $\frac{3}{4}$. After this change, fractions were added using the common denominator of 4.

Examples - Subtracting Fractions

$$\frac{6}{8} - \frac{1}{16} = \frac{12}{16} - \frac{1}{16} = \frac{11}{16}$$

$$\frac{24}{34} - \frac{12}{17} = \frac{24}{34} - \frac{24}{34} = 0$$

$$\frac{7}{9} - \frac{2}{8} = \frac{56}{72} - \frac{18}{72} = \frac{38}{72} = \frac{19}{36}$$

$$\frac{3}{4} - \frac{10}{20} = \frac{3}{4} - \frac{2}{4} = \frac{1}{4}$$

Does it sound strange that the denominator remains the same when adding or subtracting fractions? Think about this. If you had half a pizza, and your brother had half a pizza, how much would you have together?

$$\frac{1}{2} + \frac{1}{2} = \frac{2}{2} = 1$$

Yes, you would have a total of one whole pizza, not $\frac{2}{4} = \frac{1}{2}$. 1/2 is what you each started with.

$$\frac{1}{2} + \frac{5}{10} \neq \frac{6}{12}$$

When adding or subtracting integers, it was necessary to keep each numerical place aligned. Ones must be added to ones. Tens must be added to tens. Using common denominators is similar to keeping columns aligned when adding integers or decimals. Numbers can be compared only if the denominators are the same.

You know that 2 + 3 = 5. However, this can also be written as shown. Obviously, the denominator remains the same when adding.

$$\frac{2}{1}+\frac{3}{1}=\frac{5}{1}=5$$

Another way of understanding the addition of fractions is to use the Distributive Law of Multiplication. Using the Distributive Law of Multiplication, we see that the following is true.

$$\frac{1}{2}(1+1)=\frac{1}{2}(2)=1$$

- or -

$$\frac{1}{2}(1+1)=\frac{1}{2}+\frac{1}{2}=\frac{2}{2}=1$$

You should understand how to add or subtract any valued fractions.

5-14 Conversion of Mixed Numbers

We have already shown how to multiply two fractions. Simply multiply the numerators and denominators together, and then reduce the fraction to lowest terms. There is no need to find common denominators when multiplying fractions.

Examples - Multiplying Fractions

$$\frac{1}{2}\bullet\frac{1}{2}=\frac{1}{4}$$

$$\frac{3}{4}\bullet\frac{5}{12}=\frac{15}{48}=\frac{5}{16}$$

$$\frac{8}{3}\bullet\frac{1}{15}=\frac{8}{45}$$

Based on your knowledge of fractions, you should be able to determine how to convert a mixed number to an improper fraction. Your logic should follow the given example.

Example - Converting a Mixed Number to an Improper Fraction

$$7\frac{5}{8}=7+\frac{5}{8}=\frac{56}{8}+\frac{5}{8}=\frac{61}{8}$$

After you do a few of these conversions, you will see a pattern. The LCD must always be equal to the denominator of the fractional part.

Based on this information, a 'short-cut' may be taken when converting a mixed number to an improper fraction.

STEP - BY - STEP

To Convert a Mixed Number to an Improper Fraction

1. Multiply the integer of the mixed number by the denominator of the fractional part.

2. Add the resulting number to the numerator of the fractional part.

3. Place the result in the numerator, keeping the denominator the same.

From the above example,

$$7 \frac{5}{8} \quad \text{then add}$$

first multiply

Step 1: Multiply.

$$7 \bullet 8 = 56$$

Step 2: Add step #1 result to numerator.

$$56 + 5 = 61$$

Step 3: Place result over denominator.

Answer: $\dfrac{61}{8}$

Examples - Converting Mixed Numbers to Improper Fractions

$$4\frac{3}{2} = \frac{11}{2}$$

$$12\frac{3}{4} = \frac{51}{4}$$

Converting an improper fraction to a mixed number has already been demonstrated in chapter 4. Divide the numerator by the denominator and add the remainder over the divisor.

Example - Conversion of an Improper Fraction into Mixed Number

Convert $\dfrac{61}{8}$ to a mixed number.

$$\begin{array}{r} 7 \\ 8\overline{)61} \\ \underline{56} \\ 5 \end{array}$$

If you carefully examine the division above, you see that the answer is 7 plus the amount that 5 divides into 8. This is the mixed number.

$$\text{Answer:} \quad \frac{61}{8} = 7\frac{5}{8}$$

This procedure was also given in section **4-14, Division with Remainders**. You can double-check that the answer is correct by converting the mixed number back into the improper fraction.

Let's try another example.

Example - Converting Improper Fractions to Mixed Numbers
$\frac{71}{2}$ equals what mixed number?

$$\begin{array}{r} 35 \\ 2\overline{)71} \\ \underline{60} \\ 11 \\ \underline{10} \\ 1 \end{array}$$

The remainder is 1.

$$\text{Answer: } 35\frac{1}{2}$$

5-15 Dividing Fractions

Finally, you need to learn how to divide fractions. This is probably not the most difficult but most confusing operation to perform.

Integer division is relatively easy to understand. If you have $6, and you split your money into two groups, $3 is in each group. This is expressed as $6 ÷ 2 = $3. However, dividing by 2 is the same as multiplying by $\frac{1}{2}$, or

$$6 \div 2 = 6 \bullet \frac{1}{2} = 3$$

2 and $\frac{1}{2}$ are reciprocals of one another. A **reciprocal** of any number is the number with the numerator and denominator reversed (or 'inverted'). In the examples below, the ⇔ symbol has

been used to show numbers that are reciprocals of each other. Any number multiplied by its reciprocal must equal one.

Example - Reciprocals

$$\frac{3}{2} \Leftrightarrow \frac{2}{3}$$

$$2 \Leftrightarrow \frac{1}{2}$$

$$\frac{16}{7} \Leftrightarrow \frac{7}{16}$$

$$\frac{a}{b} \Leftrightarrow \frac{b}{a}$$

In the previous example of 6 ÷ 2, there is nothing special about the numbers 6 or 2. They are the same as fractions $\frac{6}{1}$ and $\frac{2}{1}$. Therefore, we may say that $\frac{6}{1} \div \frac{2}{1} = \frac{6}{1} \bullet \frac{1}{2} = 3$. Since there is nothing special about the numbers used, we have a method for dividing fractions.

STEP - BY - STEP

To Divide Fractions

1. Find the reciprocal of the divisor. (Remember for $a \div b$, b is the divisor, and a is the dividend.)

2. Multiply the dividend by the reciprocal found in step #1.

Let's clarify with an example.

Example - Dividing Fractions

What is $6 \div \frac{1}{2}$?

Step 1:   The divisor is $\frac{1}{2}$. The reciprocal of $\frac{1}{2}$ is 2.

Step 2: $6 \div \frac{1}{2}$ = 6 $\bullet$ 2 = 12

Answer: 12

Does this make sense? Think of $6 being split into piles of $0.50. How many piles would exist? There would be 12 piles.

Most people don't really think about dividing fractions and it making sense. They just know how to perform the operation and they're happy. In real life, you will seldom have an example where you directly divide by a fraction. However, you often must divide by a fraction as an intermediate step in some calculation. Therefore, you must at least know how to do it, even if you have trouble imagining what the computation actually means.

You may write fractional division in any of the normal forms used for division.

$6 \div \frac{1}{2}$ may also be written as $\dfrac{\frac{6}{1}}{\frac{1}{2}}$ Calculate by multiplying : $\dfrac{\frac{6}{1}}{\frac{1}{2}}$

This may seem awkward at first, but after some practice this form is actually rather convenient for dividing fractions. You can mentally flip the term in the denominator ($\frac{1}{2}$) of the entire equation upside-down ($\frac{2}{1}$) to obtain the reciprocal. Then bring it into the numerator ($\frac{6}{1}$) and multiply to get the answer of $\frac{12}{1}$ = 12.

To divide with mixed numbers, simply convert the mixed number to an improper fraction first, and then perform the division.

Examples - Dividing Fractions

$$\frac{3}{4} \div \frac{1}{2} = \frac{3}{4} \bullet \frac{2}{1} = \frac{6}{4} = \frac{3}{2}$$

$$\frac{10}{3} \div \frac{4}{7} = \frac{10}{3} \bullet \frac{7}{4} = \frac{70}{12} = \frac{35}{6}$$

$$1\frac{3}{4} \div 3 = \frac{7}{4} \bullet \frac{1}{3} = \frac{7}{12}$$

5-16   Summary of Fractions

If you understood this chapter, you should know the definition of a fraction, how to convert between fractions and decimals, and how to perform the four fundamental math operations using fractions. You should also thoroughly understand the topic of cancellation and factoring.

Remember that computing numbers with fractions is sometimes more accurate (and never less accurate) than computing with decimals due to possible rounding or truncation of decimals. Rounding or truncation errors are not significant when one is trying to calculate how much pizza is left, but these errors are very significant when trying to calculate the flight path of a shuttle to the moon.

If you understand all of the above topics, it is time once again for a pat on the back. Fractions are not simple. Your junior high math education will most likely be filled with computing fractions. The above discussion should provide an adequate foundation for the many math problems that you will practice.

Algebra is fast approaching. If you don't understand something we've discussed, please go back and review. Nothing that has been explained can be forgotten later. All of the preceding material will be used throughout your math career.

Important Definitions

Numerator

Denominator

Proper Fraction

Improper Fraction

Mixed Number

Factor

Prime Number

Even Number

Odd Number

Least Common Denominator
(LCD)

Least Common Multiple
(LCM)

Reciprocal

You should be able to ...

1. Pronounce any fraction

2. Convert any fraction to a decimal

3. Convert any decimal to a fraction

4. Multiply fractions

5. Simplify (or reduce) fractions

6. Cancel numbers and units in fractions

7. Find the prime factors of any number

8. Reduce any fraction to lowest terms

9. Find the LCM of two or more numbers
   (or find the LCD of two or more fractions)

10. Add two or more fractions

11. Subtract two or more fractions

12. Convert a mixed number to an improper
    fraction

13. Convert an improper fraction into a
    mixed number

14. Divide fractions

6

Percentages

6-1   Defining Percentages

Before beginning to understand percentages, it is helpful to begin with a short review of multiplication. For example, 4 times 5 means that the number 4 is added a total of five times to produce 20.

$$4 \bullet 5 = 4 + 4 + 4 + 4 + 4 = 20$$

In section **4-15**, you learned how to multiply decimals. Using those methods we may calculate the following.

$$4 \bullet 0.5 = 2.0$$

Is 4 added 0.5 times? It is difficult to think about multiplication with decimals in this manner. To make it more understandable, we may think of 4 • 0.5 as finding a part or proportion of 4. Look carefully at the following calculations. As 4 is multiplied by larger decimals, the answer is a larger part of 4. Finally, as 4 is multiplied by 1, the answer is 'the whole part of 4' or simply 4.

$4 \bullet 0.1 = 0.4$
$4 \bullet 0.2 = 0.8$
$4 \bullet 0.3 = 1.2$
$4 \bullet 0.4 = 1.6$
$4 \bullet 0.5 = 2.0$
$4 \bullet 0.6 = 2.4$
$4 \bullet 0.7 = 2.8$
$4 \bullet 0.8 = 3.2$
$4 \bullet 0.9 = 3.6$
$4 \bullet 1.0 = 4.0$

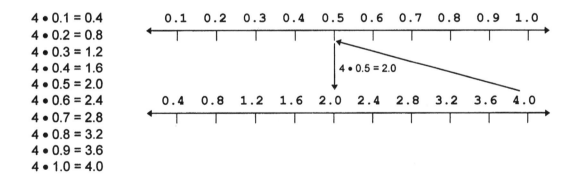

Furthermore, we may use the Distributive Law of Multiplication as shown below.

$$4 \bullet 1.1 = 4 \bullet (1 + 0.1) = 4 + 0.4 = 4.4$$
$$4 \bullet 1.2 = 4 \bullet (1 + 0.2) = 4 + 0.8 = 4.8$$

It is very useful to be able to find the part or proportion of any number. As a matter of fact, it is so useful, and so often necessary that an entirely different notation has been developed. The notation is called a percentage.

A **percentage** is any fraction with a denominator of 100. **%** is the **percent** symbol, which is used to replace the understood denominator. Therefore, 50/100 may also be written as 50%, which is read aloud as "fifty percent". The % symbol always follows the numerator of the fraction.

If you understand division, decimals and fractions, you should not find percentages difficult to use. However, percentages are very popular so you need to clearly understand how and when to use them.

Remember that dividing any number by 100 is the same as shifting the decimal point of the number two places left. The examples below show how different percentages can be represented by either fractions or decimals.

Examples - Percentages

$$50\% = \frac{50}{100} = 0.50 \text{ (or one half)}$$

$$5\% = \frac{5}{100} = 0.05$$

$$32\% = \frac{32}{100} = 0.32$$

$$25.35\% = \frac{25.35}{100} = 0.2535$$

$$100\% = \frac{100}{100} = 1.0$$

$$632.58\% = \frac{632.58}{100} = 6.3258$$

Do not be confused by a number such as 25.35%, (which is read aloud "twenty-five point three five percent"). Decimals may be included in fractions. Usually, decimals and fractions are kept separate to be consistent and make things more clear, but decimal percentages are often necessary. To obtain any value from a percentage shift the decimal point two places left, whether the number is a decimal or integer.

6-2   Operations using Percentages

Based on operations shown in previous chapters, we may already perform any of the four fundamental math operations using percentages, because a percentage may always be written as a fraction or decimal number.

Please verify the following examples. You may need to convert each number to a fraction or decimal instead of directly using percentages. However, note that there is no need to convert percentages to a fraction or decimal when adding (or subtracting) two percentages. The percentages may be treated like any other number, with the % symbol carried along. Remember, it is the same as adding (or subtracting) two numbers with a denominator of 100.

For problems that have a combination of percentages and non-percentages, first convert all numbers to either fractions or decimals. Then complete the calculation. Normally it is easier to use the decimals rather than fractions.

Examples - Adding and Subtracting Percentages

5% - 2% = 3% (since 0.05 - 0.02 = 0.03 = 3%)

13.25% + 17.75% = 31%

4% + .01% = 4.01%

6% - 10% = -4%

3.5 - 4% = 3.5 - .04 = 3.46

350% - 4% = 346% = 3.46

18 + 200% = 18 + 2 = 20

1 - 0.53 = 0.47 = 47%

Before continuing, please make sure that all of the above examples are understood. Once you become accustomed to working with percentages, converting to decimals or fractions will probably not be necessary.

HELPFUL TIP!

There are no new techniques to learn in order to perform operations with percentages. However, it is important to learn how and when to use percentages in everyday life. This will be explained in the following sections.

The examples below show how to multiply and divide numbers represented with percentages. When first learning to multiply or divide with percentages, it is least confusing if all percentages are first converted to decimals.

Examples - Multiplying and Dividing Percentages

5% • 50 = 0.05 • 50 = 2.5 = 250%

10% • 30% = 0.10 • 0.30 = 0.03 = 3%

100% • 8 = 1 • 8 = 8 = 800%

0.1% • 1000 = .001 • 1000 = 1 = 100%

5 ÷ 1% = 5 ÷ 0.01 = 500 = 50,000%

3% ÷ 5 = 0.03 ÷ 5 = 0.006 = 0.6%

20% ÷ 10% = 0.20 ÷ 0.10 = 2 = 200%

6-3   Finding the Percentage of a Number

Percentages are used often in everyday life. Every dollar earned at work requires paying a tax, which is typically expressed as a percentage. Every purchase also includes a tax. The tax money is all given to the government.

<u>Example - Cost with a Percent Tax</u>

How much must you pay for a $20 baseball glove, if the sales tax is 5%?

To purchase the glove, you must pay $20 plus an additional part of $20. The additional part in this example is 5%. The tax you must pay is 5% of $20. We know that 100% of anything is the whole thing. 100% of $20 is $20. But how much is 5% of $20?

To calculate 5% of $20, multiply 5% times $20. Therefore,

tax on glove = 5% • $20 = $1

So you must pay $21 total for the baseball glove.

Answer: $20 + 5%($20) = $20 + $1 = $21

Taxes are always based on percentages. Let's see why people don't like it when taxes increase.

<u>Example - Cost with a Percent Tax</u>

How much must you pay for a $20 baseball glove, if the sales tax is 10%?

Answer: $20 + 10%($20) = $22

Since the tax percentage doubled from 5% to 10%, the tax paid doubles from $1 to $2.

By using percentages, the larger the cost of the item, the more tax is paid. This makes sense since you should have to pay more tax money for a car than a pack of gum. 10 times more tax is paid on an item that is 10 times more expensive.

<u>Example - Cost with a Percent Tax</u>

How much must you pay for a $40 baseball glove, if the sales tax is 5%?

Answer: $40 + 5%($40) = $42

As you can see, a glove costing twice as much money requires twice as much tax.

It should be clear that finding the percentage of a number requires multiplication. Let's look at another example.

<u>Example - Using Percentages</u>

The price of a $20 shirt is reduced by 35% due to a '35% off' sale.

How much does the shift cost before taxes?

The shirt costs $20 minus 35% of $20.

Therefore, first calculate 35% of $20.

$$35\% \bullet \$20 = \$7$$

So, if the shirt cost is $20, the price is reduced by $7. The sale price is $20 - 0.35($20) = $13.

Answer: $20 - $7 = $13

If we wanted, we could find the sales tax based on the $13 price. Do you remember how?

If the sales tax were 5%, the total price of the shirt would be,

$$\$13 + 0.05(\$13) = \$13.65$$

Using the Distributive Law of Multiplication, we see that the shirt cost, including the 5% tax, is actually 105% of (or 1.05 times) the shirt cost.

$$\$13 + 0.05(\$13) = 1.05 (\$13) = \$13.65$$

We also see that a 35% price reduction is the same as 65% of the original cost (100% - 35% = 65%).

$$\$20 \bullet (0.65) = \$13$$

Many explain that the word *of* always means multiply and the word *is* always means equals. This is usually true with regards to percentages since 35% of $20 is calculated 35% • $20 which equals $7. However, do not always look for a word such as *of* and then multiply without understanding the problem. If you only look for the word *of* you would have had difficulty solving the example in the above box.

You must understand the math operation you are performing rather than looking for the 'magic word'. A clear understanding of math now will make advanced math more clear later.

Please verify the following examples.

Examples - Percentages of a Number

15% of 25 = 3.75

150% of 20 = 30

0.1% of 72 = 0.072

12.5% of 18 = 2.25

50% of 30 = 15

Let's look at a slightly different problem.

Example - Finding Percents

7 is what percent of 20 ?

In other words, 7 is what part of 20 ? From experience, we know that 20 is 100% of 20. We also know that 10 is 50% (or half) of 20, so the answer must be less than 50%.

Let x be a variable, representing an unknown number. Then the problem may be written as shown below.

$$x \bullet 20 = 7$$

Using the complementary nature of multiplication and division (section **4-11**), we see this problem requires division. We then calculate the appropriate fraction.

Answer: $x = \dfrac{7}{20} = 0.35 = \dfrac{35}{100} = 35\%$

As shown, the answer is that 7 is 35% of 20. (To check the answer we see that 20 $\bullet$ 0.35 = 7).

Another way to convert a fraction to a percentage is to make an equivalent fraction with a denominator of 100. We can make an equivalent fraction of $\frac{7}{20}$ with a denominator of 100 by multiplying the fraction by $\left(\frac{5}{5}\right)$.

$$\frac{7}{20} = \frac{7}{20}\left(\frac{5}{5}\right) = \frac{35}{100} = 35\%$$

Of course, making an equivalent fraction with a denominator of 100 is not always possible using integers, as we learned in the previous chapter on fractions.

Example - Finding Percents

7 is what percent of 17?

The LCD of 17 and 100 is 1700. Since we cannot make an equivalent fraction with a denominator of 100, division is required to calculate the percentage.

$$\text{Answer: } \frac{7}{17} \approx 41.2\%$$

Make sure that you agree with the following examples.

Example - Percentages

8 is what percent of 8?	Answer: 100%
16 is what percent of 8?	Answer: 200%
98 is what percent of 100?	Answer: 98%
98 is what percent of 50?	Answer: 196%
6 is what percent of 40?	Answer: 15%

150% of 12 = 18

50% of 12 = 6

10% of 50 = 5

20% of 50 = 10

The two types of questions presented in the above example box are very popular problems. These two problem types are summarized in the **STEP-BY-STEP** box below. Usually **STEP-BY-STEP** instructions are given before examples. However, these steps have been saved until the end of the section so that you actually understood percentages without blindly applying the given formulas. Note that *A*, *B*, and *x* may represent any number.

STEP - BY - STEP

Solving Problems with Percentages

Question:	What is x % of A?
Answer:	Multiply x % $\bullet$ A
Question:	A is what % of B?
Answer:	Compute $A \div B$, and convert to a percentage

You should apply common sense when using percentages. Common sense will help verify that your answers are correct. A test score of 100% means every answer was correct. A test score of 50% correct means that half of the answers were correct. However, a test score 200% doesn't make sense. How can you have twice as many correct as were asked? (Unless you get extra credit.) On the other hand, if the price of something increases 200%, the price doubled. This may give you a better feel of percentages.

In every day life, a person typically pays about 30% of their salary in taxes, pays 5% sales tax, earns 5% interest from money saved in the bank, and pays 15% interest on money owed. The use of percentages in daily life is endless, especially in dealing with money. Maybe this is because every dollar may be split into 100 cents, so 100 is a convenient denominator.

6-4   Percentages Shortcuts

Do you see a pattern in the box below?

<u>Examples - Percentages with Factors of 10</u>

1% of 70 = 0.7
10% of 70 = 7
100% of 70 = 70

1% of 54,322 = 543.22
10% of 54,322 = 5432.2

1% of 72.634 = 0.72634
10% of 72.635 = 7.2635

Multiples of 10 are easily calculated as shown in section **4-15** (**Multiplying Decimals**). To find 10% of a number simply move the decimal point one place to the left of the number. Therefore, it should be simple to calculate 10% of any number in your head (or 'melon' if you prefer).

If you can mentally calculate 10%, you can probably also calculate 20% of any number. 20% is simply 10% • 2. Therefore if 10% of 50 = 5, then 20% of 50 must equal 5 • 2 or 10. It is relatively easy to double one number, so after a little practice you will probably be able to mentally calculate 20% of any number.

30% is 3 • 10%, 40% is 4 • 10%, and so forth. Therefore, after enough practice, you will probably be able to mentally calculate any percentage that is a multiple of 10.

Furthermore, you can also easily calculate 15% of a number. 15% = 10% + 5%. To find 15% of a number first calculate 10%, and then add half of 10%.

<u>Example - Shortcut to Calculating 15%</u>

What is 15% of 80?

$$15\% \bullet 80 = x$$

By separating 15% into two numbers,

$$(10\% + 5\%)\, 80 = x$$

Using the Distributive Law of Multiplication,

$$(10\% \bullet 80) + (5\% \bullet 80) = x$$

$$8 + 4 = x$$

Answer: 12 is 15% of 80

That solution may not seem like a shortcut since several steps were performed. However, each step was a very simple calculation. Let's try another example.

Example - Percentage Shortcuts

What is 15% of 60?

$$10\% \text{ of } 60 = 6$$

$$6 \div 2 = 3$$

$$6 + 3 = 9$$

Answer: 9 is 15% of 60

It is customary at a restaurant to pay the server a tip that equals 15% of the meal cost. Now you don't need to bring a calculator (or a pointless little chart) to dinner. You can calculate 15% of the meal cost in your head! Verify the following example.

Example - Percentage Shortcuts

At a fancy German restaurant, your meal cost $50. If you wish to tip the server 15%, how much should you pay the server?

Answer: $7.50

6-5   Mean, Median, and Mode

Test scores are often given in percentages. Furthermore, a student receives a single grade which is dependent on all of his test scores. So, how may all of the test scores combined to find a single grade? There are three popular methods of characterizing a group (or set) of any valued numbers. These methods are the mean, median, and mode.

The **average**, or **mean**, is the sum (or addition) of all of the numbers in the set divided by the number of elements in the set. The **median** is the middle value in a set of numbers. If there are an even number of items in the set, the median is the average of the two middle values. The **mode** is the value that appears most often in the set of numbers.

An example will help clarify these definitions. Note that to find the median or mode, the elements in the set should be listed in numerical order.

Example - Finding the Mean, Median, and Mode

Find the average, median, and mode of the set of numbers: { 80, 80, 92, 95, 98 }

The sum of the numbers is 80 + 80 + 92 + 95 + 98 = 445. Furthermore, there are 5 numbers in the set. With this information, the average may be found by calculating 445 ÷ 5 = 89

The middle number in the set is 92, which is the median.

The number that appears most often is 80, which appears twice.

Answer: Average = 89   Median = 92   Mode = 80

6-6   Summary of Percentages

Most people use percentages everyday. Therefore, you should become proficient at calculating numerical relationships using percentages. Percentages allow you to find the part of any number. 100% of a number is the entire number, but 50% of a number is half of the number.

When calculating percentages, please do not only look for words such as *of* or *is* to indicate the math operator which must be used. Rather, understand what you are trying to do and apply the operation that makes sense. Once you get the hang of it, you will realize that using percentages is quite simple.

You should be able to ...

1.   Convert any percentage into an equivalent fraction or decimal

2.   Perform any of the four fundamental operations with percentages

3.   Find any given % of any number

4.   Answer questions such as *A* is what percent of *B* (where *A* and *B* are any value numbers)

5.   Calculate simple percentages (e.g. 10% or 20%) of any number in your head

6.   Understand what percentages are and why they are used

7.   Find the mean, median, or mode from any set of numbers

Negative Numbers

7-1   Defining Negative Numbers

Any number less than zero is a **negative number**. In section **2-3**, both positive and negative numbers were placed on the number line. However, examples in previous chapters have almost exclusively used positive numbers. It is now necessary to clarify the four fundamental operations using negative numbers.   Negative numbers, like positive numbers, may be in the form of integers, fractions, decimals, or percentages.

As shown in chapter 2, negative numbers are preceded by a negative or minus (-) sign. Therefore, "negative 3" is written -3.   A number written without a sign is assumed positive. Therefore, "positive 3" could be written +3,   but writing 3 is sufficient.   Positive and negative numbers may also be called **signed numbers**.

7-2   Negative Numbers are Necessary

At first you may think that you can merely avoid negative numbers by arranging equations using only positive numbers. However, you will soon find that negative numbers are unavoidable.

In a cold climate the temperature may often fall below 0°. These temperatures are represented by negative numbers.   A weatherman may say that it is "3 below" which means that the temperature is -3°.

Negative numbers are used when a reference level is established. For example, altitude is normally referenced at sea level. Locations higher than sea level have a positive altitude, and locations below sea level have a negative altitude. Therefore, the altitude at the top of Mount Everest is 29,028 feet, or 29,028 feet above sea level. However, the altitude at the Dead Sea is -1300 feet, or 1,300 feet below sea level.

In golf, par is the number of strokes required for a particular hole by an average golfer.   If you get the ball in the hole in one stroke more than par, your score for the hole is +1 ("a bogey" in golf lingo). However, if you get the ball in the hole in one stroke less than par (which is much better, and called a "birdie"), your score for the hole is -1.

There are countless examples available. Negative numbers are unavoidable and often used in everyday life.   Many math equations require them. Therefore, be sure to read this chapter if you are not familiar with negative numbers.

7-3   Addition and Subtraction with Negative Numbers

The rules of addition and subtraction presented in chapter 3 also apply to negative numbers. By using already established laws and understanding the purpose for addition (combining numbers) and subtraction (difference between numbers), the following general rules may be established.

Rules for Adding and Subtracting Negative Numbers

$$a + (-b) = a - b$$

$$-b + a = a - b$$

$$-a - (-b) = -a + b$$

$$-a - b = -(a + b)$$

Parentheses are often placed around a negative number to make the math more clear. The formula $a + - b$ looks very confusing, and therefore should be written with parentheses as $a + (-b)$.

Remember, according to the Commutative Law of Addition, reversing the order of two terms added does not affect the answer. Therefore,

$$a + (-b) = a - b = -b + a$$

By distribution,

$$-a - b = -(a + b)$$

You really do not need to 'memorize' any of these formulas, if you understand the purpose for addition and subtraction, along with the concept of negative numbers. Remember that there is no commutative law for subtraction, as shown below.

$$4 - 3 = 4 + (-3) = (-3) + 4 = 1$$

$$3 - 4 = 3 + (-4) = (-4) + 3 = -1$$

Before moving on to some examples for you to try on your own, let's briefly review each of the combinations in the box above.

First, the addition of a positive and negative number is the same as finding the difference between the two numbers. The difference between two numbers requires subtraction. In the examples below, note that the answer has the same sign as the number with the larger magnitude. Does this make sense to you?

$$-5 + 8 = 8 - 5 = 3 \qquad\qquad 8 + (-5) = 8 - 5 = 3$$

- or -

$$-8 + 5 = 5 - 8 = -3 \qquad\qquad 5 + (-8) = 5 - 8 = -3$$

Second, subtracting a negative number is the same as adding a positive number.

$$-5 - (-8) = -5 + 8 = 3 \qquad\qquad 8 - (-5) = 8 + 5 = 13$$

Finally, if you start with a negative number and subtract more, the answer becomes more negative. As a simple example, if the temperature is $5°$ below zero, and it drops $8°$ more, the final temperature must be $-13°$.

$$-5 - 8 = -13 \qquad\qquad -8 - 5 = -13$$

Use your understanding of signed numbers to verify the many examples that follow.

<u>Examples - Adding/Subtracting Negative Numbers</u>

$$16 + (-17) = -1$$

$$-12 + 20 = 8$$

$$14 + (-3) = 11$$

$$-14 + 3 = -11$$

$$-45 + 45 = 0$$

$$-9 + (-3) = -9 - 3 = -12$$

$$-4 + (-18) = -22$$

$$-18 - 4 = -22$$

$$-20 + (-20) = -40$$

$$4 - (-3) = 4 + 3 = 7$$

$$-3 - 4 = -7$$

$$-3 - (-4) = 1$$

$$-4 - (-6) = -4 + 6 = 2$$

$$20 - (-5) = 25$$

$$-20 - (-20) = 0$$

Remember that subtraction finds the difference between two numbers, and the difference between two equal numbers is zero. Therefore $-20 - (-20) = 0$, or $-a - (-a) = -a + a = 0$.

Subtracting negative numbers may seem more confusing than adding negative numbers. However, remember that subtracting a negative number is the same as adding a positive number. If you subtract two losses from a team, the team must have two more wins.

Let's think about negatives in a different manner. In English you were taught not to use double negatives.

<u>Example - An English Refresher of Double Negatives</u>

"I am **not** going to learn English **no** more."

The reason that this sentence is poor grammatically is the use of a double negative. If you are NOT going to learn English NO more, then you ARE going to learn more English.   As in English, in mathematics a double negative is the same as a positive.

Remember to understand the formulas and examples presented, rather than only using memorization. In the long run, understanding formulas is actually easier than memorizing them. Mathematician say: *It's much easier to forget something memorized than forget something understood.* (A little Ancient Chinese proverb, maybe?)

<u>Example - Using Negative Numbers</u>

Based on the numbers presented in section **7-1**, what is the difference in altitude between the top of Mount Everest and the Dead Sea?

Answer: 29,028 - (-1300) = 30,328 feet

7-4   Multiplying and Dividing Negative Numbers

Multiplying and dividing two positive numbers was demonstrated in chapter 4. Multiplying or dividing two negative numbers also produces the same positive result.

<u>Examples - Multiplying Two Negative Numbers</u>

$$(-5) \bullet (-8) = 40$$

$$(-0.1) \bullet (-150) = 15$$

$$-\left(\tfrac{1}{4}\right) \bullet (-12) = 3$$

Note in the last example that the negative applied to the entire fraction. This is the reason that the negative sign was placed outside of the parentheses. You'll understand negative fractions better after completing this section.

$$-\left(\tfrac{1}{4}\right) = -0.25$$

Dividing two negative numbers also produces a positive number as shown below.

<u>Examples - Dividing Two Negative Numbers</u>

$$(-10) \div (-2) = 5$$

$$(-1) \div (-2) = \tfrac{1}{2}$$

$$-\left(\tfrac{1}{4}\right) \div -\left(\tfrac{1}{4}\right) = 1$$

Therefore, the answers are the same whether the two multiplied numbers are both positive or negative. The same is true for division.

However, when multiplying or dividing and one number is positive while the other is negative, the result is always a negative number.

Examples - Multiplying Negative and Positive Numbers

$$(-4) \bullet (12) = -48$$

$$(-15) \bullet (2) = -30$$

$$16 \bullet -\left(\frac{1}{4}\right) = -4$$

$$-1 \bullet 100{,}000 = -100{,}000$$

$$-100{,}000 \bullet 10\% = -10{,}000$$

Do these results make sense? The first example is $(-4) \bullet (12)$. To find the answer, start at zero on the number line and move four places to the left (or -4) 12 times. The result is the correct answer of -48.

Below is a proof of the stated rule.

$$
\begin{aligned}
-a \bullet b \quad &= ? \\
&= -1(a) \bullet b \qquad &&\text{by factoring} \\
&= -1 \, (a \bullet b) \qquad &&\text{by associate law} \\
&= - \, (a \bullet b)
\end{aligned}
$$

Rules for Multiplying and Dividing Negative Numbers

$$a \bullet b = ab$$
$$a \bullet (-b) = -ab$$
$$-a \bullet (-b) = ab$$

$$a \div b = a/b$$
$$a \div (-b) = -(a/b)$$
$$-a \div (-b) = a/b$$

Examples - Dividing Positive and Negative Numbers

$$10 \div (-2) = -5$$

$$(-10) \div 2 = -5$$

$$-500 \div 500 = -1$$

$$-\left(\frac{1}{4}\right) \div 4 = -\left(\frac{1}{16}\right)$$

Let us look at fractions a little more carefully. So far the negative sign has been placed outside of the fraction in parentheses. However, the negative sign may go inside the parentheses. Furthermore, the negative sign may apply to the numerator or denominator or to the entire fraction. Any of these forms gives the exact same decimal number.

$$-\left(\tfrac{1}{4}\right) = \left(-\tfrac{1}{4}\right) = \left(\tfrac{-1}{4}\right) = \left(\tfrac{1}{-4}\right) = -0.25$$

It does not matter mathematically where the negative is placed. Any of the above locations is satisfactory. Remember,

$$-a \bullet b = -b \bullet a$$

7-5   Performing Operations with More than 3 Numbers

What if more than two numbers are divided or multiplied?

Example - More than Three Values Multiplied
-5 • -3 • -10 = ?

To obtain this answer, simply perform one operation at a time.

First,

$$-5 \bullet -3 = 15$$

Then,

$$15 \bullet -10 = -150$$

Therefore,

$$\text{Answer: } -5 \bullet -3 \bullet -10 = -150$$

Obviously, you could have multiplied the numbers in any order by the Commutative Law of Multiplication. You would have obtained the same result.

To add, subtract, or divide more than three numbers, follow the same rule. Perform the operation in steps with two numbers at one time.

Examples - Working with More than Two Signed Numbers
10 - (-3) + (-4) + 6 = 15
(-8) - (-8) + 6 - 10 = -4
12 ÷ [(-4) • (-3)] = 1

Do not forget the use of the absolute value symbol given in section **3-8**. This symbol will make a negative number positive.

Example - Absolute Values

$$| -2 | \bullet 2 = 4$$

$$| -6 \bullet 3 | = 18$$

$$-| 4 | \bullet | -6 | = -4 \bullet 6 = -24$$

$$| 4 - 3 | = 1$$

$$| -4 + 3 | = 1$$

$$| -2 \bullet 5 \bullet 10 | = 100$$

7-6   Summary of Negative Number Operations

There is no doubt that it is difficult to picture each operation with negative numbers using physical examples and objects. However, do your best and try to satisfy yourself by simply remembering the procedures for performing the four operations with negative numbers.

Remember the number line when adding and subtracting. When multiplying and dividing, remember that the answer is negative only if one of the two factors is negative. Go back and reread the section **2-1, The Definition of a Number** if needed. This will remind you that a number is merely a symbol that obeys certain rules. The rules and symbols for negative numbers were established in this chapter.

Algebra is quickly approaching.

You should be able to ...

1. Add and Subtract with negative numbers

2. Multiply and Divide with negative numbers

3. Use negative decimals, fractions, and percentages

4. Use absolute values to make a negative number positive

5. Understand what negative numbers are, and why they are necessary

Exponents

8-1   Defining Exponents

Multiplication is a shorthand notation for adding the same number together a certain number of times. 3 added 5 times is written 3 • 5 rather than 3 + 3 + 3 + 3 + 3. There is often a need to multiply the same number together many times. In these cases, **exponents** are used as a shortcut notation.

The number to be multiplied is called the **base**. The number of times the base is to be multiplied by itself is called the **exponent**. A number written in exponential notation is given below, where *base* and *exponent* are variables representing any valued numbers. The exponent is always written in the upper right hand corner of the base, using a smaller sized writing than the base.

$$\text{base}^{\text{exponent}}$$

Following are some examples of exponential notation. If you would like to skip the examples for now, and just look at all the rules that will be developed in this chapter, see section **8-5**.

<u>Examples - Exponential Notation</u>

$$5 \bullet 5 \bullet 5 \bullet 5 = 5^4$$

$$3 \bullet 3 \bullet 3 \bullet 3 \bullet 3 = 3^5$$

$$(-1) \bullet (-1) \bullet (-1) = (-1)^3$$

$$4 = 4^1$$

$$0.5 \bullet 0.5 \bullet 0.5 \bullet 0.5 = (0.5)^4$$

$$3^2 = 3 \bullet 3$$

$$13.6^6 = 13.6 \bullet 13.6 \bullet 13.6 \bullet 13.6 \bullet 13.6 \bullet 13.6$$

In the first example 5 is the base, and 4 is the exponent. You should be able to determine the base and exponents of the other examples. Take special note that:

$$4 = 4^1$$

Every number that is written without an exponent has an implied exponent of 1. In general,

$$b^1 = b$$

Sometimes exponents are written with a (^) which called a **carot**. This is often the notation that computers use for exponents. When programming in a computer language, or using a formula in a spreadsheet, exponents cannot be entered as superscripts. Therefore, the carot is used. However, use the standard notation whenever possible.

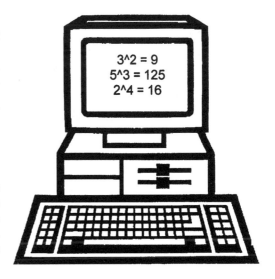

```
3^2 = 9
5^3 = 125
2^4 = 16
```

You need to know how to read exponents aloud. Another word for the exponent is **power**. Therefore 5^2 is read as "5 raised to the second power"; 5^3 is read "5 raised to the third power"; 5^4 is read "five raised to the fourth power" and so forth. Sometimes the word "raised" is not used, and 5^2 is simply read "5 to the second power."

There are often special names for number representations that contain 2's and 3's. For example the fraction $\frac{1}{2}$ can be read as "one over two" or "one half". Special names also exist for exponents of 2 and 3. If the exponent is 2, the base is called **squared**. Therefore 5^2 is also read aloud as "five squared". If someone needs to "square 5", they want to multiply 5•5. If the exponent is 3, the base is called **cubed**. Therefore 4^3 is read aloud "four cubed". If you "cube 3", the answer is 27. Virtually every calculator has a special button for squaring a number. There is also usually a button which takes the place of the ^ symbol and allows the base to be raised to any power needed. This button is typically marked with an x^y on most calculators.

At this point, it may seem that pronouncing the notation is more difficult than using it!

Fractions can also be raised to a power. Note that parentheses around the fraction indicate that the entire fraction is raised to a power, rather than only the numerator or denominator.

Examples - Fractions with Exponents

$$\left(\frac{2}{3}\right)^3 = \frac{2}{3} \cdot \frac{2}{3} \cdot \frac{2}{3} = \frac{2 \cdot 2 \cdot 2}{3 \cdot 3 \cdot 3} = \frac{8}{27}$$

$$\frac{2^3}{3} = \frac{2 \cdot 2 \cdot 2}{3} = \frac{8}{3}$$

$$\frac{2}{3^3} = \frac{2}{3 \cdot 3 \cdot 3} = \frac{2}{27}$$

Multiplication made adding a number many times easier and quicker. However, exponents are not used to make multiplication easier. There is no chart of exponents to memorize. Exponents are simply used as a shortcut notation.

However, exponents may often be manipulated directly when performing operations. Therefore, exponents are a powerful mathematical tool. The following sections describe how to work with various types of exponents.

There are no sections on adding or subtracting numbers with different exponents. There are no shortcuts for these operations. If numbers with exponents are to be added or subtracted, the numbers must first be multiplied to remove all exponents other than one. Then, the addition or subtraction may be performed as shown in previous chapters.

Example - Adding Numbers with Exponents Other than 1

$$3^3 + 3^2 = ?$$

$$3^3 = 3 \bullet 3 \bullet 3 = 27^1$$
$$3^2 = 3 \bullet 3 = 9^1$$
$$27 + 9 = 36$$

Answer: $3^3 + 3^2 = 36$

Example - Subtracting Numbers with Exponents Other than 1

$$3^3 - 3^2 = ?$$

$$3^3 = 3 \bullet 3 \bullet 3 = 27$$
$$3^2 = 3 \bullet 3 = 9$$
$$27 - 9 = 18$$

Answer: $3^3 - 3^2 = 18$

8-2   Multiplying with Positive Exponents

It is necessary to learn how to perform operations with numbers that are raised to various powers. Remember that in previous chapters, every number was written without an exponent. Therefore, an exponent of 1 has always previously been assumed.

Example - Multiplying Numbers with Same Base, but Different Exponents

What does ($3^2 \bullet 3^3$) equal?

It is simple to perform this calculation based on the known rules.

$$3^2 = 3 \bullet 3$$

$$3^3 = 3 \bullet 3 \bullet 3$$

Therefore,

$$(3^2 \bullet 3^3) = (3 \bullet 3) \bullet (3 \bullet 3 \bullet 3) = 243$$

We can also use exponents to describe the answer, since 3 is multiplied together 5 times.

$$(3 \bullet 3) \bullet (3 \bullet 3 \bullet 3) = 3^5 = 243$$

Therefore

$$\text{Answer:} \quad 3^2 \bullet 3^3 = 3^5 = 243$$

For now, do not concern yourself with the answer of 243. Exponents do not help us calculate 243. To calculate the answer we must use multiplication. However, focus on the fact that

$$3^2 \bullet 3^3 = 3^5$$

Keeping the answer in exponential form indicates a pattern. There is nothing special about the base's value or the exponents used in the example. The base and exponents could be replaced with any other integer. Therefore, we can make the following general rule for any number *b*, and integers *n*, and *m*. (Actually, *n* and *m* need not be integers for the law to remain valid. This will be explained in section **8-6**.)

Law of Exponents

$$b^n \bullet b^m = b^{n+m}$$

IMPORTANT LAW!

Therefore to multiply two numbers with the <u>same base</u>, keep the base the same and add exponents. All other rules regarding exponents are based on this fundamental law.

Examples - Multiplying Numbers with the Same Base

$$3^2 \bullet 3^6 = 3^8$$

$$21^3 \bullet 21^2 = 21^5$$

$$\left(\frac{1}{3}\right)^2 \bullet \left(\frac{1}{3}\right)^1 = \left(\frac{1}{3}\right)^3$$

What if the bases are not the same? Let's try an example.

$$4^2 \bullet 3^3 = (4 \bullet 4) \bullet (3 \bullet 3 \bullet 3)$$

The only way to reduce this answer to a simpler form is to actually perform the multiplication. Therefore, there is no easy way of multiplying numbers with different bases.

Finally, what if the bases are different, but the exponents are the same? Again, let's try an example.

$$2^3 \bullet 5^3 = (2 \bullet 2 \bullet 2) \bullet (5 \bullet 5 \bullet 5)$$

Let's regroup the numbers by utilizing the commutative, and associative laws of multiplication.

$$(2 \bullet 2 \bullet 2) \bullet (5 \bullet 5 \bullet 5) = (2 \bullet 5) \bullet (2 \bullet 5) \bullet (2 \bullet 5)$$

Multiply all of the quantities in parentheses.

$$(2 \bullet 5) \bullet (2 \bullet 5) \bullet (2 \bullet 5) = 10 \bullet 10 \bullet 10$$

Use exponential notation.

$$10 \bullet 10 \bullet 10 = 10^3$$

Therefore,

$$2^3 \bullet 5^3 = (2 \bullet 5)^3 = 10^3$$

Again, this method works using any numbers. A general rule may be written.

Rule for Multiplying Different Bases with the Same Exponent

$$a^n \, b^n = (ab)^n$$

Verify the following examples, using the newly developed rules.

Examples - Using Exponents

$$5^1 \bullet 5^1 = 5^2 = 25$$

$$5^1 \bullet 5^2 = 5^3 = 125$$

$$13^4 \bullet 2^4 = 26^4$$

$$13^2 \bullet 2^3 = (13 \bullet 13) \bullet (2 \bullet 2 \bullet 2) \quad \text{(no simplification)}$$

$$(0.5)^4 \bullet 2^4 = 1^4 = 1$$

Note that the fourth example presented above could be slightly simplified with a little effort.

$$13^2 \bullet 2^3$$
$$= (13 \bullet 13)(2 \bullet 2 \bullet 2)$$
$$= (13 \bullet 2)(13 \bullet 2) \bullet 2$$
$$= (26)(26)\,2$$
$$= 2\,(26^2)$$

8-3   Using Negative Exponents

So far, only positive integer exponents have been discussed.   However, as you may have guessed, exponents can also be negative. Previous laws and rules regarding exponents must still apply -- otherwise they wouldn't be called laws or rules.

Section **5-15** explained reciprocals. To review, the reciprocal of 2 is $\frac{1}{2}$, the reciprocal of $\frac{3}{2}$ is $\frac{2}{3}$, and so on. A reciprocal reverses the position of a number's numerator and denominator. As explained in section **5-15**, any number multiplied by its reciprocal equals one.

$$\left(\frac{a}{b}\right)\left(\frac{b}{a}\right) = \frac{ab}{ba} = 1$$

A negative exponent may always be converted to a positive exponent. To make a negative exponent positive, change the base to its reciprocal. Changing the base to its reciprocal will also make a positive exponent become negative. So remember, to change the sign of the exponent, invert the base. Let's clarify with examples.

Examples - Changing the Sign of the Exponent

$$2^{-3} = \left(\frac{1}{2}\right)^{3} = \frac{1}{2}\bullet\frac{1}{2}\bullet\frac{1}{2}$$

$$4^{-2} = \left(\frac{1}{4}\right)^{2} = \frac{1}{4}\bullet\frac{1}{4}$$

$$\left(\frac{1}{2}\right)^{-3} = 2^{3} = 2\bullet 2\bullet 2$$

$$6^{2} = \left(\frac{1}{6}\right)^{-2}$$

We can state the general rule as follows:

Rule for Changing the Sign of the Exponent

$$b^{-m} = \left(\frac{1}{b}\right)^{m}$$

Why does inverting the base change the sign of the exponent?

The law of exponents states that

$$b^{n}\bullet b^{m} = b^{n+m}$$

This law must be true for negative exponents and positive exponents.   Let's apply the law using a negative exponent and see what happens.

> **Example - Using the Law of Exponents with Negative Exponents**
>
> What does $(2^3 \bullet 2^{-2})$ equal?

Using the law,

$$2^3 \bullet 2^{-2} = 2^{3-2} = 2^1 = 2$$

Check to ensure this is correct with multiplication. Remember, remove the negative exponent by finding the reciprocal of the base.

$$2^3 \bullet 2^{-2} = (2 \bullet 2 \bullet 2) \bullet (\tfrac{1}{2} \bullet \tfrac{1}{2})$$

Use the commutative and associative laws of multiplication to rearrange the problem.

$$(2 \bullet 2 \bullet 2)\,(\tfrac{1}{2} \bullet \tfrac{1}{2}) = (2 \bullet \tfrac{1}{2})\,(2 \bullet \tfrac{1}{2}) \bullet 2$$

Multiplying,

$$(2 \bullet \tfrac{1}{2})\,(2 \bullet \tfrac{1}{2}) \bullet 2 = 1 \bullet 1 \bullet 2 = 2$$

By inverting the base to change the exponent's sign, answers agree with those obtained from the law of exponents.

What types of problems require negative exponents? That's a difficult question. You probably will never directly need to raise a number to a negative power to solve a simple question. However, negative exponents often occur as intermediate steps in more complicated math problems.

Although it is difficult to imagine what it means for a number to be raised to a negative exponent, negative exponents are mathematically just as valid as positive exponents. Both negative and positive exponents obey the mathematical laws which we stated earlier. Remember, mathematics is the manipulation of symbols that obey developed laws. The symbols do not always represent something physical.

> **Examples - Multiplying with Negative Exponents**
>
> $$4^{-2} \bullet 4^6 = 4^4$$
>
> $$3^{-5} \bullet 3^{-6} = 3^{-11}$$
>
> $$\left(\frac{1}{4}\right)^{-2} \bullet \left(\frac{1}{4}\right)^{-1} = \left(\frac{1}{4}\right)^{-3} = 4^3$$
>
> $$6^{-2} \bullet 2^{-2} = 12^{-2} = \left(\frac{1}{12}\right)^2$$

8-4 More Rules for Using Exponents

Laws and rules from previous sections must apply for numbers of any value. However, look at the following example.

Example - Exponent Equals Zero

What does $4^3 \bullet 4^{-3}$ equal?

Using our law of exponents,

$$4^3 \bullet 4^{-3} = 4^{(3-3)} = 4^0$$

But what does 4^0 equal? The value of 4^0 can be found using multiplication in the original problem.

$$4^3 \bullet 4^{-3} = (4 \bullet 4 \bullet 4)\left(\tfrac{1}{4} \bullet \tfrac{1}{4} \bullet \tfrac{1}{4}\right)$$

Using the commutative and associative laws of multiplication,

$$(4 \bullet 4 \bullet 4)\left(\tfrac{1}{4} \bullet \tfrac{1}{4} \bullet \tfrac{1}{4}\right) = (4 \bullet \tfrac{1}{4})\ (4 \bullet \tfrac{1}{4})\ (4 \bullet \tfrac{1}{4})$$

Multiplying the numbers in parentheses yields,

$$\text{Answer:}\quad (4 \bullet \tfrac{1}{4})\ (4 \bullet \tfrac{1}{4})\ (4 \bullet \tfrac{1}{4}) = 1 \bullet 1 \bullet 1 = 1$$

A number to the zero power may also be factored.

Examples - Determining Exponents of Zero by Factoring

$$\left(\tfrac{1}{2}\right)^0 = \left(\tfrac{1}{2}\right)^1 \bullet \left(\tfrac{1}{2}\right)^{-1} = \tfrac{1}{2} \bullet 2 = 1$$

$$-8^0 = (-8^1)\bullet(-8^{-1}) = (-8)\bullet(-\tfrac{1}{8}) = 1$$

We can substitute any number for the base and obtain the result of 1. Therefore, we find that ANY number raised to the zero power equals 1. This is very important. The only exception is 0 itself. For now, we'll say that 0^0 is not defined. We can even prove that any number raised to the zero power equals one by using variables.

$$a^0 = a^b a^{-b}$$
$$= a^b\left(\frac{1}{a^b}\right)$$
$$= \frac{a^b}{a^b} = 1$$

Examples - Numbers Raised to the Zero Power

$$3^0 = 1$$

$$0.3^0 = 1$$

$$-135,689^0 = 1$$

$$(14 \div 62.5 + 23000)^0 = 1$$

Division with exponents is not difficult. Remember that multiplying by 1/*a* is the same as dividing by *a*. Furthermore, multiplication with exponents has already been explained.

Using previously established rules, we may develop a formula for dividing numbers with exponents for any numbers *b*, *m* and *n*.

$$\frac{b^n}{b^m} = b^n \cdot \frac{1}{b^m} = b^n \cdot b^{-m} = b^{(n-m)}$$

We have developed a rule for division. To divide numbers with equal bases, subtract the exponent in the denominator from the exponent in the numerator.

Examples - Division of Numbers with Exponents

$$\frac{4^3}{4^2} = 4^1 = 4$$

$$\frac{6^4}{6^{-3}} = 6^{(4-(-3))} = 6^7$$

$$\frac{0.5^{-2}}{0.5^3} = 0.5^{-5} = 2^5$$

One final operation is possible -- multiplying a number raised to an exponent many times.

Example - Raising a Power to Another Power

What does $\left(4^2\right)^3$ equal?

Determine the answer by expanding the value with an exponent of 3, and using the law of exponents.

$$\left(4^2\right)^3 = 4^2 \cdot 4^2 \cdot 4^2 = 4^6$$

Answer: $\left(4^2\right)^3 = 4^6$

8-5   Summary of Exponential Rules

DO YOU KNOW THE RULES?

Many different rules have been developed. It is time to 'clear the air' and summarize all of the rules for exponents already presented in this chapter. Remember that every rule was developed from the law of exponents developed in section **8-2**.

As usual, the letters b, m, and n can represent <u>any</u> number. (Although, 0^0 is not defined.)

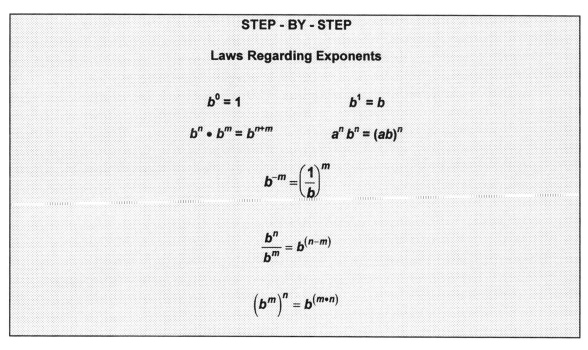

STEP - BY - STEP

Laws Regarding Exponents

$$b^0 = 1 \qquad\qquad b^1 = b$$

$$b^n \bullet b^m = b^{n+m} \qquad\qquad a^n b^n = (ab)^n$$

$$b^{-m} = \left(\frac{1}{b}\right)^m$$

$$\frac{b^n}{b^m} = b^{(n-m)}$$

$$\left(b^m\right)^n = b^{(m \bullet n)}$$

Maybe it's time for you to take a break?

Make sure you understand the previous sections and examples before moving onto section **8-6**.

The section is not simple, so please be patient.

8-6   Fractional Exponents

Rules have been developed for exponents of any value. However, all previous examples have used integers for exponents. The next step is to learn how to calculate bases with fractional or decimal exponents.

Decimal exponents are very rare. If there is a need to calculate a number with a decimal exponent, first convert the decimal into an equivalent fraction. Then use the method presented in this section. At this point in our mathematical development, there is no easy way to evaluate a number with decimal power directly (unless you have a calculator).

Start by writing the law of exponents 'backwards' from the previous sections.

$$b^{n+m} = b^n\, b^m$$

Use this law to calculate the following problem.

Example - Fractional Exponents

What does $9^{1/2}$ (or $9^{0.5}$) equal?

First remember,

$$9 = 9^1$$

Using the law stated above, factor 9^1 into two equal factors.

$$9^1 = 9^{1/2} \bullet 9^{1/2}$$

This is interesting. $9^{1/2}$ multiplied by $9^{1/2}$ equals 9. What two equal numbers, when multiplied together equal 9? After thinking a short time and using knowledge from the times table, we realize that,

$$3 \bullet 3 = 9 \quad \text{and} \quad -3 \bullet -3 = 9$$

Therefore, $9^{1/2}$ must equal 3 or -3.

$$\text{Answer:} \quad 9^{1/2} = 3 \text{ or } -3$$

Another way of writing the answer is to use the $\pm$, read "plus or minus":

$$9^{1/2} = \pm 3$$

But which is the correct answer, -3 or 3? Either answer could be correct, depending on the question. If you cannot determine whether the answer should be positive or negative from the question, you must state that the answer is 3 or -3. Either answer is correct mathematically. However, the question will often require the answer to be either positive or negative. For example, the age of a person must be a positive answer.

Both $3^2 = 9$ (read "three squared equals nine"), and $-3^2 = 9$. Another name for a number raised to the one half power is the **square root**. You should see where the name of square root originated. Rather than finding the value of a number squared, we must work backwards to find the square root. A **root** of a number is one of the equal factors whose product equals the number. The roots of 9 are 3 and -3.

Roots other than square roots will be mentioned shortly. However, square roots are often used, and are the focus of the immediate discussion.

> **Definition - What is a Square Root?**
>
> The square root of any number **a** is one of two equal numbers
> that when multiplied together equal **a**.

In the previous example, we found the square root of 9 equals ±3.

A symbol may be used for roots, rather than a fractional exponent. The $\sqrt{}$ symbol replaces the fractional exponent, and is called a **radical**. $\sqrt{}$ is also read aloud as "the square root". The base is placed inside the radical.

For example, $\sqrt{9}$ is read aloud "the square root of 9". Technically, the $\sqrt{}$ symbol is actually slightly different than the fractional exponent. This symbol specifies that the given answer should only be the positive root.

$$\sqrt{9} = 3$$

Therefore, to be mathematically correct

$$9^{1/2} = \pm 3 \quad \text{but} \quad \sqrt{9} = 3$$

Don't be surprised if you see $\sqrt{9} = \pm 3$ written in other texts. However, now you know what is technically correct. This text assumes that the radical requires only the positive root. Verify the following examples using your knowledge of multiplication.

Examples - Square Roots

$$\sqrt{25} = 5$$

$$\sqrt{81} = 9$$

$$\sqrt{625} = 25$$

A number with an exponent of 1/3 is called a **cubed root**. Therefore, $27^{1/3}$ is read aloud as "27 to the one third power" or "the cubed root of 27". This means that there is some equal factor that when multiplied together three times equals 27. Three cubed (3^3) equals 27. So, the cubed root of 27 equals 3. Negative 3 cubed equals $-3 \cdot -3 \cdot -3 = -27$. Therefore, the cubed root of 27 only has a positive solution.

The radical symbol may also be used for roots of any value. The notation is shown below.

$$27^{1/3} = \sqrt[3]{27} = 3$$

As you can see, the denominator of the fractional exponent has been written in small type in front of the radical sign. If no value is written outside the radical, a 2 is implied and therefore a square root is assumed.

Roots higher than three do not have special naming conventions. 1/4 is called the "fourth root". 1/5 is called the "fifth root". In each circumstance the denominator of the exponent indicates how many equal factors must be multiplied together to equal the base. Verify the examples using multiplication.

Examples - Higher Roots

$$\sqrt[4]{16} = 2$$

$$\sqrt[5]{3125} = 5$$

In all previous examples, the numerator of the exponent equaled one.   The following law is required if the numerator does not equal one.

$$\left(b^m\right)^n = b^{(m \cdot n)}$$

Using this law, any fractional exponent may be factored into an integer and a fraction with numerator one.

Example - Fractional Roots

What does $(32)^{\frac{2}{5}}$ equal?

First, rewrite the problem using the law stated above.

$$(32)^{\frac{2}{5}} = \left((32)^{\frac{1}{5}}\right)^2$$

We can now calculate the fifth root of 32 which equals 2.

$$\left((32)^{\frac{1}{5}}\right)^2 = 2^2$$

Answer: 4

Since,

$$\frac{2}{5} = 0.4$$

the example problem can also be written,

$$(32)^{0.4} = 4$$

You can also see from this example that in order to calculate a base raised to a decimal exponent, first find an equivalent fraction of the decimal. Then find the answer as shown above.

As section **4-14** stated, a rational number is a ratio of integers. However, an **irrational number** cannot be expressed as a ratio of integers and consists of a never-ending, never-repeating decimal number.

The discovery of irrational numbers is important, and was made by Hippasus of Metapontum in about 500 B.C. Both irrational numbers and rational numbers are real numbers since they may be represented on the number line. Exact expressions for irrational numbers often requires the use of radicals.

Examples - Irrational Numbers

$$\sqrt{2} = 1.41421356237...$$
$$\sqrt{3} = 1.73205080757...$$
$$\sqrt[3]{7} = 1.91293118277...$$

If a ratio of integers cannot exactly represent an irrational number, how do we calculate a problem such as $10^{\sqrt{2}}$? The practical answer is to approximate the exponent as a rational number. However, much thought, effort, and complicated theory has been developed for calculating numbers with irrational exponents. It is a very difficult problem. We will only concern ourselves with calculating numbers with rational exponents. This problem is difficult in itself.

So far, roots have only been verified to be correct. But, how are roots found in the first place?

It is relatively simple to find a number raised to an integer power, since the base is just multiplied a certain number of times. It is significantly more difficult to calculate the value of bases with fractional powers. It is difficult enough to find square roots, but higher roots can be extremely tedious. There are basic mathematical techniques for finding square roots, cube roots, and higher order roots. There are also advanced mathematical and computer techniques.

However, this book will not attempt to show you these methods. In practice, you can probably get close enough to the answer by guessing at the value of the root and using trial and error. Calculus will provide another method for finding the root of a number (as shown in **section 22-9**). Furthermore, almost every modern day calculator can find roots.

Being proficient at calculating roots is not necessary in today's society. However, it is very important that you understand the definition of roots, notation involving exponents, and especially how to manipulate exponents using the mathematical laws. It is not important at this point that you memorize special techniques for finding roots, since you will probably forget them anyway.

8-7   Scientific and Exponential Notation

In section **2-4**, we said that there was a popular alternative notation for writing very large or very small numbers. Now that we have learned exponents, we can learn how to write these numbers using scientific and exponential notation.

The base 10 raised to a power is unique since the exponent indicates the number of decimal point shifts of the number 1. A positive exponent indicates a shift of the decimal point right. A negative exponent indicates a shift left. The following examples can be proven with multiplication and the rules for exponents.

Examples - Powers of 10

$10^0 = 1$ (The decimal point on the number 1 = 1.000 is shifted 0 times)

$10^1 = 10$	(1 decimal point shift right)	$10^{-1} = 0.1$	(1 decimal point shift left)
$10^2 = 100$	(2 decimal point shifts right)	$10^{-2} = 0.01$	(2 decimal point shifts left)
$10^3 = 1000$	(3 decimal point shifts right)	$10^{-3} = 0.001$	(3 decimal point shifts left)
$10^4 = 10,000$	(4 decimal point shifts right)	$10^{-4} = 0.0001$	(4 decimal point shifts left)

This property of the number 10 may be used to rewrite numbers of any value.

Example - Factoring Using Powers of 10

$$600 = 6 \bullet 100 = 6 \bullet 10^2$$

$6 \bullet 10^2$ is equal to the value of 6 with the decimal point shifted twice right.

Example - Factoring Using Powers of 10

What does $6 \bullet 10^4$ equal?

10^4 indicates that 4 shifts right of the decimal place are required. Therefore,

$$6.00000 \ => \ 60,000$$

Answer: 60,000

Exponential notation is the expression of a number multiplied by a power of 10. Verify the following examples using exponential notation.

Examples - Exponential Notation

$$80 \bullet 10^3 = 80,000$$

$$1 \bullet 10^{-2} = 0.01$$

$$345.67 \bullet 10^{-3} = 0.34567$$

$$345.67 \bullet 10^4 = 3,456,700$$

$$1.23 \bullet 10^{17} = 123,000,000,000,000,000$$

Exponential notation allows any number to be multiplied by a factor of 10. In **scientific notation** a number is rewritten as a value between 1 and 10 multiplied by a factor of 10. Usually the (×) operator for multiplication is used rather than the (•) operator, since (×) will not be confused with a variable.

Example - Using Scientific Notation

The distance from the earth to the sun is approximately 150 billion meters. Use scientific notation to express the distance of the earth to the sun.

$$150{,}000{,}000{,}000 = 1.5 \times 10^{11}$$

Answer: 1.5×10^{11} meters

Example - Scientific Notation

The wavelength of red light is about 0.0000004 meters.
Express this wavelength using scientific notation.

Answer: 4×10^{-7} meters

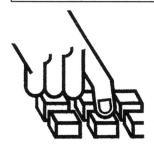

Most calculators have a button which automatically converts numbers to scientific notation.

In some math books and on most calculators, numbers in scientific notation use the letter *E* rather than the base 10. The power of 10 is written after the *E*.

Example - Scientific Notation using *E*

Express the distance of the earth to the sun using scientific notation.

$$150{,}000{,}000{,}000 = 1.5 \times 10^{11} = 1.5 \text{ E+11}$$

Answer: 1.5 E+11 meters

The wavelength of red light can be written as 4 E-7 meters. This notation is easier to type since superscripts are not used.

8-8   Summary of Exponents

Exponents and roots are often used in mathematics. We have covered the basic manipulations and definitions. However, more advanced manipulations of powers and roots will be shown later to help us understand how different areas of mathematics are related. As with just about everything in math, the topics may seem difficult at first but with practice and further understanding, you will soon become an expert.

Logarithms are closely related to exponents and are explained in chapter 18. However, the next chapter is a preparation for Algebra and the final chapter in Part I.

Important Definitions

Exponent

Base

Power

Root

Square Root

Cubed Root

Radical

Irrational Number

Exponential Notation

Scientific Notation

You should be able to ...

1. Change the form of a number repeatedly multiplied into a base with an exponent

2. Find the value of a number raised to any integer power

3. Multiply numbers with any base and integer exponent

4. Divide numbers with any base and integer exponent

5. Understand and be able to use all rules stated in section **8-5** for any number

6. Understand and be able to find the values of numbers with fractional exponents

7. Write any number using scientific or exponential notation

Pre-Algebra

9-1 Review of the Past and Goals for the Future

Let's review topics explained in previous chapters.

- Chapter 2 presented the basic definitions of numbers and symbols.

- Chapters 3 and 4 explained the four fundamental math operators.

- Chapters 5 and 6 focused on manipulating numbers using fractions and percentages.

- Chapter 7 clarified the use of negative numbers.

- Chapter 8 introduced the shorthand notation of exponents.

Chapter 9 is the final chapter of the first of three parts of this text. At the end of this chapter, all topics normally taught from first grade through eighth grade will have been covered. The next part of the text explains mathematics normally taught in high school, starting with Algebra in chapter 10. It is the goal of chapters two through nine to prepare the student for Algebra.

There are two objectives for the student of Algebra:

1. The student must learn to write mathematical equations which represent problems with unknown solutions.

2. The student must find the unknown solution in a mathematical equation.

The first objective is taught using word problems which is the topic of chapter 12. In a word problem, you are not given a math equation to solve, but must write your own based on given information. This subject is best taught after learning how to solve simple equations.

The second objective is taught by solving a variety of equations. No new operators or notations are taught prior to the completion of Algebra. *The entire topic of Algebra is merely the application of mathematics presented in chapters 2 through 8.* If there are any topics in previous chapters which are not thoroughly understood, you should review them once again before continuing.

9-2   Definitions for Algebra

Algebra is the first branch of mathematics that requires the use of variables which represent unknown values. (Section **3-4** introduced variables.) In fact, the names *variable* and *unknown* will often be used interchangeably.

The letter *x* is the standard letter used to represent an unknown value. If more than one unknown exists, then the letters *y* and *z* are normally used. Obviously, there is nothing special about using these letters. However, virtually every math text normally abides by this convention. Advanced sciences and mathematics often use Greek letters as variable names, since many variables are often used simultaneously and English only contains 26 letters.

Variables can be any letter or name, and are often chosen so that the problem makes sense. To determine how quickly a car is moving, the variable could be *x*, *s*, *speed*, or any other name which makes sense to you. Time is usually described using the variable *t*. Distance is normally represented by the variable *d*.

A mathematical statement using variables, such as 5 + *x*, is also called an **algebraic expression**. On the other hand, a mathematical statement with no variables, such as 5 + 2(3) is called an **arithmetic expression**. An equals sign is required to change an expression into an **equation**. Therefore, 5 + *x* = 1 is an algebraic equation.

An expression containing an unknown may be simplified but the unknown may not found because an expression does not have an equals sign. However, an unknown in an equation may be found.

IMPORTANT

Finally, an algebraic equation which indicates a mathematical relationship is called an **algebraic formula**. The commutative, associative, and distributive laws stated in earlier chapters were all algebraic formulas.

Do not be overly concerned with memorizing all of these definitions. Rather, concentrate on understanding the math and examples. The terminology will be learned automatically with enough practice.

<u>Example - Using Variables</u>

$$x^2 + 2y = 14 - x$$

How many variables are used in the above equation?

There are two values which are unknown, represented by the variables *x* and *y*.

Answer: 2 variables (or unknowns)

Chapter 10 will focus on solving one equation with one unknown. Chapter 11 will focus on solving more than one equation with more than one unknown.

9-3   Operations with Variables

Operations with variables have been performed in earlier chapters. However, this section should clarify any misunderstandings regarding the use of variables. A few more definitions are required. The definitions should make more sense after studying the examples.

A **term** is a group of numbers or variables combined by multiplication or division (*not* addition or subtraction). A number multiplied or divided by one or more variables is called a **coefficient**. **Like terms** are terms with exactly the same variables and exponents, though not necessarily the same coefficient.

In the examples, pay special attention to the sign of the coefficients.

<u>Examples - Terms</u>

$5a$	one term
$5a + 2a$	two like terms
$5a + 2b$	two terms
$5a + 2a^2$	two terms
$5ab$	one term
$5ab + 2ab + 3c$	three terms, $5ab$ and $2ab$ are like terms

<u>Examples - Coefficients</u>

$5a^2$	coefficient is 5
$5ab$	coefficient is 5
$1.5c$	coefficient is 1.5
$-25x$	coefficient is -25
x	coefficient is 1
$12x - 13x$	coefficient of first term is 12, second term coefficient is -13

Only like terms may be added or subtracted in simplifying expressions. Any terms may be multiplied or divided, with exponents and cancellation utilized as necessary. Verify the following examples.

<u>Examples - Simplification of Expressions</u>

$$x + x = 2x$$

$$5a + 2a = 7a$$

$$23ab - 10ab = 13ab$$

$$64c - 9b = 64c - 9b \text{ (no simplification possible)}$$

$$3a \bullet 6b = 18ab$$

$$3a \bullet 6a = 18a^2$$

$$2abc \div 0.5abc = 4$$

$$2ab \div 0.5c = 4ab/c$$

Why can only like terms be added or subtracted?

Mathematically, this can be understood by factoring with the Distributive Law of Multiplication.

<u>Example - Using the Distributive Law to Factor</u>

Prove that $5a + 2a = 7a$ using the Distributive Law of Multiplication.

$5a + 2a =$
$\quad = a(5 + 2)$ according to the distributive law
$\quad = a7$ after adding numbers in parentheses
$\quad = 7a$ after Commutative Law of Multiplication

The coefficient is <u>always</u> written before the variable to avoid confusion. This is the reason that a7 was changed to 7a.

**EVERYBODY DOES IT
THIS WAY.**

The Distributive Law of Multiplication allows like terms to be added or subtracted. As you can see, the following terms cannot be reduced with the distributive law, and therefore unlike terms cannot be added or subtracted.

$$5a + 2b$$

Furthermore, adding or subtracting unlike terms does not make sense. Remember the definition of multiplication. $2 \bullet a$ means that there are two a's.

$$a + a = 2a$$

However, $a + b$ cannot be reduced further since a and b are unknown values, or variables.

9-4   Order of Operations

In preceding chapters, this text has explained how to use the four basic operators to manipulate expressions with numbers and variables. However, few examples of combining the operators have been shown. The goal of this section is to explain the order that operations must be performed to obtain the correct answer.

STEP - BY - STEP

Order of Operations

1. Perform calculations in parentheses. If there are more than one set of parentheses, perform the operation on the innermost parentheses first.

2. Perform all calculations that contain exponents (or roots) from left to right.

3. Perform all multiplication and division computations from left to right.

4. Perform all addition and subtraction computations from left to right.

 I have a wonderful aunt Sarah who is always bumping into things because she is so busy. When visitors come, we always have to say **P**lease **E**xcuse **M**y **D**ear **A**unt **S**arah (*PEMDAS* for short). Without knowing it, Sarah helps me remember the order of operations.

Parentheses,   then
Exponents,   then
Multiplication   and
Division,   then
Addition   and
Subtraction

Note that brackets [ ] or braces { } may also be used rather than parentheses. Parentheses, brackets, or braces all can form a group of terms. A group of terms is called a **quantity**.

Example - Understanding Quantities

Write an expression for 3 times the quantity of four minus seven.
Then find the solution.

Answer: 3(4 - 7) = -9

A few examples demonstrating the order of operations are provided.

Example - Simplification using the Order of Operations

What is $5^2 + 3 \bullet 4$?

Step 1: No parentheses exist.

Step 2: Calculate exponents.

$$5^2 + 3 \bullet 4 = 25 + 3 \bullet 4$$

Step 3: Perform multiplication and division from left to right.

$$25 + 3 \bullet 4 = 25 + 12$$

Step 4: Perform addition and subtraction from left to right.

$$25 + 12 = 37$$

Answer: 37

The correct answer will only be obtained using the order of operations. The following example should demonstrate the importance of performing multiplication and division (or addition and subtraction) from 'left to right'.

> <u>Example - Simplification using the Order of Operations</u>
>
> What is $5^2 + 3 \bullet 4 \div 6 - (6 - 3 + 4)$?

Step 1: Calculate the quantities in parentheses.

$$5^2 + 3 \bullet 4 \div 6 - (6 - 3 + 4) = ?$$

$$5^2 + 3 \bullet 4 \div 6 - 7 = ?$$

Step 2: Calculate exponents.

$$5^2 + 3 \bullet 4 \div 6 - 7 = ?$$

$$25 + 3 \bullet 4 \div 6 - 7 = ?$$

Step 3: Perform multiplication and division from left to right. Parentheses have been inserted to highlight the operations performed first.

$$25 + (3 \bullet 4) \div 6 - 7 = ?$$

$$25 + (12 \div 6) - 7 = ?$$

$$25 + 2 - 7 = ?$$

Step 4: Perform addition and subtraction from left to right.

$$25 + 2 - 7 = ?$$

$$27 - 7 = ?$$

$$20 = ?$$

Answer: 20

As you can see, the order of operations is absolutely necessary to obtain the correct answer. Review the previous example and make sure that you understand why the operations were performed as shown.

In step #1, the quantity $(6 - 3 + 4 = 7)$ was calculated. However, note what happens if operations are not performed left to right. Assume that the addition of $3 + 4$ was performed first.

$$6 - (3 + 4) = 6 - 7 = -1$$

The change shown in the above example is that 4 is subtracted from 6, rather than added to 6. Of course, the Commutative Law of Addition could also be applied in step #1 above to obtain the correct answer.

$$6 + 4 - 3 = 7$$

A complicated example is presented. Verify that the steps were performed according to the order of operations. Bold type and underlines are used to indicate the calculation to be performed in the ensuing step.

Example - Using the Order of Operations

What is $5 \bullet (6^2 - (3 \bullet (2 + 9(5-4)^3))) - 14 = ?$

$5 \bullet (6^2 - (3 \bullet (2 + 9(\underline{5-4})^3))) - 14 = ?$

$5 \bullet (6^2 - (3 \bullet (2 + 9\underline{(1)^3}))) - 14 = ?$

$5 \bullet (6^2 - (3 \bullet (2 + \underline{9(1)}))) - 14 = ?$

$5 \bullet (6^2 - (3 \bullet \underline{(2+9)})) - 14 = ?$

$5 \bullet (6^2 - \underline{(3 \bullet 11)}) - 14 = ?$

$5 \bullet (\underline{6^2} - 33) - 14 = ?$

$5 \bullet \underline{(36 - 33)} - 14 = ?$

$\underline{5 \bullet (3)} - 14 = ?$

$15 - 14 = ?$

Answer: 1

Make sure you understand the above example, since every operation has been used. Innermost parentheses always have the **highest priority**, or must be performed first. After practice, you will find that following the order of operations is not difficult, but essential.

Verify the following examples to test your knowledge of the order of operations.

Examples - Using the Order of Operations

$12 \div 4 \bullet 3 = 9$

$4x^2 - 9x^2 + x(6x - 5x) = -4x^2$

$13 \bullet 8 - x(4x^2 - (2x)^2) = 104$

9-5   Summary

Chapters two through nine are the foundation upon which all ensuing math skills will be built. Algebra is normally first taught at the eighth or ninth grade level. For many, Algebra is the deciding factor in convincing a student whether to pursue advanced mathematics or to quit mathematics and attempt a career in English or History.

To reiterate chapter 1, advanced mathematics is used by millions of people everyday at work. Mathematics is the key to many professions from working on Wall Street to working in national laboratories. Algebra is the first step in advanced mathematics. It is a tool which allows you to find information that cannot be found using any other discipline.

Think about the progression that has been demonstrated in Part I of this text. First, you learned addition of single digit integers. By separating multi-digit numbers into places, addition of any valued integer or decimal was possible. Addition required an inverse operation to "undo" addition, so subtraction was developed. Multiple additions of the same number were tedious, so multiplication was created. Multiplication also required an inverse operation to "undo" numbers multiplied, so division was established. This concluded the development four fundamental math operators.

Some quantities are best represented by a division statement, so fractions were developed. After learning how to perform any of the four fundamental operations with fractions, the special fraction with denominator 100 was defined as a percentage. Percentages proved very useful, especially in dealing with money. Since sometimes you owe more money that you have, using negative numbers became necessary.

Repeated multiplication became tedious, so exponents were developed. Exponents also need an inverse operator, but that subject will not be explained until chapter 18 (logarithms). Finally, sometimes we don't even know the value of numbers to be modified with the various operations. Therefore, we learned how to perform operations using variables. Now it's time for Algebra!

Important Definitions

Algebra

Expression

Equation

Term

Like Terms

Coefficient

Quantity

You should be able to ...

1. Perform any of the four fundamental operations with variables

2. Recognize like terms

3. Find the coefficient in a term

4. Simplify expressions according to the Order of Operations

5. Use everything you have learned in the first nine chapters

Solving One Algebraic Equation

10-1   Introduction

Algebra is the first topic presented in this text that may be called "advanced math." The word *advanced* does not necessarily imply that the mathematics from this point forward will be more difficult. However, this does imply two things.

1. Algebra is a large subject area with much to learn. High schools generally teach the courses Algebra I and Algebra II. However, other subjects such as Abstract Algebra and Linear Algebra also exist, and there is much to learn beyond that explained in Algebra II texts. No one book can explain all of Algebra or all of any of the other math disciplines that are explained from this point forward. However, all of the algebraic topics necessary for daily life and further mathematical development are presented herein.

2. Solving algebraic problems is not as straightforward as solving problems in earlier chapters. There is no precise step-by-step solution to every problem. Therefore, only a general method of solution may be presented. The student must not only follow the general steps to find the solution, but also rely on past knowledge and acquired skills to solve a particular problem.

 Again, do not worry. If you have thought the explanations in previous chapters clear, you will find ensuing topics explained with equal clarity. It is assumed at this point that the reader has already acquired a solid mathematical foundation. The use of mathematical language to describe problems will intensify in order that the reader get accustomed to reading mathematical texts. Special efforts are made to keep the reader informed of the goals of each chapter.

10-2   Algebraic Definitions

Many definitions are presented at the outset. However, understanding these definitions is a prerequisite to understanding the goals that need to be accomplished in this important chapter. The definitions will make more sense as additional examples are presented.

In the past, many different letters have been used as variables or unknowns. A **constant** is a fixed value. A constant may be simply a number. (For example, 1, 5, and 20 are constants.) A constant may also be a letter that represents a fixed value. Typically, a, b, c and d are used as constants. If more than four constants are required, then typically subscripts are used such as a_0, a_1, a_2, a_3, a_4, etc. Constants are often used to represent coefficients.

Example - Variables and Constants

How many variables and constants are in the following equation?

$$ax^2 + bx + c = d$$

Answer: One variable is used: x
Four constants are used: a, b, c, and d

Example - Variables and Constants

How many variables and constants are in the following equation?

$$ax^2 + bx + c = y$$

Answer: Two variables are used: x and y
Three constants are used: a, b, and c

Both examples presented are answered by knowing that the letters x and y are used to represent variables, and a, b, c, and d represent constants. Most books assume you understand this method of writing general equations.

Example - Writing Equations

Write an equation using the following general form,
replacing all constants with chosen numbers.

$$ax^2 + bx + c = d$$

An infinite number of equations fit the given form. Some examples are given below.

Answer(s): $3x^2 + 2x + 4 = 5$ with $a = 3$, $b = 2$, $c = 4$, $d = 5$

$x^2 + x + 2 = 3$ with $a = 1$, $b = 1$, $c = 2$, $d = 3$

$2x^2 + 3 = 4$ with $a = 2$, $b = 0$, $c = 3$, $d = 4$

$x^2 - 4x = 6$ with $a = 1$, $b = -4$, $c = 0$, $d = 6$

- A **monomial** is an algebraic expression with one term.   ("mono" = one)
- A **binomial** is an algebraic expression with two terms.   ("bi" = two)
- A **trinomial** is an algebraic expression with three terms.   ("tri" = three)
- A **polynomial** is an algebraic expression with one or more terms.   ("poly" = many)

Technically speaking, the variable in a polynomial must be raised to a whole number power. Otherwise, the expression is called a **multinomial**.

The term polynomial is most often used. Obviously, both polynomial expressions (i.e. without an equals sign), and polynomial equations (i.e. with an equals sign) exist.

<u>Example - Different "-nomial" Expressions</u>

5	monomial
x	monomial
$x + 1$	binomial
$3x^2 + 2x + 4$	trinomial
$3x^2 + 2x + 4$	polynomial
$ax^2 + c$	polynomial
$a^{0.5}x + 2$	polynomial (remember, a represents a constant)
$ax^{0.5} + 2$	multinomial

- The **order** or **degree** of a polynomial is the greatest power of the variable in a polynomial. If there is more than one variable in a term, the degree is the sum of the exponents in the variables of the term. (See final example in box below.)

- A **linear equation** is the same as a first-order or first-degree polynomial equation.

- A **quadratic equation** is the same as a second-order or second-degree polynomial equation.

<u>Examples - Polynomials</u>

5	zero-order polynomial expression ($x^0 = 1$)
$x + 1 = 0$	first-degree polynomial or linear equation
$x^2 + 1 = 0$	quadratic equation, or second-degree polynomial
$3x^2 + 2x + 4 = 0$	quadratic equation, or second-degree polynomial
$3x^3 + 4 = 0$	third-degree or third-order polynomial equation
$3ab^2 + 3b^2$	third-degree polynomial expression

The examples should make the given definitions clear. Future examples will provide further clarification. Note that a standard convention is to write the variables with the highest degree first.

10-3   Two Basic Methods for Solving An Algebraic Equation

The goal of this chapter is to learn how to find the unknown value(s) of one variable in a given polynomial equation containing one variable. There are two methods of accomplishing this goal.

1. Isolate the variable -- used for linear equations
2. Factorization -- used for polynomials of degree two or higher

Review sections **4-6**, **4-7**, and **5-8**, if necessary, in order that you clearly understand the distributive law and factorization. These previous sections performed factorization of numbers. This chapter will perform factorization of polynomials.

10-4   Isolating the Variable

The first method for solving an algebraic equation is to isolate the variable. **Isolate the variable** by placing the variable on one side of the equation and placing the constant(s) on the other side of the equation.

Example - Isolating the Variable

Solve the following equation for x by isolating the variable.

$$\frac{x}{2} = 4$$

Using the complementary nature of multiplication and division as described in section **4-11**, we find the answer.

Answer: $x = 8$

x is isolated on one side of the equals sign and the constant of 8 is on the other side. Isolation of x resulted in the answer 8. Methods for isolating the variable, and thus finding the value of the unknown are given in this section.

The most simple method of solving an algebraic equation is to isolate the variable to one side of the equation. This can be accomplished by remembering the following simple rules developed in previous chapters.

$$\frac{a}{a} = 1$$

$$a \bullet 1 = a$$

$$a - a = 0$$

$$a + 0 = a$$

$$a = a$$

These equations are very simple, yet very powerful. Every operation performed in this section can be verified correct by one of the above equations.

The complementary nature of multiplication and division described in section **4-11** is verified with the first two rules stated above. The complementary nature of addition and subtraction given in section **3-9** are verified with the third and fourth equations given above. Examples in the following pages will give further insight.

Look at the following problem, from the previous example.

$$\frac{x}{2} = 4$$

The solution may be obtained by multiplying both sides of the equation by 2. This is the exact same as multiplying the left side by $\frac{2}{2} = 1$, which is valid according to the first rule listed above. This is shown on the next page.

$$\left(\frac{2}{2}\right)\frac{x}{2} = 4$$

- or -

$$\left(\frac{2}{1}\right)\frac{x}{2} = 4\left(\frac{2}{1}\right)$$

$$\left(\frac{2}{1}\right)\frac{x}{2} = 4\left(\frac{2}{1}\right)$$

$$x = 8$$

A slightly more complicated example is also helpful.

Example - Isolating the Variable

Solve the following equation.

$$\frac{x}{2} = 10.5 + 2x$$

Remember, the goal is to isolate the variable x. To accomplish the goal in this example, first multiply both sides of the equation by 2 to cancel the denominator of the fraction.

$$2\left(\frac{x}{2}\right) = 2(10.5 + 2x)$$

Then, after applying the Distributive Law of Multiplication to the right side,

$$x = 21 + 4x$$

Subtracting $4x$ from both sides of the equation will remove $4x$ from the right hand side. Again, this is the exact same as adding $4x - 4x = 0$ to one side, which is valid.

$$x - 4x = 21 + 4x - 4x$$

$$-3x = 21$$

Dividing both sides by -3, to isolate the variable x, provides the answer.

Answer: $x = -7$

A general procedure for isolating the variable is provided. A detailed procedure cannot be provided since every algebraic problem requires different steps.

STEP - BY - STEP

To Isolate the Variable

Whatever operation is performed on one side of the equation must be repeated on the other side of the equation.

Perform any operation(s) necessary to isolate the variable on one side of the equation and the constant on the other side of the equation to determine the solution.

THIS IS THE KEY CONCEPT TO ALL OF ALGEBRA!

If the same operation is performed on both sides of the equation, the simple equations listed at the start of this section will be followed. Does this make sense?

For example, assume that you have two cartons with an equal number of tomatoes in each carton. The goal is to keep the number of tomatoes the same in both cartons. The number of tomatoes in a carton may represent the value on one side of an equation.

tomatoes in carton *A* = # tomatoes in carton *B*

A

- If I eat (subtract) five tomatoes from carton *A*, I must eat (subtract) five in carton *B* to keep the number of tomatoes the same in each carton.

- If I add three tomatoes to one carton, I must add three to the other.

B

- If I multiply the number of tomatoes in carton *A* by seven, I must multiply the tomatoes in carton *B* by seven.

- If I eat the square root of the number of tomatoes in each carton, the number of tomatoes remain equal in both cartons.

An equation always has two equal values, written on opposite sides of the equals sign. You may add, subtract, multiply, or divide by any number or find the square root of any value on one side of the equation. However, whatever operation is performed on one side of the equation must also be performed on the other side of the equation to ensure that the values on both sides of the equation remain equal.

The concept of variable isolation is not difficult, but it does take practice.

Example - Solving the Variable

Solve $3x = -6x + 81$

It is difficult to solve for *x* by just looking at the problem. However, isolating the variable provides an easy method of solution. There are several ways of isolating the variable. Only one sequence of steps is presented.

Step 1: Add 6x to both sides of the equation to remove x from the right side of the equation.

$$3x + 6x = -6x + 81 + 6x$$

$$9x = 81$$

Step 2: Divide both sides of the equation by 9 to simplify the problem.

$$\frac{9x}{9} = \frac{81}{9}$$

$$x = 9$$

The variable has been isolated.

Answer: $x = 9$

Let's check the answer to verify that no errors were made. We will substitute the value of 9 for x.

$$3x = -6x + 81$$

$$3(9) = -6(9) + 81$$

$$27 = -54 + 81$$

$$-27 = -27 \qquad \sqrt{} \text{ yes, } x = 9 \text{ is correct}$$

Example - Solving the Variable

Solve $21 + 13x = 14x - 2^3$

Step 1: Subtract 13x from both sides to remove x from the left side of the equation.

$$-13x + 21 + 13x = -13x + 14x - 2^3$$

$$21 = x - 2^3$$

Step 2: Add 2^3 (or 8) to both sides to remove the constant from the right hand side of the equation.

$$21 + 8 = x - 2^3 + 8$$

$$29 = x$$

The variable has been isolated.

Answer: $x = 29$

You should verify that the answer is correct.

ON TO ANOTHER EXAMPLE!

Example - Solving for the Variable

Solve: $5x + 3(x + 1) = 51 - 4x$

Step 1: Use the distributive law to remove the quantity in parentheses and simplify the problem.

$$5x + 3(x + 1) = 51 - 4x$$

$$5x + 3x + 3 = 51 - 4x$$

Step 2: Combine like terms for further simplification.

$$5x + 3x + 3 = 51 - 4x$$

$$8x + 3 = 51 - 4x$$

Step 3: Subtract 3 from both sides of the equation to remove the constant from the left side of the equation.

$$8x + 3 - 3 = 51 - 4x - 3$$

$$8x = 48 - 4x$$

Step 4: Add $4x$ to both sides of the equation to remove the variable x from the right side.

$$4x + 8x = 48 - 4x + 4x$$

$$12x = 48$$

Step 5: Divide both sides by 12 to make the coefficient of x equal 1.

$$\frac{12x}{12} = \frac{48}{12}$$

Answer: $x = 4$

Check the solution.

$$5(4) + 3(4 + 1) = 51 - 4(4)$$

$$20 + 3(5) = 51 - 16$$

$$35 = 35 \qquad \sqrt{}\ \text{yes}$$

Example - Solving the Variable

Solve $\dfrac{x^2 + 80}{x + 4} = 20$

Step 1: Multiply both sides by $x + 4$ to cancel the denominator of the fraction.

$$\left(\frac{\cancel{x+4}}{1}\right)\frac{x^2+80}{\cancel{x+4}} = 20(x+4)$$

$$x^2 + 80 = 20x + 80$$

Step 2: Subtract 80 from both sides to remove 80 from the right side of the equation.

$$x^2 + 80 - 80 = 20x + 80 - 80$$

$$x^2 = 20x$$

Step 3: Divide both sides by x to simplify the problem, removing the variable from the right side.

$$\frac{x^2}{x} = \frac{20x}{x}$$

Answer*: $x = 20$

Check:

$$\frac{20^2 + 80}{20 + 4} = \frac{480}{24} = 20$$

$$20 = 20 \qquad \sqrt{} \text{ yes}$$

With practice and knowledge obtained from previous chapters, isolating the variable should not seem too difficult. You probably now realize some of the importance of learning cancellation, and the laws of addition and multiplication shown in earlier chapters.

You must be careful if each side of the equation is squared. For illustrative purposes, begin with the following simple equation.

$$x = 5$$

Square both sides.

$$x^2 = 25$$

Taking the square root of both sides yields:

$$x = \pm 5$$

Although it is known that the answer is $x = 5$, the process of squaring and taking the square root of a number produces positive and negative answers. To determine which answer is correct, separately insert the positive and negative solutions in the original equation. The correct solution will satisfy (or 'make true') the original equation.

Please verify the following examples.

---

*Note: $x = 0$ is also a solution to this equation. In general, you should always check to see if 0 is a valid solution to the given problem.

Examples - Isolating the Variable

$x = x + 11(2 + x)$ Answer: $x = -2$

$x / 10 = (x - 9)$ Answer: $x = 10$

$3x \div 2 = 9$ Answer: $x = 6$

$(4x)^2 = 64$ Answer: $x = \pm 2$

$x / x = 1$ Answer: $x = $ <any number>

Maybe it's time for a break?

Isolating the variable to solve an algebraic equation is a very important method and is a key to understanding more advanced math.

Please make sure you understand the previous sections, and the given examples before moving on to the second method of solving algebraic equations -- factorization. The next section is also very important, and very long!

10-5   Factorization of Quadratic Equations by Inspection

Linear equations and quadratic equations are the most popular polynomials used in mathematics. *A linear equation may always be solved by isolating the variable,* as shown in section **10-4**. However, it is usually quite difficult or impossible to isolate the variable in polynomial equations of higher orders. For example, observe the following quadratic equation.

$$x^2 + 3x + 2 = 0$$

Let's try to isolate the variable. First, isolate the constant term to one side of the equation.

$$x^2 + 3x = -2$$

Then, factor an x from the left-hand side.

$$x(x + 3) = -2$$

As you can see, we are no closer to solving the problem. The variable x cannot be isolated without using some math 'tricks' or non-obvious manipulations. A new method for solving equations is required, factorization. In sections **5-8** and **5-10**, factorization of numbers was performed. In this section, factorization of quadratic expressions is necessary. *Quadratic equations may always be solved with factorization* and an understanding of the usefulness of the simple equation given below.

$$a \bullet 0 = 0$$

STEP - BY - STEP

Solving Quadratic Equations by Inspection

1. Make one side of the equation equal to zero through algebraic manipulations.
2. Factor the quadratic expression into two linear factors.
3. Set each linear factor equal to zero, and solve the variable in each linear expression.
4. Verify the answers found in step #3 are correct.

The section title words 'by inspection' mean 'by observation'. Therefore, this section will demonstrate how to solve particular quadratic equations by only looking at the problem and using prior knowledge of multiplication. The following section (**10-6**) will demonstrate how to solve quadratic equations using a general formula.

Let's clarify the steps listed above with an example. Further explanation is given after the example is presented.

<u>Example - Solving a Quadratic Equation</u>

Solve $x^2 + 3x = -2$

Step 1: Add 2 to both sides of the equation to make one side of the equation zero.

$$x^2 + 3x + 2 = -2 + 2$$

$$x^2 + 3x + 2 = 0$$

Step 2: Factor the quadratic equation into two linear factors. With knowledge of the distributive law, we can verify the following statement. This step will be explained more clearly in the paragraphs below.

$$x^2 + 3x + 2 = (x + 1)(x + 2) = 0$$

Step 3: The linear factors are $(x + 1)$ and $(x + 2)$. Set each factor equal to zero and solve.

$x + 1 = 0$	Answer:	$x = -1$
$x + 2 = 0$	Answer:	$x = -2$

Step 4: Verify answers obtained in step #3 by substituting answers into the original equation.

First, verify $x = -1$ is a solution in the original equation ($x^2 + 3x = -2$).

$$(-1)^2 + 3(-1) + 2 = 0$$
$$1 - 3 + 2 = 0$$
$$0 = 0 \quad \sqrt{} \text{ yes}$$

Second, verify $x = -2$ is a solution to the original equation.

$$(-2)^2 + 3(-2) + 2 = 0$$
$$4 - 6 + 2 = 0$$
$$0 = 0 \quad \sqrt{} \text{ yes}$$

Answers: $x = -1$ and $x = -2$

More clarification of *why* the steps were performed is necessary.

The key to understanding this method of solution is the following simple equation containing variables *x* and *y*.

$$x \bullet y = 0$$

Either *x* or *y* (or both) must equal zero for the above equation to be true since

$$a \bullet 0 = 0$$

In quadratic equations, the quadratic is factored into two binomial linear factors, which are represented here by *x* and *y*. One or both of the binomials must equal zero if their product equals zero.

Therefore, the idea is to factor a quadratic into two linear factors whose product equals zero. The two factors can then be solved individually with variable isolation as presented in section **10-4**. Since there are always two linear factors, two solutions always exist. You should now understand *why* factorization works, and *why* all of the steps are presented as shown in **STEP-BY-STEP**. Now we move to *how* step #2 was performed.

GETTING THE IDEA?

Section **4-7** provided a detailed explanation of distribution and the Distributive Law of Multiplication. Using the distributive law to multiply two binomials is repeated from section **4-7** below. Numbers indicate the order that operators are normally performed, although the order may be altered by the Commutative Law of Addition.

$$(a + b)\,(c + d) = ac + ad + bc + bd$$

Most Algebra books describe the method of multiplying two binomials as shown above as the FOIL method. **FOIL** is an acronym for **F**ront **O**utside **I**nside **L**ast.

<u>One Valid Order for Multiplying Two Binomials</u>
1. First Terms
2. Outside Terms
3. Inside Terms
4. Last Terms

Apparently the word FOIL helps some remember how to multiply binomials. However, FOIL is the exact same method as the distributive law. If FOIL helps you remember how to multiply two binomials, then use it. However, understanding the Distributive Law of Multiplication should suffice. Look once again at step #2 from the previous example which contained the following expression.

$$x^2 + 3x + 2$$

As stated, every quadratic expression may be factored into two linear binomials.

$$x^2 + 3x + 2 = (x + ?)(x + ?)$$

At this point, we are not sure what numbers should replace the question marks. Therefore, let's first represent the values with b and d.

$$x^2 + 3x + 2 = (x + b)(x + d)$$

Now it is necessary to determine values for b and d. With a little thought, we reach the following conclusions.

1. The term x^2 is developed by multiplying the first terms in each binomial. Furthermore, the values of b and d do not affect the term x^2.

$$x \bullet x = x^2$$

2. The term $3x$ is developed by multiplying the inside and outside terms of the binomials.

$$3x = bx + dx = (b + d)x$$

3. The term 2 is developed by multiplying the last terms in each binomial.

$$bd = 2$$

To conclude, we know that both of these statements are true for some value b and d.

$$b + d = 3$$
$$b \bullet d = 2$$

Using knowledge of multiplication and addition, we must think of two factors of 2, which added together equal 3. After a little thought, you should realize that the factors must be 2 and 1. Obviously, it does not matter which value is assigned to b and which is assigned to d, since both are added to the same x.

$$2 + 1 = 3$$
$$2 \bullet 1 = 2$$

$$x^2 + 3x + 2 = (x + 1)(x + 2)$$

We have completed factorization of a quadratic by inspection. *Factorization takes much practice.* However, more explanation should not be required since the concepts are not too difficult. Let's look at several more examples of factoring, and a few tricks which make factorization easier. Don't forget *why* we are factoring in the first place -- to solve a quadratic equation.

Example - Quadratic Factorization

Factor $6 + x^2 + 5x$

It is always best to arrange the polynomial with higher orders listed first. This makes the problem easier to solve by inspection.

$$x^2 + 5x + 6$$

We need to find two factors of 6 which add to 5. Six may be factored as (6 • 1) or (2 • 3). Since 2 and 3 are factors of 6, and also sum to 5, they must be the constants in the binomials.

Answer: $(x + 2)(x + 3)$

We may check the answer with binomial multiplication, using the distributive law (or FOIL).

$(x + 2)(x + 3) = x^2 + 3x + 2x + (2)(3) = x^2 + 5x + 6$ $\sqrt{}$ yes, correct

---

Example - Quadratic Factorization

Solve for x in the equation: $2x^2 + 10x + 12 = 0$

After looking at the problem a moment, realize that the entire equation may be divided by 2 to simplify the problem. It is easiest to factor by inspection if the coefficient of x^2 is 1.

$$\frac{2x^2 + 10x + 12}{2} = \frac{0}{2}$$

or

$$x^2 + 5x + 6 = 0$$

This problem is the same as the last example.

$$(x + 2)(x + 3) = 0$$

This statement is true if either $x = -2$ or $x = -3$.

Answer: $x = -2$ and $x = -3$

Check:

$$2(-2)^2 + 10(-2) + 12 = 2(4) - 20 + 12 = 0 \quad \sqrt{}\ \text{correct}$$

$$2(-3)^2 + 10(-3) + 12 = 2(9) - 30 + 12 = 0 \quad \sqrt{}\ \text{correct}$$

Example - Quadratic Factorization

Factor $x^2 + 6x - 7$

Which two factors of -7 add to 6? The only factors meeting this requirement are (7) and (-1).

Answer: $(x + 7)(x - 1) = 0$

You should verify this answer is correct by using the Distributive Law of Multiplication.

Example - Quadratic Factorization

Factor $x^2 - 6x - 7 = 0$

Similar to the last example, the factors are (-7) and (1). Note the signs of 7 and 1 are reversed from the previous example, since the two factors added must equal -6 rather than +6.

Answer: $(x - 7)(x + 1) = 0$

Example - Quadratic Factorization

Factor $x^2 - 1 = 0$

At first glance, this equation appears more complicated. But, the equation may be rewritten to look more familiar.

$$x^2 + 0x - 1 = 0$$

Which two factors of (-1) add to 0? (-1) and (1) add to 0 and their product is (-1).

Answer: $(x + 1)(x - 1)$

You should verify the following general formulas with the distributive law. With practice, you will soon memorize the commonly encountered equations given below.

Common Multiplication of Binomials

$$(a + b)(a - b) = (a - b)(a + b) = a^2 - b^2$$

$$(a + b)^2 = (a + b)(a + b) = a^2 + 2ab + b^2$$

$$(a - b)^2 = (a - b)(a - b) = a^2 - 2ab + b^2$$

Example - Quadratic Factorization

Factor $x - 6x + 9$

Using the correct form above, we immediately find the answer:

Answer: $(x - 3)^2$

Example - Quadratic Factorization

Factor the quadratic in the equation: $4x^2 + 4x - 3 = 0$

If the coefficient of the x^2 term is not 1, factorization is usually more difficult to perform by inspection. To factor this equation, let's first write general forms for the binomials. This equation must be true for some values of a, b, c and d since every quadratic may be factored as two binomials.

$$4x^2 + 4x - 3 = (ax + c)(bx + d)$$

Using the distributive law, we know the following statements for constants a, b, c and d must be true.

$$ab = 4$$
$$cd = -3$$
$$bc + ad = 4$$

With our knowledge of multiplication, we may determine,

$ab = (4)(1)$ or $(2)(2)$ Therefore, $a = 4$ and $b = 1$, or $a = 2$ and $b = 2$.

$cd = (1)(-3)$ or $(-3)(1)$.   Therefore, $c = 1$ and $d = -3$, or $c = -3$ and $d = 1$.

We may try these different combinations to determine the correct answer. (Note that we ignored the combination $a = 1$, $b = 4$ since we are trying both combinations of factors for c and d.)   After trying different combinations we find that $bc + ad = 4$ is true only for $2(3) + 2(-1) = 4$.

$$a = 2 \quad b = 2 \quad c = 3 \quad d = -1$$

By substituting these factors into the expression above, we find the answer.

Answer: $4x^2 + 4x - 3 = (2x + 3)(2x - 1)$

You should verify that the answer is correct. With practice, you will be able to factor a problem such as the example above, merely by looking at the problem and using your previous knowledge of the multiplication table, rather than writing everything down step-by-step.

Also, remember that any quadratic may only be factored into two unique binomials. Therefore, in the above example, after the correct combination of constants (a, b, c and d) were found, there was no need to try other combinations of constants. Only one set will be valid. Test your factorization skills by solving the following examples.

Examples - Factorization by Inspection to Solve Quadratics	
$x^2 - 4x + 3 = 0$	Answer: 1 and 3
$x^2 - 4x + 4 = 0$	Answer: 2
$32x^2 - 64x + 32 = 0$	Answer: 1
$x^2 - 2x - 24 = 0$	Answer: 6 and -4

Note that a few of the examples above have only one solution. The example below also has just one solution.

$$x^2 - 6x + 9 = (x - 3)(x - 3) = (x - 3)^2 = 0$$

Answer: $x = 3$

10-6 Factorization Using the Quadratic Formula

As you may have guessed, it is not always possible to factor a quadratic expression by only looking at the problem and using simple multiplication. This is because the solution(s) may not be an integer.

$x^2 - 4x + 3$ is easily factorable, but

$x^2 + 4x + 1$ is not easily factorable

It is necessary to develop a general solution to solve any quadratic equation. The steps to find the general solution are given below. They are quite interesting, but rather tricky. However, the result rather than the derivation is of primary importance, and it is the result that should be memorized.

Problem: What is x, given constants a, b, and c in the general equation $ax^2 + bx + c = 0$?

Step 1: Let's begin by making the coefficient of x^2 equal 1. This requires dividing both sides by a.

$$\frac{ax^2 + bx + c}{a} = \frac{0}{a} \quad \text{or} \quad x^2 + \frac{bx}{a} + \frac{c}{a} = 0$$

Step 2: Move the constant of c/a to the right side of the equation so that we can try and somehow factor the left side, whose terms both contain x.

$$x^2 + \frac{bx}{a} = -\frac{c}{a}$$

Step 3: The goal is to obtain x by itself on one side of the equation. Since there is an x^2 term, and we need to isolate for x, we know that it is necessary to somehow take the square root of the left side of the equation.

We have already learned the following formula.

$$(x + d)^2 = x^2 + 2dx + d^2$$

This gives us an idea. If we can get the left side of the equation in step #2 into a form like $x^2 + 2dx + d^2$, we can take the square root of both sides of the equation and then isolate for x. Let's equate the two quadratic expressions we have and see how close we are to having the necessary form.

$$x^2 + \frac{bx}{a} \overset{?}{=} x^2 + 2dx + d^2$$

The expression on the left needs a constant term like d^2 in the right-hand expression. Then, the left-hand expression can be factored into a form like $(x + d)^2$. To determine the missing constant, the coefficients of x from each expression above are set equal to each other.

$$\frac{b}{a} = 2d \quad \text{or} \quad d = \frac{b}{2a} \qquad \text{-or-} \qquad d^2 = \left(\frac{b}{2a}\right)^2 = \frac{b^2}{4a^2}$$

We now know the missing constant term that will allow us to factor the left-hand expression in step #2. Therefore, let's add the constant term to both sides of the equation that we had in step #2.

$$x^2 + \frac{bx}{a} + \frac{b^2}{4a^2} = -\frac{c}{a} + \frac{b^2}{4a^2}$$

Step 4: As we planned, the left side of the above equation may be factored, so we now rewrite it as such.

$$\left(x + \frac{b}{2a}\right)^2 = -\frac{c}{a} + \frac{b^2}{4a^2}$$

Step 5: To isolate for x, we first take the square root of both sides of the above equation. Don't forget that both positive and negative solutions are possible.

$$\left(x + \frac{b}{2a}\right) = \pm\sqrt{-\frac{c}{a} + \frac{b^2}{4a^2}}$$

Step 6: Then, we subtract $b/(2a)$ from the left side of the equation, and x is finally isolated.

$$x = -\frac{b}{2a} \pm \sqrt{-\frac{c}{a} + \frac{b^2}{4a^2}}$$

Step 7: We can make the answer look more simple, by finding a common denominator in the radical. The LCM of a and $4a^2$ is $4a^2$.

$$x = -\frac{b}{2a} \pm \sqrt{\frac{-4ac + b^2}{4a^2}}$$

Step 8: Finally, we see that the denominator in the radical is also a square since $(2a)^2 = 4a^2$. Therefore, we may factor a denominator of $2a$ out of the radical, and rewrite the final form of the solution of x.

$$x = \frac{-b \pm \sqrt{b^2 - 4ac}}{2a}$$

**WHEW!
THAT WAS LONG!**

The general solution to any quadratic equation is given by the **quadratic formula** as shown above in step #8. Note that a value was added to one side of the equation in step #3 to make the quantity a perfect square. A **perfect square** is a whole number or algebraic quantity squared (e.g. 16, $4a^2$ and $\{2a + 1\}^2$). The process of adding a number or variable (as found above in step #3) to form a perfect square is called **completing the square** and is often required in advanced mathematics. We now have a formula for solving any quadratic equation.

STEP - BY - STEP

Solving any Quadratic Equation Using the Quadratic Formula

For any quadratic equation (where $a \neq 0$):

$$ax^2 + bx + c = 0$$

The solution(s) are given by inserting the appropriate constants into the quadratic formula:

$$x = \frac{-b \pm \sqrt{b^2 - 4ac}}{2a}$$

The $\pm$ in the quadratic formula shows that there are two possible answers for a quadratic equation. Also note that b^2 must be greater than $4ac$ for the square root to be a positive number. Taking the square root of a negative number is possible, but has not been explained yet. (This will be shown in chapter 19.) All examples given in this chapter assume $b^2 > 4ac$.

An example using the quadratic formula is given.

<u>Example - Solving a Quadratic Equation</u>

Solve $x^2 + 11x + 24 = 0$ first using inspection and then the quadratic formula

---

By inspection,

$$x^2 + 11x + 24 = (x + 8)\,(x + 3)$$

Answers:　-8 and -3

From the original equation, we can easily determine the values to use in the quadratic formula by looking at the coefficients.

$$a = 1 \quad b = 11 \quad c = 24$$

Using the quadratic formula and values for constants a, b, and c,

$$x = \frac{-11 \pm \sqrt{11^2 - 4(1)(24)}}{2(1)} = \frac{-11 \pm \sqrt{121 - 96}}{2} = \frac{-11 \pm \sqrt{25}}{2} = \frac{-11 \pm 5}{2} = \text{-8 and -3}$$

As expected, the quadratic formula produces the same answers as factorization by inspection. You should memorize the quadratic formula. It will be used throughout your math career. The quadratic formula gives the solutions of x. From these solutions, the two binomial factors may easily be obtained.

Applying the quadratic formula is usually more time-consuming than solving a quadratic equation with integer solutions by inspection. However, the formula allows factorization and solutions for every quadratic equation.

**CAN YOU REMEMBER THE
QUADRATIC FORMULA?**

Example - Solving with the Quadratic Formula

Solve and factor $x^2 + 4x + 1 = 0$

This equation cannot easily be solved by inspection. The quadratic formula is necessary.

Constants are: $a = 1$ $b = 4$ $c = 1$

Using the quadratic formula,

$$x = \frac{-4 \pm \sqrt{4^2 - 4(1)(1)}}{2(1)} = \frac{-4 \pm \sqrt{12}}{2} = \frac{-4 \pm \sqrt{4(3)}}{2} = \frac{-4 \pm 2\sqrt{3}}{2}$$

$$x = -2 + \sqrt{3} \quad \text{and} \quad x = -2 - \sqrt{3}$$

The factors may then be determined.

$$x^2 + 4x + 1 = (x - (-2 + \sqrt{3}))\ (x - (-2 - \sqrt{3}))$$
$$= \left(x + 2 - \sqrt{3}\right)\ \left(x + 2 + \sqrt{3}\right)$$

We will verify that no mistakes were made by using the Distributive Law of Multiplication. Obviously, you may choose to convert values such as $-2 + \sqrt{3}$ to a decimal if desired. However, rounding or truncation errors will result. Leaving a number in radical form shows that it is exactly correct.

$$\left(x + 2 - \sqrt{3}\right)\ \left(x + 2 + \sqrt{3}\right) = x^2 + 2x + \sqrt{3}\,x + 2x + 4 + 2\sqrt{3} - \sqrt{3}\,x - 2\sqrt{3} - 3$$

$$= x^2 + 2x + 2x + \sqrt{3}\,x - \sqrt{3}\,x + 2\sqrt{3} - 2\sqrt{3} + 4 - 3$$

$$= x^2 + 2x + 2x + \cancel{\sqrt{3}\,x} - \cancel{\sqrt{3}\,x} + \cancel{2\sqrt{3}} - \cancel{2\sqrt{3}} + 4 - 3$$

$$= x^2 + 4x + 1 \quad \sqrt{}\ \text{yes}$$

Answer: $$x = -2 \pm \sqrt{3}$$
$$x^2 + 4x + 1 = \left(x + 2 - \sqrt{3}\right)\ \left(x + 2 + \sqrt{3}\right)$$

This section demonstrated a formula for solving any quadratic equation. You will use the quadratic formula often.

HANG IN THERE!

Solving algebraic equations is not always easy. It requires much work, understanding and practice. But after a while, you'll get the hang of it.

10-7   Factorization of Higher Order Polynomials

Factorization of polynomials with order greater than two is quite difficult. The quadratic formula allows factorization of any quadratic expression. However, there is no general formula for solving polynomials of order three or higher. The solutions to a polynomial of any degree are also known as **roots**.

The most practical method for solving an equation with an order higher than two is often numerical analysis. In **numerical analysis**, you basically first make an educated numerical guess at the answer. Then, by a repetitive process of modifying the guess, and checking the result, an answer of appropriate accuracy is achieved. There are entire college courses devoted to the single topic of numerical analysis. This topic also uses Calculus extensively, and is therefore beyond the scope of this text. However, after the chapter 14 discussion on **Graphing**, you will begin to understand how to make educated guesses to arrive at the correct answers.

The computer has greatly simplified numerical analysis, because it is simple to program an equation and allow the computer to make repeated guesses until the answer is correct. Numerical analysis with the computer has allowed the quick solution to many complicated mathematical problems. This is one reason for the tremendous increase in recent technologies. Scientists and engineers knew how to perform tasks theoretically, but they did not have the time to solve all of the necessary equations. Today the computer can help.

The other method of solving a higher order polynomial (order > 2) is again by factorization. A quadratic equation required two linear factors. As you may guess, a third-order polynomial requires three linear factors and a fourth-order polynomial requires four linear factors. Furthermore, a linear equation has at most one solution and a quadratic equation has, at most, two solutions. Therefore, a third-order polynomial has at most three solutions, and so forth. There is one solution for each linear factor.

The concept of finding answers to polynomials of higher orders is the exact same as finding the answers to polynomials of order two. First set the polynomial equal to zero. Then, factor the polynomial into linear factors and find solutions which make each linear factor zero.

**MAKE SURE YOU
UNDERSTAND THE CONCEPT**

Assume that it is necessary to find the roots (or solutions) of the third-order polynomial given below. Since the polynomial is not linear, it is necessary to factor the polynomial to find its roots. As shown, the values of *-a*, *-b*, and *-c* are the three solutions to the third-order equation.

$$x^3 - 4x^2 + x + 6 = 0$$

$$(x + a)(x + b)(x + c) = 0$$

Factoring an equation with an order higher than two is <u>not easy</u>. It often requires trial and error or an educated guess to obtain at least one solution. It is often helpful to try a few simple solutions such as $x = 1$ or $x = -1$.

$$1^3 - 4(1)^2 + (1) + 6 = 4 \qquad \text{so 1 is not a solution}$$

$$(-1)^3 - 4(-1)^2 + (-1) + 6 = 0 \qquad \text{so -1 is a solution}$$

In most Algebra texts, the problems normally will be arranged so that at least one simple integer solution exists. In real life problems (which seldom turn out to be 'nice and neat'), numerical analysis is probably necessary. However, the following discussion of factoring higher order polynomials demonstrates another method to add to your mathematical toolbox and is often taught in Algebra class.

One solution is $x = -1$, but what are the other solutions?

$$(x + 1)(x + b)(x + c) = x^3 - 4x^2 + x + 6 = 0$$

The goal is to determine the values of *b* and *c*. Therefore, we'll divide both sides of the equation by the known linear factor $(x + 1)$. After cancellation of $(x + 1)$ we have the following equation.

$$(x + b)(x + c) = \frac{x^3 - 4x^2 + x + 6}{(x + 1)}$$

The next step is to divide the two polynomials on the right side of the equation. This process is actually quite similar to long division with numbers as presented in chapter 4.

Let's quickly compare a long division problem with numbers (e.g. $3375 \div 15$) and the long division problem above. The comparison is most clear by writing the numerical expression using scientific notation. As shown, polynomial division uses coefficients of various powers of *x*, but the numerical problem uses coefficients of various powers of 10.

All (+) operators

$$\frac{3(10)^3 + 3(10)^2 + 7(10)^1 + 5(10)^0}{1(10)^1 + 5(10)^0}$$

Either (+) or (-) operators

$$\frac{1(x)^3 - 4(x)^2 + 1(x)^1 + 6(x)^0}{1(x)^1 + 1(x)^0}$$

Therefore, we can use long division with polynomials in a manner similar to using long division with numbers. Long division to divide a polynomial by a binomial is called **synthetic division**. When dividing numbers, only the coefficients of the powers of 10 are used, since the column of the number indicates the correct power of 10.

$$
\begin{array}{r}
225 \\
15\overline{)3375} \\
3000 \\
\hline
375 \\
300 \\
\hline
75 \\
75 \\
\hline
0
\end{array}
$$

Step 1: There are 2 hundreds of 15 in 3375. $2(100) \cdot 15 = 3000$

Step 2: There are 2 tens of 15 in 3375. $2(10) \cdot 15 = 300$

Step 3: There are 5 ones of 15 in 3375. $5(1) \cdot 15 = 75$

Step 4: There is no remainder $(200 + 20 + 5) \cdot 15 = 3375$

Two aspects differ between dividing numbers and dividing polynomials. These aspects are listed below.

1.   There are no carries between numerical places.

2.   Values in each numerical place of the quotient may be added <u>or subtracted</u>.

Furthermore, usually the entire polynomial is written since placing only coefficients in columns could get confusing. After this section, maybe you will want to develop your own method of dividing polynomials using only coefficients!

Let's solve our problem using synthetic division. Since there are no carries between places, and values in each place of the quotient may add or subtract it is easiest to only look at the leftmost value of the divisor and intermediate dividend to methodically develop the answer. The steps listed below should help clarify.

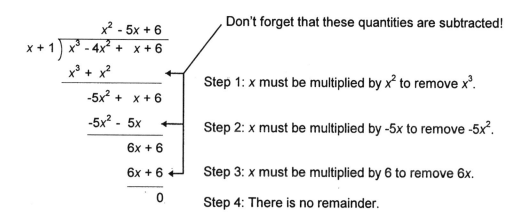

Don't forget that these quantities are subtracted!

Step 1: x must be multiplied by x^2 to remove x^3.

Step 2: x must be multiplied by $-5x$ to remove $-5x^2$.

Step 3: x must be multiplied by 6 to remove $6x$.

Step 4: There is no remainder.

The remainder was zero in this example, so no fractional answer was necessary. If the remainder was not zero, you must add the remainder divided by the divisor in the same manner as shown with numbers in sections **4-14** and **5-14**.

We may now write the polynomial as a product of a linear and quadratic factor.

$$(x + 1) (x^2 - 5x + 6) = x^3 - 4x^2 + x + 6 = 0$$

Factoring the quadratic polynomial by inspection allows determination of the solutions of the polynomial. Remember that you can check that the answer is correct by substituting each solution for x in the original equation.

$$(x + 1) (x - 2) (x - 3) = x^3 - 4x^2 + x + 6 = 0$$

<table>
<tr><td colspan="3" align="center">To summarize,</td></tr>
<tr><td>Problem:</td><td>Factor and solve the third order polynomial:</td><td>$x^3 - 4x^2 + x + 6 = 0$</td></tr>
<tr><td>Answer:</td><td>The polynomial may be factored as:
Solutions of the value of x are:</td><td>$(x + 1) (x - 2) (x - 3)$
$x = -1$, $x = 2$ and $x = 3$</td></tr>
</table>

Synthetic division is relatively simple if division of numbers is understood. However, finding the proper divisor to use is <u>not</u> easy. When dividing polynomials, do not forget to keep the columns properly aligned. If dividing a polynomial such as $4x^3 + 1$, write the polynomial as $4x^3 + 0x^2 + 0x^1 + 1$ for proper alignment prior to dividing.

Also, remember that you may always check your answer with multiplication. Please verify the following examples.

<table>
<tr><td align="center"><u>Examples - Division of Polynomials</u></td></tr>
</table>

$$4x^3 - 17x^2 + 21x - 18 \div (x - 3) = 4x^2 - 5x + 6$$

$$\frac{10x^4 + 22x^3 - 5x^2 + 9x - 9}{2x^2 + 4x - 3} = 5x^2 + x + 3$$

$$\frac{2x^3 - 5x^2 - 7x - 15}{x - 4} = 2x^2 + 3x + 5 + \frac{5}{x - 4}$$

10-8   Reducing an Algebraic Expression to Lowest Terms

As you can tell, working with long polynomials in algebraic expressions is hard work. Therefore, it is often helpful, if not necessary, to reduce polynomials to lowest terms. In other words prior to performing steps such as factorization or division, polynomials should be simplified as much as possible by combining terms and using cancellation. Then the solutions are easier to find.

This section applies topics learned previously such as cancellation and factorization. There is no more understanding to impart, but you will only become proficient with practice.

Example - Reduction of Expressions

Reduce (or 'simplify') the expression: $\dfrac{x^2 - 1}{x + 1}$

First, notice that the numerator is a quadratic expression and may be factored by inspection.

$$x^2 - 1 = (x + 1)(x - 1)$$

Rewriting the numerator and canceling the factor $(x + 1)$ reduces the expression.

$$\frac{(x - 1)(x + 1)}{x + 1}$$

Answer: $(x - 1)$

Note that if the denominator were anything other than $(x + 1)$ or $(x - 1)$, the expression could not be reduced.

Example - Reduction of Expressions

Add the following terms: $3 + \dfrac{x - 1}{x + 1} + x$

As with adding any fractions, it is first necessary to find a common denominator. The denominators consist of the values (1) and $(x + 1)$. Therefore, $(x + 1)$ is the lowest common denominator. Equivalent fractions must be made of each term with the common denominator.

$$\frac{3(x + 1)}{(x + 1)} + \frac{x - 1}{(x + 1)} + \frac{x(x + 1)}{(x + 1)} = \frac{3x + 3 + x - 1 + x^2 + x}{x + 1}$$

Adding like terms in the numerator simplifies the answer.

Answer: $\dfrac{x^2 + 5x + 2}{x + 1}$

You may think that the expression could be further simplified with synthetic division. However, synthetic division usually does not simplify an expression, but makes an expression more complicated (due to remainders). Use synthetic division if the problem specifically requests it, or if it is necessary to find the linear factors of a higher order polynomial.

<u>Example - Reduction and Solution</u>

Solve for x in the equation: $\dfrac{3x}{x-y} \bullet \dfrac{x^2-y^2}{9x} - \dfrac{y-x}{3} = 6$

There are two variables but only one equation. The only way this problem can be solved is if one of the variables can be removed from the equation through cancellation. (Solving problems with more than one variable is the subject of chapter 11.)

According to the order of operations, multiplication of terms must be performed before addition or subtraction. However, before multiplying, notice that $x^2 - y^2$ may be factored, and cancellation is possible.

$$\frac{3x}{x-y} \bullet \frac{(x-y)(x+y)}{9x} - \frac{y-x}{3} = 6$$

Both $(x - y)$ and the factor $3x$ cancel in the two multiplied terms. Of course, nothing may cancel with the term $(y - x)/3$ since that term is subtracted from the others, not multiplied.

The expression may now be rewritten, simplified, and solved using variable isolation.

$$\frac{1}{1} \bullet \frac{(x+y)}{3} - \frac{y-x}{3} = 6$$

$$\frac{(x+y)-(y-x)}{3} = 6$$

$$\frac{x+y-y+x}{3} = \frac{2x}{3} = 6$$

Answer: $x = 9$

Verify the answer is correct by substituting 9 for x in the original equation. Any value may be substituted for y, since y canceled, (except for $y = 9$ which would divide the first term by 0).

C'MON. I'll SHOW YOU ONE MORE EXAMPLE. BUT, DON'T SAY I DIDN'T WARN YOU. IT'S LONG...

REMEMBER, JUST SOLVE IT ONE STEP AT A TIME!

Example - Reduction of Expressions

Reduce the expression: $\dfrac{y^2 - y}{x + y} - \dfrac{x^2 + x}{x - y} + \dfrac{x^2 - y^2}{y - x} + \dfrac{x^2}{7}$

To add fractions, each must have an equal denominator. In this example, the denominators are:

$$x + y \qquad\qquad x - y \qquad\qquad y - x \qquad\qquad 7$$

Therefore, it appears that the lowest common denominator is simply the multiplication of each factor since all of the factors are different. However, note that,

$$y - x = -(x - y)$$

Therefore, $(y - x)$ and $(x - y)$ only differ by a negative sign, and the most simple common denominator is $7(x + y)(x - y)$. Using this common denominator, the expression is rewritten below. Note that changing $(y - x)$ to $-(x - y)$ in the third term was expressed by changing the factor in the denominator and subtracting the third term, rather than adding the term.

$$\dfrac{7(y^2 - y)(x - y)}{7(x + y)(x - y)} - \dfrac{7(x^2 + x)(x + y)}{7(x - y)(x + y)} - \dfrac{7(x^2 - y^2)(x + y)}{7(x - y)(x + y)} + \dfrac{x^2(x + y)(x - y)}{7(x + y)(x - y)}$$

Look carefully at the above expression. It does look complicated. However, do you see that cancellation of common factors in each term would produce the exact same expression as the original question? The factors missing from the common denominator in each term were multiplied by each term's numerator and denominator.

Rewriting the expression using the common denominator,

$$\dfrac{7(y^2 - y)(x - y) - 7(x^2 + x)(x + y) - 7(x^2 - y^2)(x + y) + x^2(x + y)(x - y)}{7(x + y)(x - y)}$$

Repeatedly using the distributive law, the numerator may be rewritten as shown below. (The denominator will be ignored while the numerator is simplified.) Note the importance of keeping each term in quantities so that the correct sign (+ or -) may be applied to the entire term.

$$7(y^2x - y^3 - yx + y^2) - 7(x^3 + x^2y + x^2 + xy) - 7(x^3 + x^2y - y^2x - y^3) + x^2(x^2 - y^2)$$

or

$$7y^2x - 7y^3 - 7yx + 7y^2 - 7x^3 - 7x^2y - 7x^2 - 7xy - 7x^3 - 7x^2y + 7y^2x + 7y^3 + x^4 - x^2y^2$$

Wow. We know that like terms may be added. Therefore, we'll rewrite the numerator one step at a time with higher orders written first. You may choose a different order if you like, as long as like terms are collected. You may want to place a check next to each term in the above expression after it has been collected, so that you don't forget any terms.

Step 1: An x^4 exists. No other variables have an order of four (or higher).

$$x^4 + ...$$

Step 2: The last term is $-x^2y^2$.

$$x^4 - x^2y^2 + ...$$

Step 3: Collect all x terms with order three.

$$x^4 - x^2y^2 - 14x^3 + ...$$

Step 4: Collect all y terms with order three. A $+7y^3$ and $-7y^3$ exist, so these terms cancel.

$$x^4 - x^2y^2 - 14x^3 + ...$$

Step 5: Collect all y^2x terms. There are two such terms with coefficient 7.

$$x^4 - x^2y^2 - 14x^3 + 14y^2x + ...$$

Step 6: Collect all x^2y terms. There are two such terms with coefficient (-7).

$$x^4 - x^2y^2 - 14x^3 + 14y^2x - 14x^2y + ...$$

Step 7: Collect all xy terms. There are two such terms with coefficient (-7).

$$x^4 - x^2y^2 - 14x^3 + 14y^2x - 14x^2y - 14xy + ...$$

Step 8: There is only one term with $-7x^2$ and one term with $7y^2$.

$$x^4 - x^2y^2 - 14x^3 + 14y^2x - 14x^2y - 14xy - 7x^2 + 7y^2$$

The numerator is complete, since all like terms have been collected.   Therefore, the entire expression may be rewritten in simplest form. To check that the reduction is correct, we could substitute numbers for x and y in the reduced expression and in the original expression to verify that the expression reduces to the same value.

Answer:

$$\frac{x^4 - x^2y^2 - 14x^3 + 14y^2x - 14x^2y - 14xy - 7x^2 + 7y^2}{7(x + y)(x - y)}$$

This form may not appear 'simplified', but there are no other mathematical techniques that will reduce the number of terms. If desired, the denominator factors could be multiplied to change the binomial factors into a quadratic, but usually factored form is preferred since it is easier to multiply polynomials than to factor them.

This book could show hundreds of pages of these examples. However, you must first clearly understand the mathematical rules.   After the rules are understood, you will only become proficient at solving algebraic problems with practice. You may look in other texts, or make up your own problems for practice. Designing and checking your own problems is actually an excellent way to get a 'feel' for the mathematics.

10-9   Reducing Algebraic Equations Containing Absolute Values

Section **3-8** introduced the absolute value symbol. The absolute value of a number provides the distance the number is away from zero on the number line. Therefore, the absolute value of a number is never a negative. We may state the following definition.

Removing Absolute Value Signs for Algebraic Reduction
$\|a\|$ = *a* if *a* $\geq$ 0
= *-a* if *a* < 0

Let's clarify the definition with a simple example.

Examples - Using Absolute Values
$\| 5 \| = 5$
$\| -5 \| = -(-5) = 5$

To reduce any algebraic equation, it is first necessary to remove all absolute value signs. It is impossible to move variable expressions in and out of absolute value signs without knowing if the expression is positive or negative. In some questions, the problem will state whether an expression in an absolute value sign is positive or negative. If the question does not specify, there are optional solutions to the problem as shown in the example below.

IMPORTANT POINT

Example - Reduction of Expression with Absolute Value Signs
Reduce $\| x - 2 \| + \| 2x + 6 \|$ by removing the absolute values.

Since we do not know if the quantities in the absolute value signs are positive or negative, there are four possibilities for the answer. Each possibility uses the definition for removing absolute value signs, as given previously.

Option #1:   If $(x - 2) > 0$ and $(2x + 6) > 0$ the expression may be reduced to:

$$x - 2 + 2x + 6$$

Answer: $3x + 4$

Option #2:   If $(x - 2) > 0$ and $(2x + 6) < 0$ the expression may be reduced to:

$$x - 2 - (2x + 6)$$

Answer: $-x - 8$

Option #3:   If $(x - 2) < 0$ and $(2x + 6) > 0$ the expression may be reduced to:

$$-x + 2 + 2x + 6$$

Answer: $x + 8$

Option #4:   If $(x - 2) < 0$ and $(2x + 6) < 0$ the expression may be reduced to:

$$-(x - 2) - (2x + 6)$$

Answer: $-3x - 4$

As shown, there are four possible answers to the problem. However, the following example only has one solution.

Example - Reduction of Expression with Absolute Value Sign

Reduce the following expression knowing that $x < 8$

$$x + 3 + |x - 8|$$

Since $x < 8$, $|x - 8| < 0$. Therefore, the equation may be rewritten,

$$x + 3 - (x - 8)$$

Answer: 11

As shown, the expression containing x may be reduced to a constant. Any value of x less than 8 will yield a result of 11 in the original equation. For example, assume $x = 7$. Then,

$$7 + 3 + |7 - 8|$$
$$= 10 + |-1|$$
$$= 10 + 1$$
$$= 11$$

To reiterate, in any algebraic expression containing absolute values, the absolute value signs must be removed prior to any algebraic reduction. Use your understanding of absolute values to verify that the following formulas make sense.

Formulas for Absolute Values

$$|a| |b| = |ab|$$

$$|a| \div |b| = |a \div b|$$

$$|a + b| \leq |a| + |b|$$

10-10 Summary

There are two algebraic methods of solving any polynomial equation.

1. Isolating the Variable   (used for linear equations)

2. Factorization   (used for polynomial equations with order > 1)

This chapter has shown both methods for various order polynomials. Before attempting to solve an equation, you should reduce the polynomials using cancellation and techniques learned in previous chapters. Also, remove any absolute values signs prior to reduction.

At first you will find these concepts difficult. However with practice and acquired understanding, solving algebraic equations will become clear. Understanding the basic concepts presented in earlier chapters cannot be overemphasized.

This chapter has demonstrated how to solve for one variable in one equation and is the foundation for all of Algebra. The next chapter will demonstrate how to find the value of multiple variables in multiple equations.

Important Definitions

Constant

Polynomial

Order or Degree

Linear Equation

Quadratic Equation

Isolation of the Variable

Quadratic Formula

Roots of a Polynomial

Synthetic Division

You should be able to ...

1. Find the order of any given polynomial

2. Solve any linear equation by isolating the variable

3. Factor certain quadratic expressions by inspection

4. Factor any quadratic expression with the quadratic formula

5. Perform synthetic division with high degree polynomials

6. Reduce algebraic expressions

7. Solve an algebraic equation containing absolute values

Solving a System of Equations

11-1   Introduction

The previous chapter has shown how to solve an algebraic equation with one variable. However, sometimes there is more than one unknown that must be determined in a group of related equations. This chapter develops methods for finding the values of multiple variables in multiple equations. We begin with a simple example, so you get an idea of where we are headed.

Example - Multiple Unknowns in Multiple Equations

Mary is 5 years older than Joe. Joe's age plus twice Mary's age equals 25.
How old are Mary and Joe?

Based on the information in the question, we may write the following two equations.

Let Mary's Age = M
Let Joe's Age = J

$$J + 5 = M$$
$$J + 2M = 25$$

Using one of several different methods developed in this chapter, we find that the only values which make both equations true are $M = 10$ and $J = 5$.

Answer: Mary is 10 years old and Joe is 5

In related equations with multiple variables, it is always assumed that the value of each variable is the same in each equation. For example, if $x = 3$ and $y = 2$ for the first equation to be true, then $x = 3$ and $y = 2$ in the second equation. Such a group of related equations is called a **system of equations**. Since all equations are true at the same time (the variables have the same values), the equations are also called **simultaneous equations**. A system of equations with at least one solution is called **consistent**. A system of equations with no solutions is called **inconsistent**. (e.g. The system $x + y = 1$ and $x + y = 0$ is inconsistent since both equations cannot be true at the same time for any value x and y.)

The System of Equations Golden Rule

A system of equations may only be solved if
there are at least as many independent equations as unknowns.

In other words, one variable may be found with one equation. However, solving for two variables requires at least two independent simultaneous equations. Solving for three variables requires at least three independent simultaneous equations. Before continuing, it is necessary to define an independent equation.

One equation is **independent** from another equation if both cannot take the same form by algebraic manipulation.   A system of two equations is given below.

$$2x = y$$

$$x + y = 6$$

It is impossible to algebraically modify one equation to look exactly the same as the other equation. Therefore, the equations are independent. Furthermore, by methods demonstrated in this chapter, we find that the unique solution to the given system of equations is

$$x = 2 \quad \text{and} \quad y = 4$$

Verify that these values are true for both equations in the system.

On the other hand, look at the following system of equations.

$$x + y = 6$$

$$2x + 2y = 12$$

The first equation, when multiplied by 2, is in the exact same form as the second equation. Therefore, these equations are **dependent**. A system of dependent equations has an infinite number of solutions. Observe that the following sets of solutions are all valid for this simple system of equations.

$$x = 0.5 \text{ and } y = 5.5$$
$$x = 1 \text{ and } y = 5$$
$$x = 2 \text{ and } y = 4$$
$$x = 3 \text{ and } y = 3$$
$$x = 4 \text{ and } y = 2$$
$$\ldots \text{etc}$$

Please verify the following example.

Example - Independent or Dependent Equations

Are the following simultaneous equations independent or dependent?

$$3x + 4y + 9 = 8$$
$$3x + 4y = -1$$

Answer: Dependent

This chapter (in addition to most Algebra texts) will only present techniques and examples for simultaneous <u>linear</u> equations which are consistent. Remember from chapter 10 that quadratics and higher order equations may be factored into linear equations.

The values of variables in a system of independent linear equations may be found by one of the following methods.

1. Substitution of Equations

2. Elimination of Variables

3. Matrix Reduction

4. Cramer's Rule

The first two methods are commonly presented in Algebra I and Algebra II texts. Solving systems using the last two methods is usually first explained in Linear Algebra, but is also presented in this chapter. Every method accomplishes the same purpose -- multiple unknowns are found from a system of simultaneous equations. Different methods are easier to use depending on the problem. That's why so many different methods are shown.

THEY DO THE SAME THING, BUT IN DIFFERENT WAYS

11-2   Substitution of Equations

From topics learned in chapter 10, we can solve for one unknown in any one algebraic equation. Based on this information, if we can reduce a system of equations with multiple unknowns into one equation with one unknown, the value of a single variable may be found. Once the value of a single variable is found, the values of other variables may be found. This is the goal of the substitution of equations method.

Steps for using this method on a system of two equations are given below. Steps may be slightly modified for a system of more than two equations. (Just like steps for adding two numbers may be slightly modified to add three numbers.)

STEP - BY - STEP

Solving a System of Two Equations Using Substitution

1. Isolate for either variable in one equation.

2. Replace the isolated variable (from step #1) in the other equation.

3. Solve for the only variable in the equation from step #2.

4. Solve for the second variable using either equation and the result from step #3.

Let's clarify the steps with an example.

Example - Solving Simultaneous Equations with Substitution

Solve the following system of two equations.

$$3x + 4y + 9 = 8$$

$$x + y = 0$$

Step 1: Isolate for either variable in one equation. It is simple to isolate for either x or y in the second equation. Let's choose x just for fun.

$$x = -y$$

Step 2: x was isolated in step #1, and found to equal $-y$. Therefore, we can now replace x with $-y$ in the first equation.

$$3(-y) + 4y + 9 = 8$$

Step 3: y is the only variable in the equation, and therefore the equation may be solved for y.

$$3(-y) + 4y + 9 = 8$$

$$y + 9 = 8$$

$$y = -1$$

Step 4: Solve for x by substituting $y = -1$ in either original equation since both equations are true. The second equation is less complicated, so we'll use the second equation.

$$x + (-1) = 0$$

$$x = 1$$

Therefore, the solutions are $y = -1$ and $x = 1$. Check the answers by inserting the values into each equation, and verifying that both equations are true or 'satisfied'.

$$3(1) + 4(-1) + 9 = 8$$
$$8 = 8 \quad \sqrt{} \text{ yes}$$

$$1 + (-1) = 0$$
$$0 = 0 \quad \sqrt{} \text{ yes}$$

Answers: $x = 1$ and $y = -1$

Let's solve the same system again, except isolate for x in the first equation rather than the second. We had better get the same answer!

Step 1: Isolating for x yields,

$$3x + 4y + 9 = 8$$

$$3x + 4y = -1$$

$$3x = -1 - 4y$$

$$x = \frac{-1 - 4y}{3}$$

Step 2: Replace x in the second equation to get one equation with one unknown.

$$\frac{-1 - 4y}{3} + y = 0$$

Step 3: Solve for y.

$$-1 - 4y + 3y = 0$$

$$-1 = y$$

Step 4: Solve for x by substituting $y = -1$ in either equation.

$$x + (-1) = 0$$

$$x = 1$$

This is the same result obtained earlier. It is helpful to isolate and substitute in the equations which make the problem easier to solve.

Let's try substitution with two <u>dependent</u> equations and see what happens. Look at the following system of dependent equations.

$$x + y = 3$$
$$3x + 3y = 9$$

Step 1: Using the first equation,

$$y = 3 - x$$

Step 2: Substituting for y in the second equation yields

$$3x + 3(3 - x) = 9$$
$$3x + 9 - 3x = 9$$
$$9 = 9$$

$9 = 9$ is obvious, but nothing has been solved. x was canceled and no variables remain. The problem is that the equations are dependent, so an infinite number of x and y combinations are valid. A system of dependent equations will always cancel the variable and produce a result as shown in step #2 (i.e. $a = a$).

Verify the following examples using the substitution of equations method. You should be able to solve a system of three (or more) equations using this method. Substitute variables to obtain one equation and one unknown. Then solve, and use the result to find the value of other variables.

Examples - Solving Systems of Equations with Substitution

Solve the following system.
(*Hint: Substitute for 2 variables in the final equation*)

$$x + y = 5$$
$$z = 3 - x$$
$$x + y + z = 9$$

Answer: $x = -1$, $y = 6$, $z = 4$

11-3   Elimination of Variables

The goal of this method is to generate one <u>new</u> equation with one unknown from the system of equations. The new equation is created by subtracting (or adding) the existing equations in the system. The equations must be carefully subtracted (or added) such that the resulting new equation only contains one variable.

Steps for solution are given below for a system of two equations. Again, steps may be slightly modified for a system with more than two equations.

STEP - BY - STEP

Solving a System of Two Equations Using Elimination

1. Algebraically modify one equation (or both equations), such that the magnitude of a variable's coefficient is the same in both equations.

2. Subtract (or add) the two equations to create a new equation with only one variable.

3. Solve for the variable in the newly generated equation.

4. Solve for the second variable using an original equation and the result from step #3.

Let's clarify the steps with an example.

Example - Solving Simultaneous Equations with Elimination

Solve the following system of two equations.

$$3x + 4y + 9 = 8$$

$$x + y = 0$$

Step 1: Let's modify the second equation by multiplying it by 3. Then the coefficient of x will be the same in both equations.

Remember from chapter 10 that if the left side of the equation is multiplied by three, the right side of the equation must also be multiplied by three.

$$3(x + y) = 3(0)$$

$$3x + 3y = 0$$

Step 2: Subtract equations so that the variable x cancels in the result.   (Adding the equations would not produce a new equation with only one variable.)

$$3x + 4y + 9 = 8$$
$$- (\,3x + 3y \qquad = 0)$$
$$\overline{}$$

The subtraction is more clear if all coefficients are aligned. Therefore, move 9 to the right side of the first equation to align the constants. Remember that the entire equation must be subtracted from the other, not just the term $3x$.

$$3x + 4y = -1$$
$$- (\,3x + 3y = \;\;0)$$
$$\overline{}$$
$$0x + \;y\; = -1$$

Step 3: The subtraction produced one equation with one unknown. In this example, the variable has already been isolated.

$$y = -1$$

Step 4: Solve for x by substituting $y = -1$ in one of the original equations. We'll choose the second.

$$x + (-1) = 0$$

$$x = 1$$

Answers: $y = -1$, $x = 1$

This is the same example and same solution as that obtained in the previous section.

Why does this method work?

This approach applies rules demonstrated in section **10-4**. As you know from that section, if one value is added to one side of the equation, the same value must be added to the other side of the equation to keep the equation true.

In the elimination of variables method the exact same process is repeated. The only twist is that different forms of a particular value are subtracted (or added) from each side of the equation. In the above example, we were given

$$x + y = 0$$

Therefore, subtracting $(x + y)$ is the same as subtracting 0. Elimination uses this technique to eliminate variables. The newly generated equation is simply a modification of an original equation.

We have stated that equations may be subtracted or added to eliminate a variable. Look at the following system of equations. Note that the magnitude of the coefficient of x is the same in both equations (i.e. 3).

$$3x + 4y + 9 = 8$$

$$-3x - 3y = 0$$

In this example, the equations may be added rather than subtracted to eliminate the variable x. This example is actually the same system as that presented earlier, and results in $x = 1$, $y = -1$.

Verify the following example using elimination of variables.

Example - Solving Simultaneous Equations with Elimination

Solve the following system of two equations using elimination.

$$2x - 3y = -7$$
$$x + 6y = 34$$

Answer: $y = 5$, $x = 4$

If subtracting (or adding) equations results in a newly developed equation such as $0 = 0$, no variables may be solved. The equations in such a system are dependent, as shown in the substitution method. If subtracting (or adding) equations results in a newly developed equation such as $0 = 1$, or another false mathematical statement, the system is inconsistent, and no solution exists.

HELPFUL TIP

WAIT !!

The remaining sections of this chapter are advanced and show two optional methods of solving simultaneous equations. You may skip the remainder of this chapter if you do not need (or want) to know how to use matrices. Matrices are not used elsewhere in this text.

11-4 Using Matrices

It becomes difficult to use either the substitution or the elimination method if the system contains more than two equations. One problem is simply writing all of the equations with the proper signs and variables. Mistakes can easily be made in merely copying equations.

Upon reviewing the elimination method, we realize that the values of the coefficients are the important aspects since each equation in the system uses the same variables. (Remember, the coefficient of a variable not listed is simply zero.) Therefore, a shortcut notation for writing the system of equations has been developed, a matrix.

We begin with some important definitions. Examples of each will be given shortly.

A **matrix** is a rectangular array of numbers. In general, the **size** of a matrix is referred to as "# rows by # columns." An **augmented matrix** is a matrix which contains all of the coefficients in a set of linear simultaneous equations, and the constants equal to the linear equations. A matrix containing only variable coefficients (no constants) is a **coefficient matrix**.

A matrix with the same number of columns as rows is called a **square** matrix. In all of our examples, we will assume that every system of equations has the same number of variables as equations (which is a necessary condition to solve a system of equations). Therefore, every coefficient matrix developed in this chapter will be square.

Each number in a matrix is called an **element**. In general, we may refer to each element as

$$a_{r,c}$$

where r represents the row in the matrix, and c represents the column in the matrix. You may also remember the element as $a_{row,column}$ or $a_{down,across}$.

Let's clarify some of the definitions with an example.

Example - Writing Matrices

Write an augmented matrix for the following system of equations.
What is element $a_{3,4}$ in the augmented matrix?
Write a coefficient matrix for the system of equations.

$$x + y + 2z = 9$$
$$2x + 4y - 3z = 1$$
$$3x + 6y - 5z = 0$$

An augmented matrix is written using the coefficients of each variable and constants right of the equals sign. The size of the augmented matrix given below is 3 by 4 or equivalently 3×4.

Answer: The augmented matrix is:
$$\begin{bmatrix} 1 & 1 & 2 & 9 \\ 2 & 4 & -3 & 1 \\ 3 & 6 & -5 & 0 \end{bmatrix}$$

The element in row 3, column 4 is 0.

Answer: $a_{3,4} = 0$

The coefficient matrix is the exact same as the augmented matrix except with the column containing constants removed.

Answer: The coefficient matrix is:
$$\begin{bmatrix} 1 & 1 & 2 \\ 2 & 4 & -3 \\ 3 & 6 & -5 \end{bmatrix}$$

All coefficients of the same variable must be aligned in a single column. The same is true for constants which must be isolated on the opposite side of the equals sign. Therefore, the first step in writing a matrix is to rewrite the equations with the same variables aligned in each equation. Constants should all be placed on the right side of each equation.

You should understand that the order of the rows is not important. Usually, the rows are simply listed in the same order as the equations are given in the original problem.

Therefore, the system of equations from the previous example may equivalently be rewritten as shown.

$$4y + 2x - 3z = 1$$
$$y + x + 2z = 9$$
$$6y + 3x - 5z = 0$$

and accurately described with the following augmented matrix,

$$\begin{bmatrix} 4 & 2 & -3 & 1 \\ 1 & 1 & 2 & 9 \\ 6 & 3 & -5 & 0 \end{bmatrix}$$

We can denote some of the elements in the above matrix as follows:

$$a_{1,1} = 4 \qquad a_{1,2} = 2 \qquad a_{2,1} = 1 \qquad a_{2,4} = 9 \qquad a_{3,4} = 0$$

Each row in the matrix is simply the constant coefficients of one equation in the system of equations. Therefore, any operation allowed on an equation is also allowed on a matrix row.

Allowed Augmented Matrix Manipulations

- Any row may be multiplied by a non-zero constant.
- Any two rows may be interchanged.
- A multiple of one row may be added to another row.

Note that columns in a matrix cannot be interchanged. (The matrix will eventually provide the solutions for the system, so interchanging columns results in swapped answers for variables.)

In our discussion of using matrices to solve simultaneous equations, there is no need to know how to add, subtract, or multiply matrices. However, knowing how to perform these operations may be helpful in some other area of your education. Therefore, a brief explanation of each is given prior to describing how to solve systems of equations using matrices. The remainder of this section may be skipped if you are only trying to learn how to solve simultaneous equations, using matrices.

To add two matrices, each matrix must be the same size. Add elements corresponding to the same row and column of each matrix.

Example - Adding Matrices

$$\begin{bmatrix} 1 & 2 & 3 \\ 4 & 5 & 6 \\ 7 & 8 & 9 \end{bmatrix} + \begin{bmatrix} 3 & 3 & 5 \\ 7 & 9 & 11 \\ 3 & 11 & 4 \end{bmatrix} = \begin{bmatrix} 4 & 5 & 8 \\ 11 & 14 & 17 \\ 10 & 19 & 13 \end{bmatrix}$$

Subtracting matrices also consists of subtracting corresponding elements.

A constant number is multiplied by a matrix by multiplying each element in the matrix by the constant. This should be clear, since it is the same as multiplying each equation in the system by the same constant.

Multiplying matrices is much more complicated.

STEP - BY - STEP

Multiplying matrices

Assume the problem consists of two matrices **A** (size $r_1 \times c_1$), and **B** (size $r_2 \times c_2$). The product **AB** may only be obtained if the number of columns in matrix **A** is equal to the number of rows in matrix **B** (i.e. $c_1 = r_2$). The resulting matrix will be size $r_1 \times c_2$.

When multiplying matrices, **AB** $\neq$ **BA**, so the *Commutative Law of Multiplication does not apply to matrices.*

1. To obtain element $a_{r,c}$ in **AB**, multiply each element in row r of **A** by each corresponding element in column c of **B**, and add the resulting products.

2. Repeat step #1 for all elements.

At first, multiplying matrices is quite confusing. Row 2 of the first matrix and column 3 of the second matrix are combined as shown to obtain the element in row 2, column 3 of the product.

$$\begin{bmatrix} 1 & 2 & 4 \\ 2 & 6 & 0 \end{bmatrix}\begin{bmatrix} 4 & 1 & 4 & 3 \\ 0 & -1 & 3 & 1 \\ 2 & 7 & 5 & 2 \end{bmatrix} = \begin{bmatrix} \square & \square & \square & \square \\ \square & \square & 26 & \square \end{bmatrix}$$

$$2(4) + 6(3) + 0(5) = 26$$

Multipliying each row of the first matrix with every column of the second matrix produces the completed matrix as given below.

$$\begin{bmatrix} 1 & 2 & 4 \\ 2 & 6 & 0 \end{bmatrix}\begin{bmatrix} 4 & 1 & 4 & 3 \\ 0 & -1 & 3 & 1 \\ 2 & 7 & 5 & 2 \end{bmatrix} = \begin{bmatrix} 12 & 27 & 30 & 13 \\ 8 & -4 & 26 & 12 \end{bmatrix}$$

It is not possible to divide matrices.

11-5   Solving Systems with Matrix Reduction

Solving a system of equations with matrix reduction is basically the same as the elimination of variables. The only difference is that equations are written in matrix form, using only coefficients.

Assume that a system of equations with variables x, y, and z is described by the following augmented matrix.

$$\begin{bmatrix} 1 & 0 & 0 & 8 \\ 0 & 1 & 0 & 4 \\ 0 & 0 & 1 & 12 \end{bmatrix}$$

This matrix immediately provides answers to the values of each variable, as shown by writing the three equations represented by the matrix.

$$\begin{aligned} x + 0y + 0z &= 8 \\ 0x + y + 0z &= 4 \\ 0x + 0y + z &= 12 \end{aligned}$$

or

$$\begin{aligned} x &= 8 \\ y &= 4 \\ z &= 12 \end{aligned}$$

The above matrix form is called **reduced row-echelon** form. All variable values can be determined by looking at the augmented matrix since each row contains only a single coefficient of 1, in addition to the answer in the rightmost column.

Alternately, the following matrix also provides information from which variable values may be determined.

$$\begin{bmatrix} 1 & 1 & 2 & 9 \\ 0 & 1 & -\frac{7}{2} & -\frac{17}{12} \\ 0 & 0 & 1 & 3 \end{bmatrix}$$

Using the last row, we can immediately write:
$$z = 3$$

The equation from the middle row may be rewritten

$$y - \frac{7}{2}z = -\frac{17}{2}$$

Substituting $z = 3$ in the above equation yields $y = 2$.

Verify that $x = 1$ by substituting values for y and z into the equation determined from the top row.

The above matrix is in **row-echelon** form, which means that coefficients of 1 are on a diagonal in the matrix. The ones serve as a boundary to a group of all zeros in the matrix.

STEP - BY - STEP

Solving a System of Equations with Matrix Reduction

1. Write the appropriate augmented matrix.

2. Apply any of the allowable augmented matrix manipulations to get the matrix in either reduced row-echelon form, or row-echelon form.

3. Solve the variables using the newly developed matrix coefficients.

<u>Example - Using Row Reduction to Solve a System of Equations</u>

Solve for variables *x*, *y* and *z* in the following augmented matrix using row reduction.

$$\begin{bmatrix} 1 & 1 & 2 & 9 \\ 2 & 4 & -3 & 1 \\ 3 & 6 & -5 & 0 \end{bmatrix}$$

Step 1: Add (-2) times the first row to the second row to make the first coefficient in row two 0.

$$\begin{bmatrix} 1 & 1 & 2 & 9 \\ 0 & 2 & -7 & -17 \\ 3 & 6 & -5 & 0 \end{bmatrix}$$

Step 2: Add (-3) times the first row to the third row to make the first coefficient in row three 0.

$$\begin{bmatrix} 1 & 1 & 2 & 9 \\ 0 & 2 & -7 & -17 \\ 0 & 3 & -11 & -27 \end{bmatrix}$$

Step 3: Multiply the second row by 1/2 to make the second coefficient 1.

$$\begin{bmatrix} 1 & 1 & 2 & 9 \\ 0 & 1 & -\frac{7}{2} & -\frac{17}{2} \\ 0 & 3 & -11 & -27 \end{bmatrix}$$

Step 4: Add (-3) times the second row to the third row to make the second coefficient in row three equal 0.

$$\begin{bmatrix} 1 & 1 & 2 & 9 \\ 0 & 1 & -\frac{7}{2} & -\frac{17}{2} \\ 0 & 0 & -\frac{1}{2} & -\frac{3}{2} \end{bmatrix}$$

Step 5: Multiply the third row by -2 to make the third coefficient in row three 1.

$$\begin{bmatrix} 1 & 1 & 2 & 9 \\ 0 & 1 & -\frac{7}{2} & -\frac{17}{2} \\ 0 & 0 & 1 & 3 \end{bmatrix}$$

The matrix is now in row-echelon form, and variables may be solved. However, let's continue reduction to achieve reduced row-echelon form.

Step 6: Add (-1) times the second row to the first row to make the second coefficient in row one equal to 0.

$$\begin{bmatrix} 1 & 0 & \frac{11}{2} & \frac{35}{2} \\ 0 & 1 & -\frac{7}{2} & -\frac{17}{2} \\ 0 & 0 & 1 & 3 \end{bmatrix}$$

Step 7: Add -11/2 times the third row to the first row, and 7/2 times the third row to the second row to obtain reduced row echelon form. (Verify that you can obtain the matrix below.)

$$\begin{bmatrix} 1 & 0 & 0 & 1 \\ 0 & 1 & 0 & 2 \\ 0 & 0 & 1 & 3 \end{bmatrix}$$

Therefore,

Answer:　　　$x = 1$　　$y = 2$　　$z = 3$

By studying the example above, you will see patterns to reducing a matrix to the desired form. No one said that solving systems of equations was simple. However, with practice you will find that solving systems of equations using matrices is not difficult. Rather, it is often just a long process. You should understand *why* solving equations with matrices works. It is merely the repeated application of the elimination of variables, using only coefficients.

Verify the following example.

Example - Solving Systems of Equations with Row Reduction

Solve the following system of equations using matrices and row reduction.

$$x + 2y + 3z = 5$$
$$2x + 5y + 3z = 3$$
$$1x \qquad + 8z = 17$$

Answer: $x = 1$, $y = -1$, $z = 2$

11-6 Solving Systems with Cramer's Rule

Prior to demonstrating how to use Cramer's rule, more definitions are required. Assume a square matrix **A** exists. The **determinant** of **A** is the sum of the products of the top-left to bottom-right diagonal elements of **A** minus the sum of the products of the top-right to bottom-left diagonal elements of **A**. It may be referred to as det(**A**). Bars around the matrix represent the matrix's determinant (similar to absolute value symbols). The determinant of a matrix is a number, not another matrix.

UNDERSTANDING THIS SECTION WILL TAKE A LOT OF TIME.

Example - Determinant of a 2 × 2 Matrix

State the determinant of $\begin{bmatrix} a & b \\ c & d \end{bmatrix}$

Arrows will assist in clarification of the definition.

Answer: *ad - bc*

Example - Determinant of a 3 × 3 Matrix

Find: $\begin{vmatrix} a & b & c \\ d & f & g \\ h & k & l \end{vmatrix}$

Arrows and repeating columns where the arrows 'wrap around the matrix' to make the necessary completed diagonals help clarify. Note that a 2 × 2 did not require 'wrapping columns' to complete diagonals. Can you see the completed diagonals without repeating the columns outside the matrix?

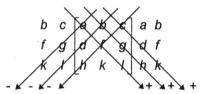

Answer: *afl + bgh + cdk - (cfh + bdl + agk)*

The determinants of 4 × 4, 5 × 5 and larger matrices all require 'wrapping around columns' to complete the diagonals and follow the example shown for a 3 × 3 matrix.

Finding the determinant using this method can get confusing. An alternative method to obtaining the determinant is given below. (Although initially you may find it equally or even more confusing!) Sorry, but more definitions are required.

The **minor of element** $a_{r,c}$ is the determinant of the matrix that remains after the rth row and c^{th} column are removed. Let's represent the minor with $M_{r,c}$. Let $C_{r,c} = (-1)^{r+c} M_{r,c}$ which is the **cofactor of** $a_{r,c}$. Again, examples will help clarify all of these definitions.

Example - Finding Minors of Matrices

Find the minor and cofactor of $a_{3,2}$ of the following matrix:

$$\begin{bmatrix} 3 & 1 & -4 \\ 2 & 5 & 6 \\ 1 & 4 & 8 \end{bmatrix}$$

First, simply remove row three and column two from the square matrix.

$$\begin{bmatrix} 3 & & 4 \\ 2 & & 6 \\ & & \end{bmatrix}$$

The resulting matrix follows:

$$\begin{bmatrix} 3 & -4 \\ 2 & 6 \end{bmatrix}$$

$M_{3,2}$ is the determinant of the above matrix.

$$M_{3,2} = 3(6) - 2(-4) = 18 + 8 = 26$$

The cofactor is $C_{3,2} = (-1)^{3+2} M_{3,2}$

$$C_{3,2} = (-1)^5 (26) = -26$$

Answer: $M_{3,2} = 26$ $C_{3,2} = -26$

From the definitions, note that the magnitude of the cofactor and minor are always equal. If the row and column are both odd or both even, the exponent of (-1) is even, and the cofactor equals the minor. However, $C_{r,c} = (-1) \bullet M_{r,c}$ if either the row <u>or</u> column number is odd.

With these new definitions, we can establish a new method for finding the determinant of a matrix. Remember, the goal is to solve simultaneous equations. We'll get to that shortly. Using determinants is merely one step in using Cramer's Rule.

STEP - BY - STEP

Finding the Matrix's Determinant Using Cofactor Expansion

For any square matrix **A**,

1. Choose any row or column in matrix **A**.
2. Multiply each element in the chosen row or column by the cofactor of the element.
3. Add all of the intermediate results in step #2 to produce the determinant.

Let's clarify with an example.

Example - Finding the Determinant

Find the determinant of the following matrix. First, use only multiplication of diagonal elements. Second, use cofactor expansion to verify the answer.

$$A = \begin{bmatrix} 3 & 1 & 0 \\ -2 & -4 & 3 \\ 5 & 4 & -2 \end{bmatrix}$$

Multiplying appropriate diagonals provides the following answer.

$$\det(\mathbf{A}) = 3(-4)(-2) + (1)(3)(5) + 0(-2)(4) - 0(-4)(5) - 1(-2)(-2) - (3)(3)(4)$$

$$= 24 + 15 - 4 - 36$$

$$= -1$$

Using cofactor expansion along the top row yields:

$$\det(\mathbf{A}) = 3(-1)^2 \begin{vmatrix} -4 & 3 \\ 4 & -2 \end{vmatrix} + 1(-1)^{1+2} \begin{vmatrix} -2 & 3 \\ 5 & -2 \end{vmatrix} + 0(-1)^{1+3} \begin{vmatrix} -2 & -4 \\ 5 & 4 \end{vmatrix}$$

$$\det(\mathbf{A}) = 3(1)(8 - 12) + 1(-1)(4 - 15) + 0(1)(-8 + 20)$$

$$\det(\mathbf{A}) = 3(-4) - 1(-11) + 0$$

$$\det(\mathbf{A}) = -1$$

Answer: $\det(\mathbf{A}) = -1$

Cofactor expansion along any row or column yields the same result. Verify the above example by performing cofactor expansion along a different row or column.

Let's pause and summarize what we already know about matrices. We've learned how to:

1. Setup a system of equations as an augmented or coefficient matrix.
2. Find the determinant of a square matrix by multiplying diagonals.
3. Find the determinant of a square matrix by cofactor expansion.

We are finally able to solve a system of equations using Cramer's Rule. A formal definition and proof of Cramer's Rule is not included due to mathematical complexity. However, the following steps are required to implement Cramer's Rule.

STEP - BY - STEP

Using Cramer's Rule to Solve a System of Equations

Assume the system of equations consists of variables x_1, x_2, ... x_n where $n \geq 2$

1. Setup coefficient matrix **A** and a 1-column matrix called **B**. **B** consists of the column of numbers that would be included in the augmented matrix, but not in the coefficient matrix.

2. Form matrix A_1 by replacing column 1 in **A** with **B**, form matrix A_2 by replacing column 2 in **A** with **B**, repeat for every matrix A_n.

3. Find determinants of all **A** matrices.

4. Solve for the desired variable x_n where $x_n = \det(A_n) / \det(A)$

Again, the process is long but not mathematically difficult. Determinants may be found by using cofactor expansions, or by summing appropriate diagonals. Use whichever method you prefer. However, as matrices become larger, using cofactor expansions is much less work than multiplying and summing diagonals. An example will clarify the steps of solving equations with Cramer's Rule.

Example - Using Cramer's Rule to Solve a System of Equations

Solve the following system of equations using Cramer's Rule

$$x \quad\quad + 2z = 6$$
$$-3x + 4y + 6z = 30$$
$$-x - 2y + 3z = 8$$

Steps 1 and 2: We need to solve for x, y, and z. Therefore, we'll first setup all of the required matrices.

$$A = \begin{bmatrix} 1 & 0 & 2 \\ -3 & 4 & 6 \\ -1 & -2 & 3 \end{bmatrix} \quad A_1 = \begin{bmatrix} 6 & 0 & 2 \\ 30 & 4 & 6 \\ 8 & -2 & 3 \end{bmatrix} \quad A_2 = \begin{bmatrix} 1 & 6 & 2 \\ -3 & 30 & 6 \\ -1 & 8 & 3 \end{bmatrix} \quad A_3 = \begin{bmatrix} 1 & 0 & 6 \\ -3 & 4 & 30 \\ -1 & -2 & 8 \end{bmatrix}$$

$$B = \begin{bmatrix} 6 \\ 30 \\ 8 \end{bmatrix}$$

Step 3: Find the determinants of all matrices. (The reader should verify that these are correct.)

$$\det(A) = 44 \qquad \det(A_1) = -40 \qquad \det(A_2) = 72 \qquad \det(A_3) = 152$$

Step 4: Solve for all variables.

$$x = \det(A_1) / \det(A) = -40/44 = -10/11$$

$$y = \det(A_2) / \det(A) = 72/44 = 18/11$$

$$z = \det(A_3) / \det(A) = 152/44 = 38/11$$

$$\text{Answers:} \quad x = -\frac{10}{11} \quad y = \frac{18}{11} \quad z = \frac{38}{11}$$

Verify the following example.

Example - Using Cramer's Rule to Solve a System of Equations

Solve the following system of equations using Cramer's Rule

$$\begin{aligned} x + 2y + 3z &= 5 \\ 2x + 5y + 3z &= 3 \\ 1x + 8z &= 17 \end{aligned}$$

Answer: $x = 1$, $y = -1$, $z = 2$

11-7   Summary

You have learned how to solve systems of equations using the following methods:

1. Substitution of Equations
2. Elimination of Variables
3. Matrix Reduction
4. Cramer's Rule

You should understand *why* the first three methods presented work. Due to mathematical complexity, discussion of Cramer's Rule did not show why this method works. However, Cramer's rule is very useful and is easily programmed on computers.

Substitution and elimination are generally used if there are only two or three equations in a system. Matrices are generally used if there are three or more matrices in the system. Only an introduction of matrices was presented in this chapter. The course Linear Algebra (usually first taught in college) expands on the introductory ideas presented in this chapter to solve a variety of problems containing simultaneous equations.

Solving systems of equations is important. Further understanding will be obtained by reading subsequent chapters.

Important Definitions

Simultaneous Equations

Consistent System of Equations

Inconsistent System of Equations

Independent Equations

Dependent Equations

Matrix

Matrix Size

Augmented Matrix

Coefficient Matrix

Reduced Row-Echelon Form

Row-Echelon Form

Determinant

Minor

Cofactor

You should be able to ...

1. Determine if equations are independent or dependent

2. Use Substitution of Equations to solve a system of linear equations

3. Use Elimination of Variables to solve a system of linear equations

4. Setup an augmented or coefficient matrix if given a system of equations

5. Add, subtract, or multiply two matrices

6. Solve a system of linear equations with Matrix Reduction to either row-echelon form or reduced row-echelon form

7. Find the determinant of a matrix by multiplying diagonals, or using Cofactor Expansion

8. Solve a system of equations using Cramer's Rule

Word Problems

12-1   Introduction

As chapter 9 stated, there are two basic goals for the student of Algebra.

1. The first goal is to learn how to solve equations. Chapter 10 explained how to solve for one unknown in a polynomial of any degree using isolation and factorization. Chapter 11 showed how to solve for multiple unknowns in a system of equations. The first goal of Algebra has been accomplished.

2. The second goal of Algebra is to solve real-world problems, not already developed algebraic equations. At a job or in everyday situations, you will seldom be given an algebraic equation to solve. Rather, you must first write the equation(s) and then solve for the unknown(s). This chapter focuses on writing equations for practical problems.

**YOU MUST UNDERSTAND
THE GOAL**

Your education will give you practice at real-world problems by proposing word problems. As the name suggests, a **word problem** is a math problem given in words not math symbols. There is no other discipline, besides mathematics, that can solve word problems. All word problems presented in this chapter can be solved by algebraic methods. Many problems in 'real life' can only be solved with Calculus, numerical analysis, or more advanced math.

To solve a word problem, you must first write the equation(s) which describe the problem. The second step is to solve the equation(s), and verify that the solution(s) answered the question. You may find that writing the correct equations is often even more difficult than solving them. The difficulty of solving word problems is one of the reasons that many dislike Algebra. Writing equations for word problems requires mathematical understanding, not just the manipulation of symbols to solve equations. A computer can solve equations. However, a computer cannot develop the necessary equations from a problem that is only explained with words (at least not yet).

Teaching how to solve word problems is difficult since every word problem is unique. Most math texts usually use common types of word problems such as chemical mixtures, moving vehicles, money (problems other than merely not having enough), and number relationships. However, there are an infinite number of 'word problems' which must be solved in everyday life. Therefore, it is best if you can understand the concepts for equation writing, and then be able to solve any type of problem. Previous chapters provide an excellent foundation to equation writing. This chapter provides a common thought process to solving any word problem. Be patient with yourself. As with almost anything worth learning, you will become proficient only with practice.

12-2 Steps to Solving Any Word Problem

There is no one set of steps that will make every word problem easily solvable. However, the following **STEP-BY-STEP** outline is a helpful guide. The key is to relax and be patient. *You are not supposed to know the answer simply by reading the question.* It is expected that the answer can only be obtained by patiently writing and solving the appropriate equations.

Remember the rules from previous chapters. Specifically, multiple variables may only be found if there are at least as many independent equations as unknowns. Most word problems in Algebra I and Algebra II texts are solved with linear algebraic equations. This is also true of word problems on standardized tests such as the GMAT, GRE, SAT, and ACT.

STEP - BY - STEP

Solving Word Problems

1. Setup appropriate variables for unknown quantities.
2. Order all of the relevant information, and draw simple pictures (if necessary) to assist in understanding the problem to be solved.
3. Look at the problem, relevant information, and unknowns. Proceed to write the necessary equations. Determine if there are any special formulas required to solve the problem.
4. Verify that you have the proper number of equations and variables, and then solve the developed equations.
5. Evaluate your answer by rereading the problem, and making sure that your answer is complete, makes sense, and (if applicable) has proper units. Check the answer.

As you may see, the five steps to solving word problems form the acronym **SOLVE**. At a minimum, this acronym should remind you that there are approximately five steps to solving any word problem, and that word problems must be solved in a step-by-step, logical manner.

With this background, examples of word problems are presented. There is no more advice, or additional explanation that can be provided, other than in the specific examples. Your math education and work environment will give you plenty of additional practice.

12-3 Word Problem Examples

Example - Related Integers

The sum of three consecutive integers is the square root of 144. The length of the Mississippi river is approximately 14(144) miles long. What are the three integers?

Step 1: Setup the variables.

There are 3 consecutive unknown integers. Therefore, variable names are assigned.

$$x = 1^{st} \text{ integer}$$
$$y = 2^{nd} \text{ integer}$$
$$z = 3^{rd} \text{ integer}$$

Step 2: Order the relevant information.

- The sum of the three integers is: $\sqrt{144}$ = 12
- The integers to be found are consecutive (i.e. one follows the next).
- The problem also provides the length of the Mississippi River, but this information is irrelevant in solving this problem.

Step 3: Look at established information and write equations.

The three integers when added equal 12.

$$x + y + z = 12$$

Since the integers are consecutive,

$$y = x + 1$$
$$z = y + 1 = (x + 1) + 1 = x + 2$$

Substituting these values into the original equation,

$$x + (x + 1) + (x + 2) = 12$$

Step 4: There is one equation and one unknown and therefore the equation may be solved.

$$x + (x + 1) + (x + 2) = 12$$
$$3x + 3 = 12$$
$$3x = 9$$
$$x = 3$$

Step 5: Evaluating the answer shows that x is indeed an integer. However, the problem requires finding all three integers. From step #3, we find the values of the other integers.

Answer: 3, 4 and 5.

Checking the solution,

$$3 + 4 + 5 = 12 \ \sqrt{} \text{ yes, answer is correct}$$

Example - Speed Related Word Problem

Two cars, separated by 1 mile, are speeding toward each other in the same lane. One driver is traveling at 55 mph. The other driver is traveling at 80 mph. How many seconds will elapse before the cars collide? Assuming the drivers do collide, and never change their speed, at what speed will the drivers impact each other?

Step 1: Setup the variables.

- Let t = time before collision
- Let s = speed at which the drivers will impact each other
- We will label the cars A and B

The two unknowns are t and s.

Step 2: Order the relevant information.

- Speed of driver *A* = 55 mph
- Speed of driver *B* = 80 mph
- Distance between drivers = 1 mile

Step 3: Look at established information and write equations. Based on the given information:

The needed formula for 'speed' problems is: rate • time = distance

or in units: miles/hour • hours = miles

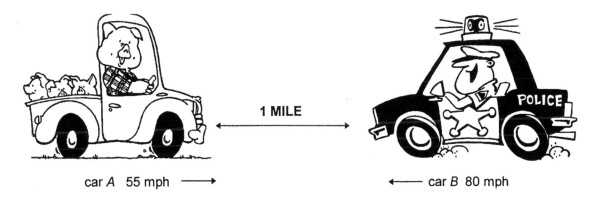

car *A* 55 mph ⟶   ⟵ car *B* 80 mph

From the picture, we see that the cars are approaching each other at *s* = 55 + 80 = 135 mph. We may develop an equation based on the general formula given above.

$$\frac{135 \text{ miles}}{1 \text{ hour}} \bullet t \text{ hours} = 1 \text{ mile}$$

Note that if one car was stopped, and the other car was moving at 135 mph, the same equation would result.

Step 4: There is one equation and one unknown.

$$t = \frac{1}{135} \text{ hour}$$

t = 0.00741 hours

Step 5: Evaluating our answer shows that *t* was found in hours, but the problem requested seconds.

0.00741 hours • 60 minutes/hour = 0.444 minutes

0.444 minute • 60 seconds/minute = 26.67 seconds

Answer: Cars will impact each other at 135 mph in 26.67 seconds

A car traveling at 60 mph travels 1 mile in one minute. Therefore, a car traveling at 120 mph travels 1 mile in 30 seconds. So, our answer of 26.67 seconds appears reasonable.

<u>Example - Speed Related Word Problem</u>

Two men drive from Chicago to Milwaukee, leaving at the same time. Mr. Clavin averaged 30 mph for the first 20 miles, and 40 mph the rest of the way. Mr. Peterson drove the entire way at a constant speed. Both men arrived in Milwaukee at the same time. What was Mr. Peterson's average speed? (The distance from Chicago to Milwaukee is 100 miles.)

Step 1: Setup the variables.

- Let s = Mr. Peterson's speed
- Let t = time required for each man to drive from Chicago to Milwaukee

Step 2: Order the relevant information.

- Total distance traveled by each man = 100 miles.
- Total time to travel for both men is equal (t)
- Mr. Clavin traveled 20 miles @ 30 mph + 80 miles @ 40 mph

Step 3: Look at established information and write equations. Based on the given information:

The needed formula for 'speed' problems is: rate • time = distance
                                             - or -   time = distance / rate
                                          in units: hours = miles / mph

We may first find how long it took Mr. Clavin to make his trip.

   1st equation: 20 miles / 30 mph + 80 miles / 40 mph = t

Mr. Peterson took the same amount of time as Mr. Clavin. Therefore,

   2nd equation: s = 100 miles / t hours

Step 4: There are two equations. t may be found by solving the 1st equation for Mr. Clavin. t may then be substituted in the second equation to find the Mr. Peterson's speed.

$$t = \frac{8}{3} \text{ hour}$$

s = 100 miles / (8/3 hours) = 300 / 8 = 37.5 mph

Step 5: The value obtained in step #4 answers the question proposed.

   Answer: Mr. Peterson's average speed was 37.5 mph

Upon reviewing the problem, Mr. Peterson and Mr. Clavin traveled the same distance for the same time. Therefore, their average speed must be the same. Mr. Clavin traveled 30 mph for 20 minutes, and 40 mph for the remainder of the trip. Therefore, Mr. Peterson's average speed must be in between 30 and 40 mph. The answer of 37.5 mph appears reasonable.

Example - Money Related Word Problem using Percentages

An engineer had her monthly wages increased by 8%, then by 10%. If she now receives $2,376 per month, find her monthly wages before the first increase.

This problem requires a good understanding of percentages.

Step 1: Setup the variables.

- Let w = the wages before the first increase

Step 2: Order the relevant information.

- Wages were first increased 8%
- Wages were then increased 10%
- Final pay is $2,376

Step 3: Look at established information and write equations. Based on the given information:

After the first increase monthly wages must be: $w + 0.08w$.
(Since wages after 1st month = starting wages + 8% increase of starting wages.)

After the second increase, monthly wages must be $(w + 0.08w) + 0.1(w + 0.08w)$.
(Since wages after 2nd month = wages after 1st month + 10% increase of those wages.)

The final pay is known ($2,376) and equals the monthly wages after the second increase.

$$w + 0.08w + 0.1(w + 0.08w) = 2376$$

Step 4: There is one equation with one unknown, so the equation may be solved.

$$w + 0.08w + 0.1(w + 0.08w) = 2376$$

$$1.188w = 2376$$

$$w = 2,000$$

Step 5: The value obtained in step #4 answers the question proposed.

Answer: She made $2000 before the first increase

We can easily calculate that after one 10% raise, she would make $2200. $2000 seems reasonable for the answer since she was making $2376 after two raises.

Example - Money Related Word Problem

Several people equally shared the payment to rent a van. If there had been one more person in the group, each person would have paid $1 less. The total cost of the van was $30. How many people were originally in the group?

Step 1: Setup the variables.

- Let p = the number of people who originally rented the van

Step 2: Order the relevant information.

- $30 is the total cost of the van
- Each person paid an equal amount, so each person paid $\dfrac{30}{p}$ dollars.

- If $(p + 1)$ people rented the van, each would have paid $\left(\dfrac{30}{p} - 1\right)$ dollars.

Step 3: Look at established information and write equations.

(Amount Each Person Paid) • (# of people) = total cost

$$\left(\dfrac{30}{p} - 1\right)(p + 1) = 30$$

Step 4: There is one quadratic equation with one unknown, which may be solved

$$\left(\dfrac{30}{p} - 1\right)(p + 1) = 30$$

$$\left(\dfrac{30 - p}{p}\right)(p + 1) = 30$$

$$(30 - p)(p + 1) = 30p$$

$$30p - p^2 + 30 - p = 30p$$

$$p^2 + p - 30 = 0$$

$$(p + 6)(p - 5) = 0$$

$$p = \text{-}6 \text{ or } 5$$

Step 5: By solving the equation from step #4, either -6 or 5 people originally rented the van.

Answer: 5 people

- If 5 people originally rented the van, they each would have paid $6, (5 • $6 = $30)
- If 6 people had originally rented the van, they each would have paid $5, which is $1 less than $6. So, the answer is correct.

Example - Chemical Mixture Word Problem

A 26 gallon mixture of acid and water contains 6 gallons of acid. If 4 more gallons of acid are added, what percent of the new mixture is water?

Step 1: Setup the variables.

- Let p = the percentage of water in the new mixture

Step 2: Order the relevant information.

- 26 gallons are originally in the mixture, consisting of 6 gallons of acid, and (26 - 6) = 20 gallons of water.

- The new mixture contains 4 more gallons of acid. Therefore, there are 6 + 4 = 10 gallons of acid total, and the new mixture is 26 + 4 = 30 gallons total.

Step 3: Look at established information and write equations. Based on the given information:

$$\text{The proportion of water} = \frac{\text{amount of water}}{\text{total solution}} = \frac{20}{30} = p$$

Step 4: There is one equation with one unknown,

$$p = \frac{20}{30} = 66.67\%$$

Step 5: The value obtained in step #4 provides the answer.

Answer: 66.67%

There is a twice as much water as acid, so the percentage of water should be higher than 50%. 66.67% sounds reasonable.

12-4 Summary

Word problems require patience, thought, hard work, and acquired confidence. This chapter has shown you how to solve word problems in steps. You may have a preferred method of solving each problem. However, the steps provide an overall, logical approach to problem solving.

One key point usually not emphasized is the importance of proper units. If the question requests hours, but the answer is miles, the value obtained cannot be correct. Proper units will also often give clues of whether multiplication or division is required. Units also provide an early indication of math errors, since unlike units may not be added or subtracted (miles - hours = ?). Review the cancellation of units in section **5-8** if necessary.

You should be able to ...

Solve Word Problems in a step-by-step manner. This includes:

1. Writing the correct equation(s)

2. Solving the equation(s)

3. Verifying that the answer makes sense and has proper units

Functions

13-1   Introduction

It seems that we already know enough math to do just about anything! Not only can we solve equations (chapters 10 and 11), but also we can write them (chapter 12). What else is there?

The fundamental goals of Algebra have been achieved. However, we can now use knowledge from previous chapters to solve new types of problems. This chapter will open the door to new areas of mathematics that are both very exciting and useful.

Chapter 10 explained that one unknown may always be determined with one equation. This chapter shows that having two unknowns and only one equation still provides much information, even without a unique solution.

<u>Example - One Equation and Two Unknowns</u>

$$y = 2x + 1$$

Some solutions to the above equation are given in the table below.   To generate values for such a table, simply choose any value for x and then find the value of y using algebraic methods.

x	y
-1	-1
0	1
0.5	2
1	3
2	5

Therefore, if we know the value of x, we can determine the value of y. Also, if we only know the value of y, we can use Algebra to find the corresponding value of x which makes the equation true. One equation with two unknowns does not provide one solution. However, it does provide a relationship between the two variables. The next chapter will develop a picture representing the relationship.

13-2   Explaining Functions

A **function** provides the mathematical relationship between two or more variables. Advanced mathematics (e.g. advanced Algebra, Calculus, and beyond) use functions extensively. Their importance cannot be overemphasized.

**LISTEN UP.
FUNCTIONS ARE
IMPORTANT!**

The relationship in the previous example is:

$$y = 2x + 1$$

Since y is isolated on one side of the equals sign, and the value of y depends on the value of x, we say that y is a function of x. If any value for x is given, a value for y may be found. Using Algebra, we see the equation may also be rewritten a shown.

$$x = 0.5 \, (y - 1)$$

In this equation, x is a function of y. If any value of y is chosen, a corresponding value of x may be found without using any Algebra. Both equations provide the same relationship between variables. However, in the first equation y is a function of x. In the second equation x is a function of y.

Because functions are so important, mathematicians have developed a new notation, **functional notation**, which may be used in writing equations. The first equation is rewritten below using two different functions, $y(x)$ and $f(x)$.

$$
\begin{aligned}
y \ &= 2x + 1 && \text{using variables} \\
y(x) \ &= 2x + 1 && \text{using functional notation } \{ \, y(x) \neq y \bullet x \} \\
f(x) \ &= 2x + 1 && \text{using functional notation } \{ \, f(x) \neq f \bullet x \}
\end{aligned}
$$

In the second equation, $y(x)$ is not equal to $y \bullet x$. $y(x)$ is a function, read aloud "y as a function of x" or simply "y of x". Unfortunately, this notation could easily cause confusion. Therefore, the original commonly used variable y is often replaced with f, or $y(x)$ is replaced with $f(x)$ (read aloud "f of x"). The letter f represents a function.

$$y = y(x) = f(x)$$

All forms given above are just different representations of a single variable. The notation $y(x)$ and $f(x)$ indicate that the value of the single variable depends on the value of x. Functions are normally referenced with letters such as $f(x)$, $g(x)$ and $h(x)$, just as constants are normally represented with a, b, c, and d, and variables are represented with x, y, and z. Virtually every math (and science) book uses this convention. Therefore, you should also use this convention since 'everybody else does it' and remain consistent.

A notation of $y(x)$ or $f(x)$ in the midst of other variables on the same side of the equals sign could be easily confused with multiplication. Therefore, functional notation is normally only used after the appropriate variable (or function) is isolated to one side of the equation. You will become accustomed to using functions quickly, although it does seem confusing at first.

Example - Using Functional Notation

DO NOT use $3 + f(x) = x - 4$

DO use $3 + y = x - 4$

DO use $f(x) = x - 7$

Example - Using Functions

Write the following equation as a function of x.

$$a - 2x + y = x + 1$$

Isolating for y, and replacing y with $f(x)$ produces the answer. (a is a constant in the equation.)

$$y = 3x - a + 1$$

Answer: $f(x) = 3x - a + 1$

13-3   Dependent and Independent Variables

Look once again at the equation,

$$y = y(x) = f(x) = 2x + 1$$

The value of y depends on the value of x. Therefore, since y <u>depends</u> on x, y is called the **dependent variable**. Since the value of x does not depend on another variable, x is called the **independent** variable. As you may guess, every function must have at least one dependent and independent variable. Otherwise, a function would not exist. If variables y and x are used, y is usually the dependent variable, and x is the independent variable.

Let's look at an example of writing functions and the dependence of variables.

Example - Writing Functions by Understanding Variable Dependence

A car travels 55 mph. Write a function relating the time and distance traveled.

---

t = time traveled in hours
d = distance

Writing this equation with two variables is simple. [Remember, (rate)(time) = distance] However, which variable should be the independent variable? In this example, distance depends on the length of time traveled. Time does not depend on the distance traveled. Time is independent.

Answer: $d = f(t) = 55t$

Time will always be the independent variable since nothing controls the passing of time. The passing of time controls everything else. (An exception may be made in working with Einstein's theory of relativity, but we'll ignore that for now.)

In the above equation $f(t)$ was used rather than $f(x)$. This is because the variable depended on t, and not x. The independent variable, written in the parentheses of a function, is called the **argument** of the function.

13-4   Examples Using Functions

Verify the following example.

<u>Example - Using Constants in the argument</u>

$$f(t) = 55t$$

What does $f(1.5)$ equal?
What does $f(6)$ equal?

Answer: $f(1.5) = 82.5$
$f(6) = 330$

$g(f(x))$ is read aloud
"g as a function of f of x"
or
"g of f of x"

This is an example of a function of a function. In the expression $g(f(x))$,

- x is the independent variable
- x is the argument of the function f
- $f(x)$ is dependent on x
- $f(x)$ is the argument of the function g
- g is dependent on $f(x)$

<u>Example - Functions of a function</u>

$$f(x) = x + 1$$
$$g(f(x)) = f(x) + 4$$

What does $g(f(2))$ equal

Answer: $f(2) = 3$
$g(f(2)) = 3 + 4 = 7$

A function may also be dependent on more than one variable as the next example shows.

Example - Functions Dependent on More than One Variable

$$f(x,y) = 3x + 2y$$

What is $f(2,4)$?

Answer: $f(2,4) = 3(2) + 2(4) = 14$

Please verify the following examples.

Examples - Using Functions

$f(x) = \lvert x \rvert$	May $f(x) < 0$ for any value of x?	Answer: no
$f(x) = 3x + 2$	$f(3) = ?$	Answer: 11
$f(x) = x^2 + x - 4$	$f(-1) = ?$	Answer: -4
$f(t,x) = t + x$	$f(4,1) = ?$	Answer: 5
$f(q) = q^2 - 1$	$f(2) = ?$	Answer: 3

13-5   Inverse Functions

An **inverse function** performs the opposite operation(s) of the original function. The word *inverse* is the same word used to state that subtraction is the inverse operation of addition. The only difference is that we are now referring to inverse functions rather than inverse operations.

Inverse Functions Defined

For any functions $f(x)$ and $g(x)$

if $g(f(x)) = x$ and $f(g(x)) = x$

then f and g are inverse functions of one another

There can only be one inverse of a function. Furthermore, not every function has an inverse. (e.g. $f(x) = 2 + 0x$ does not have an inverse.) Finding the inverse of a function often requires Calculus, so this chapter only demonstrates how to use inverse functions, not how to find them. Inverse functions usually use the following popular notation.

Inverse Function Notation

If the inverse of $f(x)$ exists, it is denoted $f^{-1}(x)$ and,

$$f(f^{-1}(x)) = x   \text{ and }   f^{-1}(f(x)) = x$$

Note: $f^{-1}(x) \neq \dfrac{1}{f(x)}$ since $f^{-1}(x)$ does **not** mean that the function has an exponent of -1.

A *-1* written above a function (which looks like an exponent), means the inverse of the function. It does not mean to raise the function to the *-1* power. If it is necessary to raise a function to the *-1* power, the function should be written with parentheses as follows.

$$(f(x))^{-1} = \frac{1}{f(x)}$$

Examples will help clarify the use of inverse functions which can be quite confusing.

Examples - Using Inverse Functions			
$f(x) = 3x$	$f(2) = 6$	$g(x) = f^{-1}(x) = x / 3$	$g(f(2)) = 6 / 3 = 2$
$f(x) = x^{0.5}$	$f(4) = 2$	$g(x) = f^{-1}(x) = x^2$	$g(f(4)) = 2^2 = 4$
$f(x) = 12x + 4$	$f(1) = 16$	$g(x) = f^{-1}(x) = (x - 4) / 12$	$g(f(1)) = (16 - 4) /12 = 1$

Inverse functions are useful for isolating a variable in a function. From the last example given above, we know that $f(x)$ and $g(x)$ are inverse functions if,

$$f(x) = 12x + 4 \quad \text{and} \quad g(x) = \frac{x - 4}{12}$$

Assume that we are given the above functions and the following equation. We are to solve for the variable x given the equation below.

$$f(x) = 28$$

One solution is to insert the above expression for the function $f(x)$, and solve for the variable.

$$12x + 4 = 28$$

$$12x = 24$$

$$x = 2$$

A second solution is to use the inverse function to isolate for the variable. As shown in the second step below, the inverse function is applied to both sides of the equation.

$$f(x) = 28$$

$$f^{-1}(f(x)) = f^{-1}(28)$$

$$x = f^{-1}(28)$$

$$x = \frac{28 - 4}{12}$$

$$x = 2$$

To solve most algebraic equations, you will use variable isolation or factorization as shown in chapter 11. However, advanced mathematics (such as Trigonometry) uses 'special' functions. The only way to isolate for the variable in such functions is to use inverse functions. Use inverse functions to verify the following example which uses the made-up function *helpme*(x).

<u>Example - Using Inverse Functions</u>

$$helpme^{-1}(x) = 3x$$

Solve for x in the equation: $helpme(x) = 10$

Answer: $x = 30$

13-6 Summary

Remember that functions are simply used in place of other variables. Functions show the relationship between two or more variables, including variable dependence. A function may be dependent on another function. Furthermore, functions may be dependent on more than one variable.

The next chapter shows how to visualize functions with pictures to further clarify the relationship between two or more variables.

Important Definitions

Function

Dependent Variable

Independent Variable

Argument of a Function

Inverse Function

You should be able to ...

1. Find many solutions to one equation with two variables

2. Change one equation with two or more variables into an equation containing a function

3. Find the dependent and independent variables in a given function

4. Use a provided inverse function to solve an equation

Graphing

14-1 Introduction

This is the final chapter in introductory Algebra. Let's review the preceding chapters of Algebra.

- Chapter 9 explained the necessary tools in preparing for Algebra.
- Chapter 10 showed how to solve one polynomial equation using isolation and factorization.
- Chapter 11 presented methods for solving systems of equations.
- Chapter 12 consisted of word problem examples and step-by-step solutions.
- Chapter 13 introduced the concept of functions.

New concepts continue to build on previous knowledge. The second chapter explained the relationship among numbers using the number line. This tool provided a visual aid for comparing numbers. You learned that the farther a number is right on the number line, the greater the value of the number. As mathematics becomes more complicated, it again helps to use visual aids. The most useful visual aid in mathematics is a graph.

There are many different types of graphs. A **graph** is a diagram that shows the relationship between numbers. The number line may be called a graph. Any number may be **plotted**, or placed, in the correct position on the number line.

We already clearly understand single numbers, and now seldom need a number line. However, understanding sets of numbers and equations would be very helpful. Sets of numbers, equations, and systems of equations may all be plotted on a graph. Graphing these items to obtain further understanding is the goal of this chapter.

Usually, graphing points is first presented in about eighth grade. This book has waited to present graphs until this stage, so that the graphs may be utilized to help us in all of the problems that have been presented thus far. This includes solving one equation and systems of equations. Graphing does not replace the material that was previously learned. But, it does help us in understanding the material more thoroughly, and from a different perspective.

Understanding all of the preceding chapters is not a prerequisite to reading this chapter. However, this entire chapter is most useful if preceding chapters have been studied.

14-2   Plotting Points on the Cartesian Coordinate System

A single point may easily be plotted on a number line. The next step is to plot a set of two numbers, also called an **ordered pair**. The pair is called ordered since the order of the numbers in the set is important. For example, one set of numbers may be (3,2) but a different ordered pair is (2,3). To plot a unique set of numbers we cannot use one number line. However, we can plot an ordered pair on two different number lines.

Others have found that it is most useful to place one number line horizontal (left to right), and the other vertical (top to bottom). The two number lines are then drawn so they cross each other where each number line equals zero. The graph consisting of two such number lines is called the **Cartesian coordinate system**. It is named after the famous mathematician Descartes. The Cartesian coordinate system is shown below.

The vertical number line is called the **y-axis** or **ordinate**. The horizontal number line is called the **x-axis** or **abscissa**.

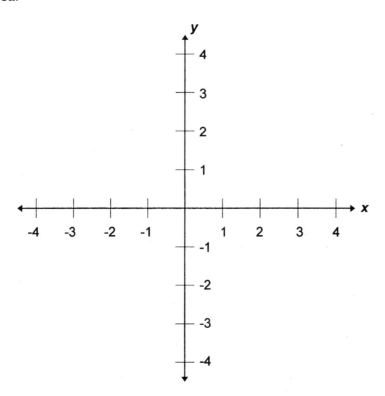

Sets of points may be easily be plotted on the Cartesian coordinate system. The first number in an ordered pair is always plotted on the x-axis. The second number in the ordered pair always represents the position on the y-axis.

<u>Example - Plotting Points</u>

Plot the following points on the Cartesian coordinate system.

(3, 2)   (-2, 2)   (-4, -1) (3, -4)

Answer:

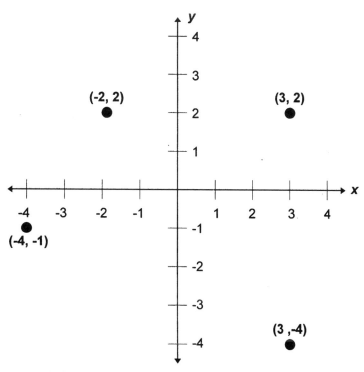

The point of intersection of the *x*-axis and *y*-axis is called the **origin** [which always occurs at (0,0)]. The Cartesian coordinate system is divided into 4 **quadrants**, or sections, as shown.

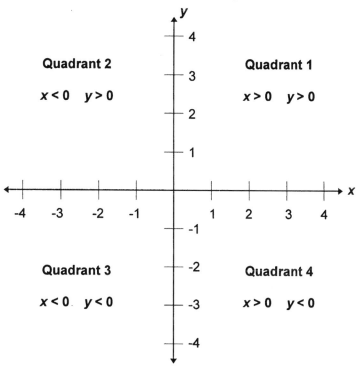

<u>Example - Naming Quadrants</u>

(4, 4) is in which quadrant?   Answer: 1
(1, -1) is in which quadrant?   Answer: 4
(-3, -124.6) is in which quadrant?   Answer: 3

14-3   Plotting Linear Equations

Plotting ordered pairs is simple. We could even connect a group of ordered pairs to create lines, circles, or any other shape. But, how is this useful to us mathematically?

Think for a moment about sets of numbers obtained in past chapters. Remember that an equation with two unknowns produces an infinite number of solutions. This fact was demonstrated in sections **11-1** and **13-1**. Let's see what happens if we plot some of the solutions of a linear equation with two unknowns.

Example - Plotting a Linear Equation

Plot a few solutions to the following equation. Connect the plotted points.

$$y = 0.5x + 2$$

We'll make a table of solutions by choosing values for x, and then determining the corresponding values of y. After making the table, we can plot the ordered pairs (x, y) on a graph. We'll plot y values on the y-axis and x values on the x-axis.

x	y
-4	0
-3	0.5
-2	1
-1	1.5
0	2
1	2.5
2	3
3	3.5
4	4

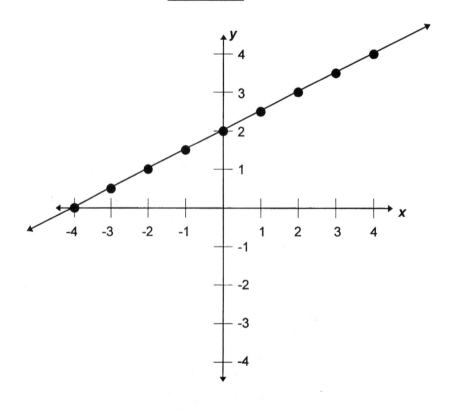

The solutions to the equation in the sample problem form a straight line. There is much that can be learned from the above example. First, remember from chapter 13 that the example equation may also be written with a function.

$$y = y(x) = f(x) = 0.5x + 2$$

Therefore, the example could have equivalently stated:

$$\text{Plot} \quad f(x) = 0.5x + 2$$

IMPORTANT

Plotting an equation implies that the ordered pairs should be connected. When plotting a function, always plot the independent variable on the *x*-axis, and the dependent variable on the *y*-axis. Therefore, time should always be plotted on the *x*-axis. If the independent variable is time, you may want to label the *x*-axis as *time* rather than *x*-axis. If the equation is not written as a function, plot the *y* value of the ordered pair on the *y*-axis and *x* on the *x*-axis.

The following observations can be made from the example problem and by plotting other linear functions (or equations).

<u>Linear Functions</u>

1. Every plot of a linear function (or equation) produces a straight line. This is the reason a polynomial with order one is called linear.

2. Every linear function of *x* will produce a straight line that crosses both axes.
   - The value of *y* where the line crosses the *y*-axis is called the **y-intercept**.
   - The value of *x* where the line crosses the *x*-axis is called the **x-intercept**.
   - The value of the *y*-intercept is usually represented with the variable *b*.

3. Every linear function has a slope. The **slope** is the slant of the plotted line.

4. Two points (or two ordered pairs) uniquely determine a straight line.

We can now define the slope of a line in mathematical terms. The slope of a line is normally represented by the variable *m*.

STEP - BY - STEP

Calculating the slope of a line

1. Choose any two ordered pairs that the line passes through.

2. Label the ordered pairs (x_1, y_1) and (x_2, y_2), and calculate the slope using the formula below.

$$\text{Slope} = \frac{\text{Rise}}{\text{Run}} = \frac{y_2 - y_1}{x_2 - x_1} = \frac{\Delta y}{\Delta x} = m$$

Δ is the Greek letter *delta*. In math terms **delta** means "change in". Therefore Δy is read out loud as "delta y", and means the change in y. **Rise** is the change in the vertical (or y) direction. **Run** is the change in the horizontal (or x) direction.

TOO MANY DEFINITIONS?

A line with a **positive slope** is drawn from the bottom-left to the top-right on a graph. The slope is positive since the rise and run are both positive or both negative.

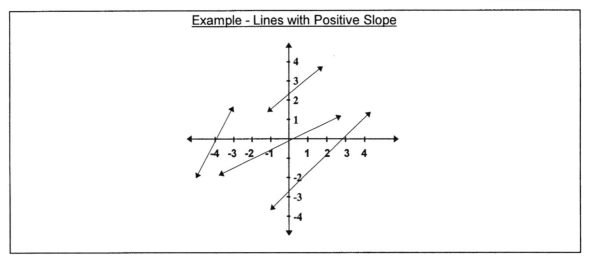

Example - Lines with Positive Slope

A line with a **negative slope** is drawn from the top-left to the bottom-right. The slope is negative since the rise increases as the run decreases, or vice versa.

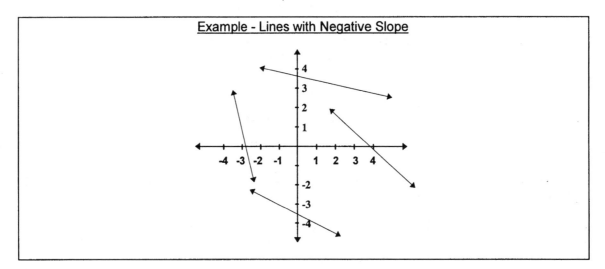

Example - Lines with Negative Slope

Example - Finding Slopes and Intercepts

Find the slope and y-intercept of $f(x) = 0.5x + 3$

We can calculate the slope by using *any* two ordered pairs which are solutions to the equation. We'll choose x values of 0 and 2 so that finding the y values of the ordered pairs is the most simple calculation. Note that in calculating the slope, it does not matter which pair is labeled first or second. The calculated slope is the same.

$f(0) = 3$ First pair: $(0, 3)$

$f(2) = 4$ Second pair: $(2, 4)$

slope $= m = \dfrac{4-3}{2-0} = \dfrac{1}{2}$

y-intercept $= b = f(0) = \dfrac{1}{2}(0) + 3 = 3$

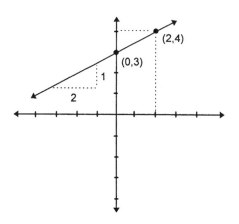

Answers: slope $= m = \dfrac{1}{2}$

y-intercept $= b = 3$

The slope indicates that for every 1 increment change in y position, 2 increments change in x position. Verify that you can obtain the same slope using any ordered pair, and then try the following example.

<u>Example - Plotting Linear Equations</u>

Plot the following equation. Determine the slope and y-intercept.

$$y = f(x) = -2x + 4$$

Answer: slope = -2, y-intercept = 4. (plot not shown)

Linear equations are very popular, and have been given two standard forms. The first form is the **point-slope form**, which is simply the definition of the slope of a line written in a different form. The second is the **slope-intercept form** of a line.

Point-Slope Form of a Line

Given a line with slope m, passing through any ordered pair (x_1, y_1), the line has the following equation.

$$(y - y_1) = m(x - x_1)$$

Slope-Intercept Form of a Line

Given a line with slope m, and y-intercept b, the line has the following equation.

$$y = mx + b$$

If an equation is given in slope-intercept form, you immediately know the slope and y-intercept. Previous examples verify that this is true. Do you understand why this is true?

$$y(0) = 0m + b = b$$

Therefore, b must equal the y-intercept. The y-intercept has no effect on the slope of the line but shifts the line up or down.

In the slope-intercept form we see that if $m = 2$, then x will be multiplied by 2. Therefore for every change of one in x, y will increase by $2 \cdot 1$ or 2. For every change of two in x, y will change by $2 \cdot 2 = 4$. Therefore, m must be the slope.

By using the slope-intercept form, the equation can easily be plotted. Alternatively, given a plot you should be able to generate the equation using the slope-intercept form.

STEP - BY - STEP

Finding the equation from a line

1. Determine the slope of the line, m.
2. Determine the y-intercept, b.
3. Replace the general equation $y = mx + b$ with values of m and b.

<u>Example - Finding the Equation of a Line</u>

Find the equation of the following line.

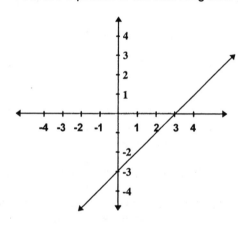

Answer: $y = x - 3$

Two lines are **parallel** if they have equal slopes. Therefore, parallel lines will never intersect on a graph even if the lines are extended indefinitely. A line parallel to the x-axis must have a slope of zero since the value of y never changes.

$$\text{Slope of Horizontal Line} = \frac{\Delta y}{\Delta x} = \frac{0}{\Delta x} = m = 0$$

Therefore $y = 3$, $y = 6$, and $y = -21$ are all lines of zero slope and parallel to the x-axis.

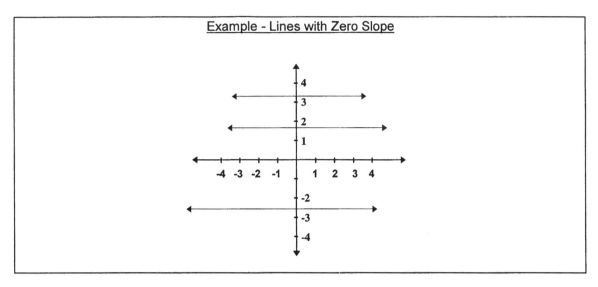

Example - Lines with Zero Slope

As a line becomes 'more vertical', the slope's magnitude increases. Finally, as the line is completely vertical and parallel to the *y*-axis we have the following equation

$$\text{Slope of Vertical Line} = \frac{\Delta y}{\Delta x} = \frac{\Delta y}{0} = m = \text{<not defined>}$$

It is not possible to divide a number by zero. Therefore, a vertical line is defined as a line which has **no slope**. No slope does not mean zero slope since a horizontal line has zero slope.

As you may guess, the definition *no slope* could get confusing. We know that the magnitude of the slope increases as a line becomes vertical. Therefore, it would be logical to say that a vertical line has an infinite slope.   However if we use the term *infinite slope*, someone who only uses formulas and doesn't understand math may try to insert infinity (∞) into the slope-intercept equation for variable *m* and get quite confused.

Lines with no slope can have any *y* value, but *x* values never change. Therefore, equations such as *x* = 3, *x* = 18, and *x* = -4 are lines of no slope. Since there is no slope, the slope-intercept form is not valid for a vertical line.

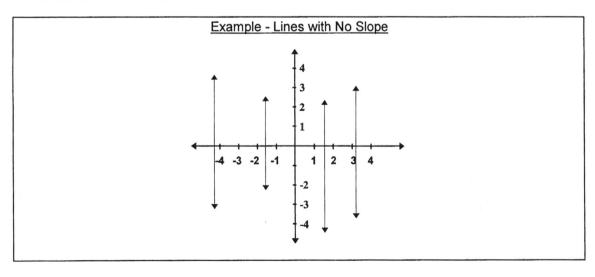

Example - Lines with No Slope

14-4   Plotting Systems of Linear Equations

Chapter 11 explained how to solve a system of two or more independent equations using several methods. However, it is also useful to plot a system of linear equations on the same graph.

Example - Plot of Simultaneous Equations

Solve and plot the following system of equations.

$$f(x) = 2x + 2$$
$$f(x) = x + 3$$

Let $y = f(x)$. Then in the first equation, $y = 2x + 2$, and from the second equation, $y = x + 3$

Substituting for y in the first equation yields the solution for the value of x.

$$x + 3 = 2x + 2$$

$$x = 1$$

Then, we may easily find the value of y from the second equation. A plot is then shown.

$$y = 1 + 3 = 4$$

Answer: $y = 4$, $x = 1$

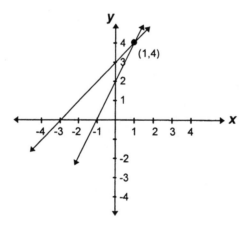

Note that the two linear equations intersect at (1, 4). This is also the <u>solution</u> to the system of equations! *Why* does this happen?

IMPORTANT!

For two simultaneous linear equations with variables x, and y, there is some unique value of x and some unique value y for which both equations are true. Therefore, the unique solution (x, y) forms an ordered pair. It is the only ordered pair which is valid for both equations. Therefore the solution to any system of two equations is the point at which the plot of the equations intersect. Reread this paragraph if necessary. This concept is very important.

By only looking at the graph and not solving the system with Algebra we can determine:

1. The solution of $x + 3 = 0$ is -3.   (-3) is *x*-intercept of this equation.
2. The solution of $2x + 2 = 0$ is -1.   (-1) is *x*-intercept of this equation.
3. The system of equations has one unique solution at (1, 4).

Let's look at a different example.

Example - Solution of Parallel Lines

Plot and solve the following system of equations.

$$y = 2x + 4$$
$$y = 2x + 1$$

The plot is given below. The lines never cross since each line has the slope of 2. The lines are parallel. Therefore, no solution is found from the graph.

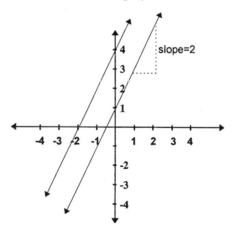

Let's try and solve the equations using algebraic methods.

Expressions in both equations equal *y*. Therefore, they may be set equal to each other.

$$2x + 4 = 2x + 1$$

$$4 = 1$$

But 4 does not equal 1, so what went wrong? The answer is that there is no solution for the system of equations. In other words, there are no values of *y* and *x* which make both equations true. We see this fact in two ways. First, our mathematical solution resulted in 4 = 1, which is not true. Secondly, our graph consisted of two parallel lines which never intersect, again demonstrating that there is no solution. As section **11-1** explained, this system is inconsistent.

Verify the following example.

Example - Simultaneous Equations

Plot and solve the following system of equations.
Verify that the plot of the equations intersect at the solution.

$$4x + 3y = 38$$
$$6x - 3y = 12$$

Answer: $x = 5$, $y = 6$ (plot not shown)

14-5   Plotting Quadratic Equations

So far we have only plotted linear equations. Linear equations could be plotted by finding only two ordered pairs and connecting the points with a straight line. Quadratic equations can be plotted by calculating and connecting several ordered pairs.

Example - Plotting Quadratic Equation

Plot the following equation.

$$y = f(x) = x^2 - 8x + 12$$

Solve the equation: $x^2 - 8x + 12 = 0$

A table of solutions is first made to find ordered pairs. The ordered pairs are then used to plot the equation

x	y
1	5
2	0
3	-3
4	-4
5	-3
6	0
7	5

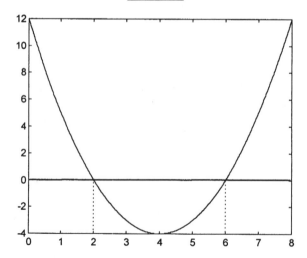

We can solve the given equation using factorization as shown in section **10-5**.

$$0 = f(x) = x^2 - 8x + 12$$

$$(x - 6)(x - 2) = 0$$

Answer: $x = 2$ and 6

There are two important things to notice about the plot in the above example. First, the plot of the function is curved. The plot is a straight line only for a linear equation. This equation has an order of two. (Two is the highest exponent of x making the equation quadratic.) A quadratic equation's plot is always a curve.

 Second, note where the plot crosses the x-axis. (Remember, $y = 0$ on the entire x-axis.) The plot crosses the x-axis at $x = 6$ and $x = 2$. These are also the solutions to the quadratic equation. You should understand why this is true based on your knowledge of graphs, ordered pairs, and quadratic equations. As you can see, plots are also useful in solving quadratic equations.

We define a **turn** as the change in the sign of the slope of the function. Moving on the x-axis from left to right in the previous function, we see that the slope of the function changes from negative to positive only once, at exactly $(4, -4)$. *A quadratic equation will only turn once.* Therefore, we can extend the plot of the function without calculating additional points with no need to worry about the plot turning again. *Why* is this true? It is true because a quadratic equation has at most two solutions, so the curve cannot turn and cross the x-axis more than twice.

Graphs do not replace the techniques learned in previous chapters. It would be much more difficult to find an exact answer of an equation with a graph than using the quadratic formula. However, plots give a good understanding of a function's characteristics. In the previous example, we see that y has its minimum value of -4 at $x = 4$. We also see that as x attains values greater than 8 or less than 0, the value of y increases rapidly. This type of insight into a function is quite valuable, since a function often represents something physical (e.g. the cost of an item, the speed of a particle, etc.). Verify the following examples.

<u>Example - Plotting Quadratic Equation</u>

Plot the function and solve $f(x) = 0$

$$f(x) = x^2 + 4x + 1$$

Answer: $x = -0.268$ or -3.732 (plot not shown)

(*Hint: Quadratic Formula is required to factor*)

<u>Example - Plotting a Quadratic Equation with One Solution</u>

Plot the function, and solve $f(x) = 0$

$$f(x) = (x - 1)^2$$

Answer: $x = 1$ (plot not shown)

14-6   Plotting Polynomials of Higher Degrees

From previous sections, we've learned a few things about plots of functions. Linear equations are always straight lines. Quadratic equations are always curves with one turn. It is necessary to learn about polynomials of higher degrees.

In general, any function can be plotted, regardless of its order or degree. This should not be surprising, since we can calculate a table of ordered pairs for any function $f(x)$. As you may have guessed, the higher the degree of an equation, the more turns may occur in the plot.

A plot of a polynomial of degree n has a maximum of (n - 1) turns

- **If n is odd:**   **The number of turns is even and the plot must cross the x-axis.**
- **If n is even:**   **The number of turns is odd and the plot might not cross the x-axis.**

Example - Plot of 3rd Degree Polynomial

Plot the polynomial $x^3 - 9x^2 + 18x + 1$

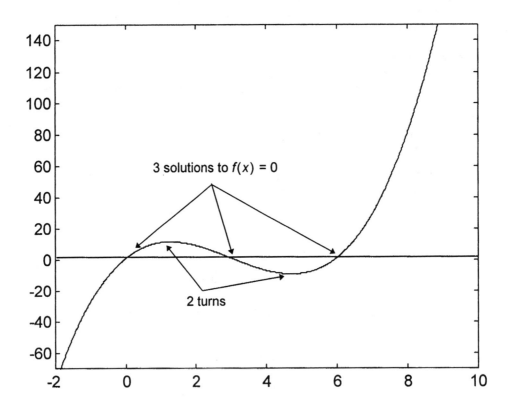

The plot is in the Cartesian coordinate system but only the section of the coordinate system that contains the x-intercepts has been used. As usual, $f(x)$ has been plotted on the vertical axis.

Factorization of higher order polynomials (section **10-7**) is made easier with plots, since approximate solutions can be found with the graph.

Verify the following example.

<u>Example - Plots of Higher Order Polynomials</u>

Plot the function $f(x) = x^3$.
How many turns are in the plot?

Answer: x^3 has no turns   (plot not included)

Plotting higher order polynomials is nothing new. You must make a table of ordered pairs, then plot them and connect the points on the graph. Remember that higher order polynomials may have more turns so you need to calculate enough ordered pairs. Computers are excellent tools for plotting polynomials.

14-7   Plotting Polynomials with Multiple Variables

All of the previous examples have been polynomials in the form $y = f(x)$. However, as we know from chapter 11, more than two variables may exist in one equation. To solve these problems, the Cartesian coordinate system must be modified.

Single numbers may be plotted on a single number line. Therefore, a single number can be plotted in one **dimension**. Ordered pairs may be plotted on two number lines or on the Cartesian coordinate system as shown in this chapter. The Cartesian coordinate system is in two dimensions. Therefore, a set of three numbers, must be plotted on three number lines in three dimensions (3-D). But where do we place the third number line?

A line has one dimension, length.

length
_____

A square has two dimensions, length and width.

length

width

A cube has three dimensions, length, width, and height. It is difficult to draw a 3-D cube on this two-dimensional paper, but you should get the idea.

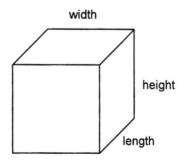

width

height

length

In order to plot a set of three numbers, a third number line must be added to the Cartesian coordinate system, such that the graph is in 3-D. A 3-D graph is given below, with point (2, 2, 2) plotted. It helps to draw lines parallel to the *x* and *z* axes, then parallel to the *y*-axis when plotting points in three dimensions.

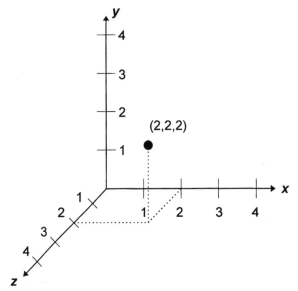

As you can see, a third axis labeled *z* has been added. The positive portion of the *z*-axis is physically meant to come directly out of the paper, toward you. However, it is drawn using a different perspective so that you do not have to read this book while wearing 3-D glasses.

As you may guess, we can plot functions on a 3-D coordinate system, just as we can plot points with coordinates (*x*, *y*, *z*). Therefore, $z = f(x, y)$ may be plotted.

You may also realize that if we have three simultaneous equations, with three variables, we can plot all three equations on a 3-D coordinate system. Once again, wherever all three lines intersect is the solution to the system of equations.

A computer generated 3-D plot of an advanced function is shown.

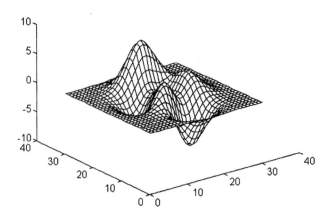

Plotting in three dimensions often requires some artistic capabilities. However, all of the concepts of plotting in two dimensions can be applied to three dimensions. The only difference is that there is one more axis.

Three dimensions is all that can be drawn on paper. You are in three dimensions, but the words on this paper are only in two. (We are ignoring the thickness of the paper of course.) Three is the most number of dimensions that just about anyone can visualize. (Some assert that a plot changing with time may be considered a 4-dimensional plot, and therefore also may be visualized.)

Generally speaking, if *n* variables exist in a system of equations, the system would require an *n*-dimensional plot. No one can imagine or draw a plot of any sized dimension, but the terminology is still used. Mathematicians will often refer to *n*-dimensional space. For example, a plot of 25 simultaneous independent linear equations with 25 different unknowns and one unique solution intersects in exactly one point in 25-dimensional space. Does that make sense? It should, even though no one has any idea what 25 dimensions looks like.

14-8   Summary of Graphing

You should understand how to plot points, functions, and polynomials of any degree. You should also understand why a linear equation plots a straight line, and how to develop an equation given a line.

WOW!

You should now be able to draw a plot when given any order polynomial. However, in more advanced mathematics (e.g. Numerical Analysis) there are methods to write multi-order polynomials from given plots. Therefore, if you plotted the high temperature for the day for every day of the year, advanced mathematics could be used to develop a function that matches the data.

You should understand that two lines which cross at an ordered pair indicate the solution to the two simultaneous equations. Linear equations make straight plots, but higher order equations make plots with curves. The higher the degree, the more turns could occur in the plot.

We can plot in one, two, or three dimensions, and even talk about *n*-dimensional plots. If you understand all of these concepts you have a firm foundation on graphing. Graphing functions will be used extensively in advanced mathematics.

We've come a long way from learning to count. Now we can talk about *n*-dimensional space!

Important Definitions

Ordered Pair

Cartesian Coordinate System

Ordinate and Abscissa

Origin

Quadrants 1-4

Delta

Slope

Rise and Run

Positive and Negative Slopes

Point-Slope Form

Slope-Intercept Form

"No slope"

You should be able to ...

1. Generate a table of values for any polynomial or function

2. Plot points from a generated table

3. Plot linear equations from two ordered pairs

4. Calculate the slope of a line, or recognize the slope from the slope-intercept form of an equation

5. Plot two or more linear equations, and understand why their point of intersection is the solution to the system

6. Plot quadratic equations, knowing that there will only be one turn

7. Plot polynomials of higher degrees

8. Understand how to plot in 3-D

15

Geometry

15-1   Introduction

The previous chapter on graphing opened the door to an entirely new area of mathematics. Rather than merely finding mathematical relationships for numbers and variables, we also may find mathematical relationships for drawings and shapes. **Geometry** is the mathematical study of shapes. This is one of the oldest branches in mathematics, but applications of Geometry coupled with other areas of advanced mathematics are in wide use today.

Geometry is normally taught at the high school level in a student's sophomore or junior year. This subject is quite a bit different than Algebra, and is usually easier to understand. Therefore, students who struggle with Algebra often feel that Geometry is a welcome break.

There are two basic goals accomplished by studying Geometry.

1.   To learn the mathematical properties of various shapes.

2.   To acquire a logical thinking process through the use of proofs.

Both this chapter and the next will demonstrate some of mathematical relationships among various shapes and will help you satisfy the first goal in studying Geometry. We now move on to the second goal.

Geometry is rooted in a few fundamental concepts and definitions. Statements accepted without any further proof are called **postulates** or **axioms**. Particular postulates may be referred to whenever it is required to prove a new conclusion called a theorem. A **theorem** is a statement to be proved. Once a theorem has been proved based on existing postulates, that theorem may be used to prove new theorems.

For example, Algebra has the following definitions. These are basic definitions requiring no proof, and could therefore be called postulates.

$$\begin{array}{ll} \textbf{Reflexive Property} & a = a \\ \textbf{Symmetric Property} & \text{if } a = b \text{ then } b = a \\ \textbf{Transitive Property} & \text{if } a = b \text{ and } b = c \text{ then } a = c \end{array}$$

Based on these fundamental ideas, new concepts in math were developed as shown in previous chapters. Geometry carefully applies postulates and proper reasoning to develop hundreds of theorems. Facts arrived at by logical thinking are more quickly obtained and soundly true than those 'facts' achieved by observation, experimentation, or educated guesses.

However, *proofs of theorems are not developed further in this text.* Therefore, the concepts of Geometry explained in this text will all be basic, fundamental concepts required for understanding more advanced mathematics. There are several reasons for this book's omission of proofs of theorems, but the main three reasons are given below.

1. **Proofs require practice and logical thinking.**
   There is little unique information that this book can provide. Since Geometry is not abstract (like Algebra), few new insights to complicated material may be presented. The material is straightforward, and it is up to the student to think logically and apply basic rules.

2. **There are literally hundreds of postulates, proofs, and theorems.**
   Each is unique and would require hundreds of pages to cover as thoroughly as the chapters on Algebra. Covering this much material would help strengthen your reasoning and logical thinking skills. However, it may also make you lose sight of the big picture regarding mathematics, as you get lost in detailed proofs.

3. **Knowing all of the theorems is not required for further mathematical study.**
   Many theorems developed in Geometry are often more elegantly proved in a Calculus course. Actually, most Calculus courses are even titled *Calculus with Analytical Geometry.* To be blunt, there are a lot of theorems proved in Geometry that you will seldom (if ever) need in more advanced mathematics.

Again, this chapter does not inspire the logical thinking required in a high school level or college level Geometry course. Furthermore, mathematically exact definitions are not emphasized. Rather, basic concepts and definitions are presented so you may acquire understanding.

15-2   Lines and Angles

A **line** in this text will always mean a straight line which extends infinitely in both directions. You should already be familiar with this definition through use of the number line.

A **line segment** is a part of a line which contains two points and all points in between. A line segment containing points *A* and *B* and all points in between *A* and *B* is shown below. The segment is represented by the symbol $\overline{AB}$. A line segment may also be simply called a **segment**. The **length** of a segment is the distance between its end points. The **midpoint** of a segment is the point which divides the segment into two equal segments. The **intersection** of two lines is the point common to both lines.

A **ray** starts at an endpoint and passes through another point, continuing indefinitely. Ray *AB* is given below.

Example - Understanding Lines

If $A = 2$ and $B = 8$ on the number line, and C is the midpoint of $\overline{AB}$,
then find the length of $\overline{AB}$ and the value of C.

Answer:

Length of $\overline{AB} = |\, 8 - 2\,| = |\, 2 - 8\,| = 6$

C = Midpoint of $\overline{AB} = (\, 8 + 2\,) \div 2 = 5$

AXIOM

A straight line is the shortest distance between two points

The length of segment $\overline{AB}$ must be shorter than the distance of $\overline{AC} + \overline{CB}$.

An **angle** is formed by two rays which intersect at a common endpoint. The point of intersection is called a **vertex**. The rays which form an angle are called **sides**.

In the example below, the angle developed by sides $\overline{AB}$ and $\overline{BC}$ is $\angle ABC$ (read aloud "angle A B C"). $\angle ABC = \angle CBA$. The vertex is B, and is always listed in between the points which makeup an angle. ($\angle BAC$ is not shown in the figure.)

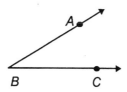

The size of an angle is measured in **degrees** ($32°$ is read aloud "32 degrees"). Following are some examples of different angles and their respective measurements in degrees.

In the examples, segments are drawn rather than rays. Quite often people use the terms lines, segments, and rays interchangeably. The formal definition of an angle requires an intersection of rays. However, you should see that angles may also be formed by segments and lines.

- **Acute Angles** are angles less than 90°.

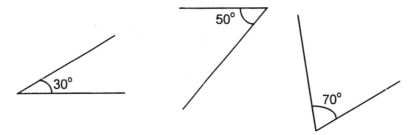

- **Right Angles** are angles equal to 90°. Two lines which are at right angles at their point of intersection are called **perpendicular lines**, and are represented by the symbol (⊥). Perpendicular lines have slopes which differ in sign (+ or -) and are reciprocals. Therefore, the two lines represented by equations $y = 2x + 3$ and $y = -0.5x + 4$ are perpendicular.

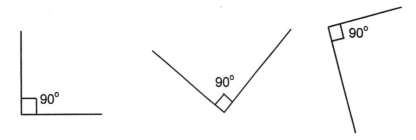

- **Obtuse Angles** are angles greater than 90° but less than 180°.

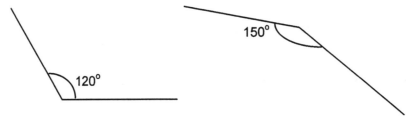

- **Straight Angles** are angles equal to 180°.

Following are some examples of the relationships among angles.

- **Adjacent Angles** have one common side and vertex.

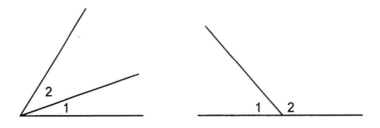

- **Vertical Angles** are formed from the intersection of two lines. Vertical Angles are equal.

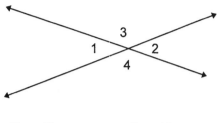

$\angle 1 = \angle 2$ $\angle 3 = \angle 4$

- **Complementary Angles** are two angles whose sum equals 90°.

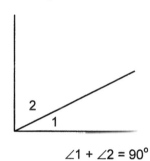

$\angle 1 + \angle 2 = 90°$

- **Supplementary Angles** are two angles whose sum equals 180°.

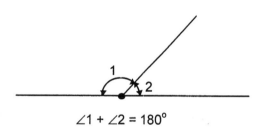

$\angle 1 + \angle 2 = 180°$

- **Equal Angles** have the same measure.

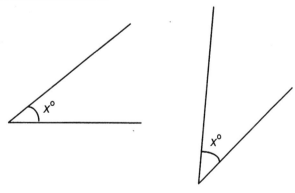

- A **bisector** is a line which divides an angle into two equal angles. The original angle is divided in half, or **bisected**.

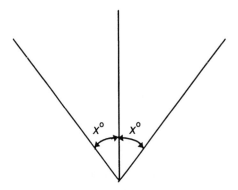

A **transversal** is a line that intersects two or more other lines.

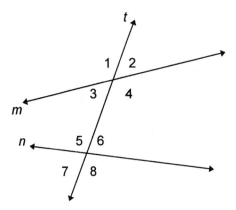

In the figure above, *t* is a transversal of lines *m* and *n*. Angles 3, 4, 5, and 6 are called **interior angles**. Angles 1, 2, 7, and 8 are called **exterior angles**. Two angles are **corresponding angles** if they are on the same side of the transversal, but with different vertices. Pairs of corresponding angles in the above figure are 3 and 7; 4 and 8; 2 and 6; 1 and 5.

If two parallel lines are cut by a transversal, corresponding angles are equal.

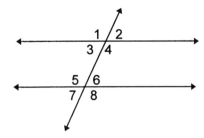

$\angle 2 = \angle 6$ $\angle 1 = \angle 5$ $\angle 3 = \angle 7$ $\angle 4 = \angle 8$

15-3 Triangles

A **triangle** is the connection of three segments, forming a three-sided figure. Therefore, a triangle is composed of three vertices, with three interior angles. A triangle with sides $\overline{AB}$, $\overline{BC}$, and $\overline{AC}$ and interior angles $\angle A$, $\angle B$, and $\angle C$ is given below.

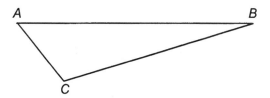

THEOREM

The sum of the angles in any triangle is 180°.

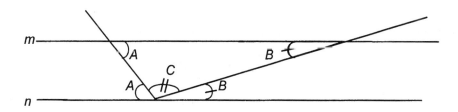

Example - Logical Thinking

Explain why the sum of the angles in any triangle is 180°.

Answer:

The figure above shows a triangle with all sides extended. *m* and *n* are parallel (or *m* ∥ *n*). Looking at line *n*, we know that $\angle A + \angle C + \angle B = 180°$. However, $\angle A$ outside the triangle and $\angle A$ inside the triangle are equal because they are corresponding angles of parallel lines cut by a transversal. The same is true of $\angle B$. Therefore, for any triangle $\angle A + \angle C + \angle B = 180°$.

There are many definitions for different types of triangles.

- A **scalene triangle** is a triangle in which no two sides are equal.
- An **isosceles triangle** is a triangle in which at least two sides are equal.
- An **equilateral triangle** is a triangle in which three sides are equal.
- An **acute triangle** is a triangle with three acute angles.
- An **obtuse triangle** is a triangle with an obtuse angle.
- A **right triangle** is a triangle with a right angle.
    - The side opposite the right angle is the **hypotenuse**.
    - The other two sides are **legs**.

Examples of each type of triangle are given below.

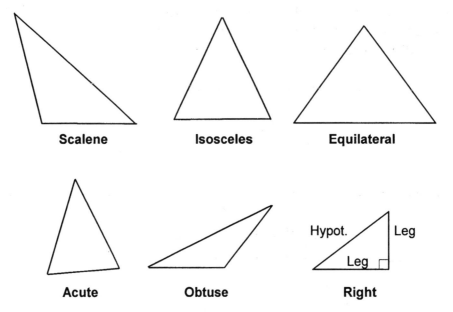

Verify the following examples based on information previously provided.

Example - Triangles

In a right triangle, which is longer the hypotenuse or the sum of the lengths of the legs?

Answer: The sum of the length of the legs is longer
(*Hint: see AXIOM regarding the length of segments*)

Example - Triangles

What is each angle in an equilateral triangle?

Answer: 60° (*Hint: All three angles are equal*)

GEOMETRY HAS MANY DEFINITIONS!

BUT YOU MUST BE ABLE TO RECOGNIZE ALL
OF THE DIFFERENT SHAPES.

15-4   Congruent Triangles

Any two figures which have the exact same size and shape are called **congruent** (≅). Three congruent triangles are shown below. Unique marks are placed on each triangle to indicate the equal parts. (The **parts** of a triangle are sides and angles.)

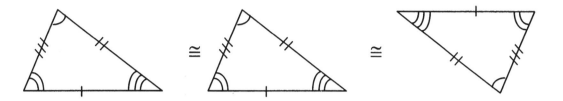

The figure indicates that every part (angle and side) of the triangles are equal, so they are congruent (even though the last one is turned a different direction).

An isosceles triangle is shown below with marks indicating the two equal length sides.

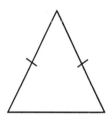

It is not necessary to indicate that all three angles and all three side of two triangles are equal to show that the triangles are congruent. If certain parts are the same, the triangles must still be the exact same size and shape.

STEP - BY - STEP

Congruence of Any Two Triangles

1. All three sides of the triangle are equal   (abbreviated SSS)
2. Two sides and the included angle are equal   (SAS)
3. Two angles and the included side are equal   (ASA)
4. Two angles and a not-included side are equal   (AAS or SAA)

Congruence of Any Two Right Triangles*

1. Sides (or legs) are equal   (LL)
2. Hypotenuse and one leg are equal   (HL)
3. Hypotenuse and one angle are equal   (HA)
4. One Leg and one angle are equal   (LA)

* These are all special cases for the congruence of any two triangles. (e.g. LL = SAS since the angle of 90° is known.)

Examples indicating triangle congruence are given.

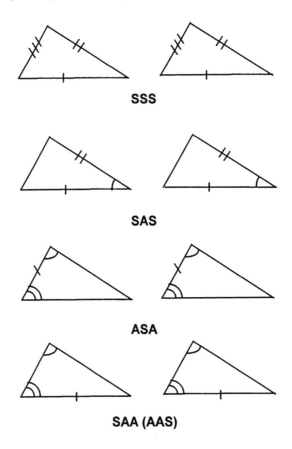

The **height** (or **altitude**) of a triangle is the perpendicular distance from a vertex to a side opposite the vertex.

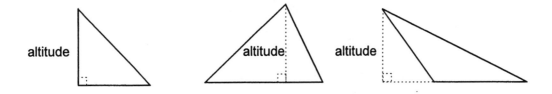

At this point, you may be thinking that it will take weeks to memorize all of the definitions given. Is memorization really necessary?

Upon further review of the previously presented information, you will find that many definitions actually repeat themselves. For example, knowing the definitions of obtuse, acute, right (meaning 90°, not the opposite of left), isosceles and equilateral provide the answer to most definitions presented. Moreover, some common sense regarding triangles will help in understanding and remembering triangle equalities and definitions.

IMPORTANT OBSERVATION

In any triangle, the larger side is opposite the larger angle.

This statement should make sense by observing a few triangles. By knowing this simple statement, you can determine other geometric properties. For example, an equilateral triangle is also equiangular. (All angles are equal in an **equiangular** triangle.) In an isosceles triangle with two equal sides, the angles opposite of the equal sides are equal. The hypotenuse of a right triangle is always larger than either leg. (A triangle with a 90° angle must have two other angles less than 90° since in a triangle $\angle A + \angle B + \angle C = 180°$.)

The above statement does not establish a proportion. That is, if one angle is twice as large as another, one side will not be twice as large as the other side. However, the larger side will always be opposite the larger angle. Chapter 17 will provide formulas for the exact relationships between sides and angles.

Finally, the above statement also allows an understanding of why SSS, SAS, ASA, and SAA triangles are congruent. These combinations of equal triangle parts force a triangle to be drawn in a unique size. On the other hand AAA is not a valid combination for congruent triangles, as shown below. One triangle is simply a larger version of the first triangle. All angles are equal (AAA), but the triangles are not congruent.

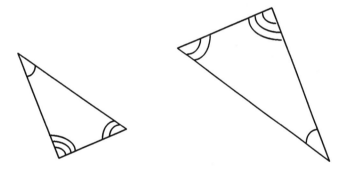

Two triangles with equal angles (AAA) are called **similar** triangles. The above figure shows two similar triangles. Two similar triangles can be made congruent by simply enlarging or reducing the sides of one triangle. Since one triangle is simply a scaled version of the other, ratios may be established. Consider the two similar triangles given below with variables indicating side lengths.

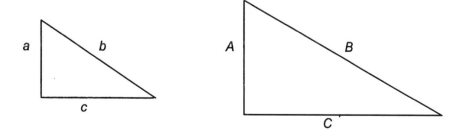

Since the larger triangle is a scaled version of the smaller triangle the following ratios of side lengths are equal.

$$\frac{a}{A} = \frac{b}{B} = \frac{c}{C}$$

We could also state that the smaller triangle was increased by a constant factor of k to generate the larger similar triangle.

$$\frac{A}{a} = \frac{B}{b} = \frac{C}{c} = k$$

Example - Similar Triangles

A mountain in Colorado is approximately in the shape of a triangle.
Some measurements of the mountain were made and given as shown below.

 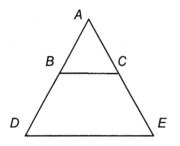

$\overline{BC}$ = 2000 feet
$\overline{AB}$ = 3000 feet
$\overline{AD}$ = 12000 feet

It is known that $\overline{BC}$ and $\overline{DE}$ are parallel.

What is the length of the base of the mountain?

Since triangles *ABC*, and *ADE* have equal angles, the triangles are similar. Therefore, a ratio of sides may be established.

$$\frac{\overline{AB}}{\overline{AD}} = \frac{\overline{BC}}{\overline{DE}}$$

$$\frac{3000}{12000} = \frac{2000}{\overline{DE}}$$

Using Algebra, we find the length of $\overline{DE}$.

Answer: Length of base = 8000 feet

15-5 Polygons

A **polygon** is a geometric figure with three or more sides. A triangle is a type of polygon.

A **quadrilateral** is a polygon with 4 sides. ("Quad" = 4)

A **trapezoid** is a quadrilateral with exactly two sides parallel. The parallel sides are called **bases**, the other sides are **legs**.

A **parallelogram** is a quadrilateral whose opposite sides are parallel.

A **rhombus** is a parallelogram with two adjacent sides equal.
A **rectangle** is a parallelogram with a right angle.

A **square** is a rectangle with 4 right angles, and 4 equal sides.

Two polygons with equal corresponding angles are called **similar**.

A tree clarifying the hierarchy of the defined polynomials is given below.

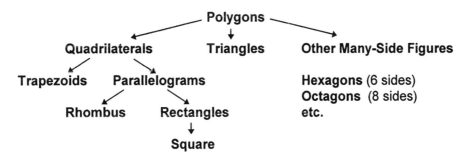

Examples of different polygons are given below.

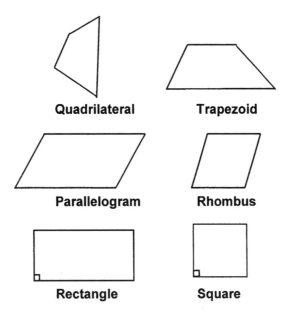

Quadrilateral	Trapezoid
Parallelogram	Rhombus
Rectangle	Square

Do you understand the following examples?

<u>Examples - Understanding Quadrilaterals</u>

Every square is a rectangle,
but every rectangle is not a square

Every rectangle is a parallelogram,
but every parallelogram is not a rectangle

Every square is a rhombus,
but every rhombus is not a square.

**EVERY QUARTER IS MONEY,
BUT EVERY FORM OF
MONEY IS NOT A QUARTER.**

15-6   Circles

Circle - the set of all points equal in distance from a unique point called the **center** of the circle.
Concentric circles - circles with the same center.

Radius   - a segment from the center of the circle to a point on the circle.
Chord   - a segment with endpoints on the circle.
Diameter - a chord which passes through the center of a circle.
Tangent - a line which intersects the circle in one point. It is also perpendicular to the radius at
the point of tangency.

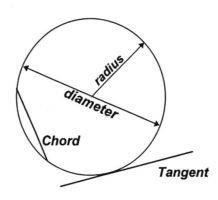

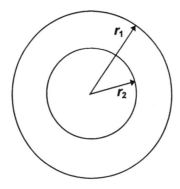

Two Concentric Circles

15-7 Summary

Unlike previous chapters, this introductory chapter on Geometry has primarily focused on definitions. All definitions and examples provided are common in mathematics, and therefore should be memorized.

As the introduction stated, Geometry is generally much more simple to understand than Algebra. The next chapter will focus on numerical measurements of all of the shapes presented.

Important Definitions

Lines

- Segment
- Intersection
- Bisector
- Length
- Ray
- Midpoint
- Transversal

Angles

- Vertex
- Acute
- Straight
- Equal
- Corresponding
- Supplementary
- Sides
- Right
- Adjacent
- Interior
- Degree
- Obtuse
- Vertical
- Exterior
- Complementary

Triangles

- Scalene
- Acute
- Similar
- Isosceles
- Obtuse
- Congruent
- Equilateral
- Right
- Equiangular

Triangle Parts

- Sides
- Legs
- Hypotenuse

Polygons

- Quadrilateral
- Rhombus
- Trapezoid
- Rectangle
- Parallelogram
- Square

Circle

- Radius
- Tangent
- Chord
- Concentric
- Diameter

You should know ...

1. The definitions

2. What parts make triangles congruent

3. How to relate two similar triangles with fractions

Measurement of Geometric Figures

16-1   Introduction

The previous chapter defined relationships between geometric figures. This chapter will show how to measure some of the most popular geometric figures. Measuring different shapes helps us build useful things like roads, cars, and even cities.

16-2   Lengths, Perimeters and Areas of Polygons

In chapter 2, the number line was introduced. Below is a segment of the number line from point 0 to 5. The length of the segment is 5 and the midpoint of the segment is 2.5.

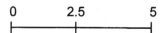

Length is the only type of measurement that may be applied to a line. Some units of length are inches, feet, meters, and miles. It is useful to measure the length of the sides of a triangle.

One of the most important formulas in mathematics is the Pythagorean Theorem. There are literally hundreds of proofs of this theorem, which was established over 2200 years ago! The formula states that the lengths of the sides of a right triangle are related as shown.

Pythagorean Theorem

In any right triangle, the length of the hypotenuse (*c*) is related to the lengths of the legs (*a* and *b*) by the formula given below.

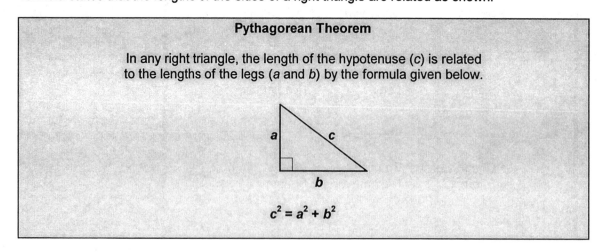

$$c^2 = a^2 + b^2$$

Example - Using the Pythagorean Theorem

If a right triangle has a hypotenuse of length 13, and one leg of length 5,
what is the length of the remaining leg?

The Pythagorean Theorem states: $c^2 = a^2 + b^2$

Substituting values, $13^2 = 5^2 + b^2$

Solving, $b = 12$

Answer: The length of the remaining leg is 12.

We may also measure the length of the sides of a polygon. The **perimeter** of a polygon is the sum of the lengths of the polygon's sides. Some examples are given below.

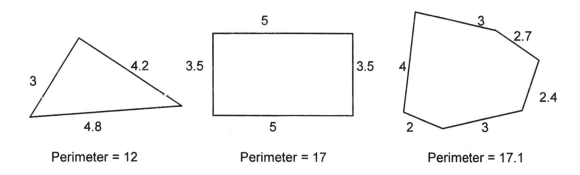

| Perimeter = 12 | Perimeter = 17 | Perimeter = 17.1 |

Not only is it helpful to know the length of the sides, but also it is helpful to know how much room is enclosed by the polygon. The **area** of a polygon is the number of square units in a polygon.

The area of a rectangle is simply the length of one side multiplied by the length of the perpendicular side. The size of the sides of a rectangle are usually referred to as length and width. However, the terms length and width may also be interchanged with base and height, or base and altitude.

Following is a figure of a rectangle with width 3, and length 4 (or a 3 by 4 rectangle).

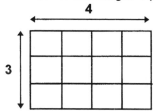

Rectangle Area = length • width

The area of the above rectangle is 4 • 3 = 12 unit squares. If each square had a side 1 inch long, the area of the rectangle would be 4 inches • 3 inches = 12 inches^2 , read aloud "12 square inches." If each square had a side 1 foot long, the area of the rectangle would be 12 feet^2 or 144 inches^2. If you would like to wallpaper a room, you must purchase the wallpaper in square feet. Therefore, to determine how much wallpaper is needed, calculate the area of each wall and add the areas together.

Similarly, the area of any parallelogram is the product of the base and the corresponding altitude. This is the same formula as a rectangle, since any parallelogram may be converted to a rectangle by adding and subtracting the same triangular area. In the figure shown, parallelogram *ABCD* may be converted to a rectangle by subtracting the area of triangle *ACX*, and adding the area of the congruent triangle *BDY*.

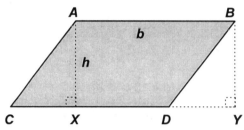

Parallelogram Area = *b* • *h*

A rectangle may be divided in half to produce two congruent right triangles. Therefore, the area of a triangle is half the area of the rectangle required to produce two equivalent triangles.

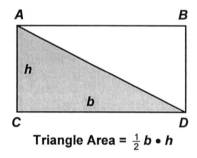

Triangle Area = $\frac{1}{2}$ *b* • *h*

Similarly, any parallelogram may be divided in half to produce two equivalent triangles. Therefore, the area of any triangle is given by the formula $\frac{1}{2}$ (base • height). Note that the base, *b*, is the entire distance from *B* to *C*.

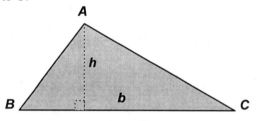

Triangle Area = $\frac{1}{2}$ *b* • *h*

The area of a trapezoid is the average of the length of the parallel sides times the height.

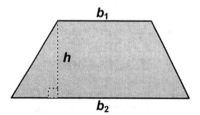

Trapezoid Area = $\frac{1}{2}$ (b_1 + b_2) • *h*

If it is necessary to find the area of a polygon which has not been included in this section, separate the polygon into several rectangles and triangles and add all of the areas.

Example - Using Measurements

What is the area of a square with one side equal to 5 miles?

Answer: 25 miles^2

Example - Using Measurements

A right triangle has two sides equal to 4. What is the perimeter of the triangle?

Answer: 13.656

(Hint: The Pythagorean Theorem is required.)

Example - Using Measurements

A rectangular room is to be painted blue. The floor is carpet, but the walls and ceiling must be painted. The floor is 10 x 12 feet, with a 15 foot high ceiling.

A gallon of blue paint will cover 50 ft^2.

How many gallons of paint should be purchased to paint the room.

Answer: 16 gallons

(Remember, paint can only be purchased by the gallon, so the answer must be an integer. Also, don't forget that the total area is the sum of the 4 walls and the ceiling.)

16-3   Circle Measurements

Assume that you are given a polygon with many equal sides. As the number of sides increases , the polygon will begin to look like a circle. The perimeter of the polygon will approach the perimeter of the circle as the number of sides increase to infinity. The proper term for the perimeter of a circle is the **circumference**.

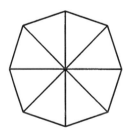

There are only 8 equal sides, and already it looks close to a circle.

It can be shown that the circumference of a circle is directly related to the diameter of the circle.

$$\frac{\text{Circumference}}{\text{Diameter}} = \pi$$

The symbol π is the Greek letter *pi*. This symbol is always used for the ratio of a circle's circumference to diameter. The value of π is a constant value for any circle. The above formula is usually written as follows, where C = circle circumference and r = circle radius.

Circumference of a Circle

For any circle,

$$C = 2\pi r$$

The value of π may be approximated by measuring the perimeter of a many-sided polygon, and by methods shown in Calculus. Early measurements estimated the value of π as $\frac{22}{7}$. Later estimates by the Chinese found the value to be closer to $\frac{355}{113}$. The exact value of π cannot be stated since pi is an irrational number. (Remember, an irrational number is a decimal number with never-ending, never-repeating digits and cannot be represented by a ratio of integers.)

However, with modern techniques and computers, mathematicians have calculated the value of π to over one billion decimal places! For practical purposes, an approximation to six decimal place accuracy is commonly used.

$$\pi \approx 3.14159$$

The area of a circle is given by a formula similar to the circle's circumference.

Area of a Circle

For any circle,

$$\text{Area} = \pi r^2$$

<u>Example - Measurements with Circles</u>

Find the area of the shaded region with the radius of the circle 5 inches as indicated.

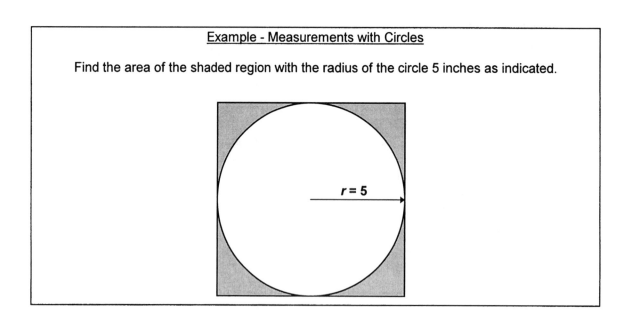

$r = 5$

The circle has a constant radius of 5 inches. Therefore, the rectangle surrounding the circle must be a square.

Area of square = 10 inches • 10 inches = 100 inches^2

Area of circle = πr^2 = π (5 inches)^2 = 25π inches^2

Area of shaded region = (100 - 25π) inches^2

Answer: 100 - 25π $\approx$ 21.46 inches^2

A polygon with sides tangent to a circle is called **circumscribed**. Therefore in the previous example, the square is circumscribed about the circle. A polygon with sides inside a circle and vertices on the circle is called **inscribed**. An odd-shaped polygon inscribed in a circle is given below.

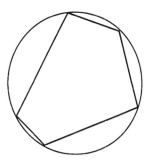

16-4   Volumes and Surface Areas

Every figure described in this chapter and the last chapter could be accurately represented as a two-dimensional figure. However many objects, including both yourself and the book that you are presently reading, are three-dimensional objects as described in chapter 14.

Plane geometry deals with two-dimensional objects. All material presented previously in this chapter would be placed under the category of plane geometry. This section describes measurements for **solid geometry** or objects with three dimensions. Whereas the area of an object is the number of square units which occupy the planar object, the **volume** of an object is the number of cubic units which occupy the solid object. A unit cube is shown below.

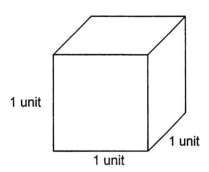

1 unit

1 unit

1 unit

A box is a common three-dimensional (3-D) rectangular object. The volume of a rectangular 3-D object is (base) • (width) • (height). An example is given.

<u>Example - Finding Volumes</u>

Find the volume of the rectangular box shown below.

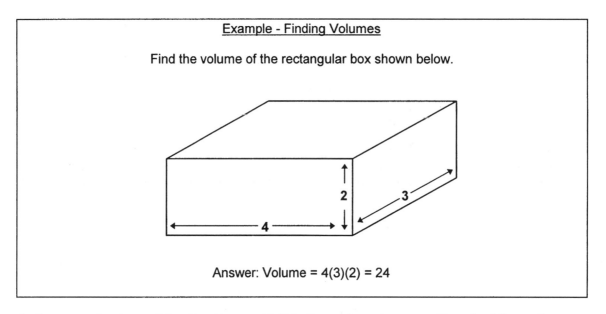

Answer: Volume = 4(3)(2) = 24

In the example above, 24 unit cubes would fit in the rectangular area. If each of the units were inches, the volume in the example would be 24 inches^3 (read "24 cubic inches").

The **surface area** of a solid is the sum of the areas of the exterior area of the solid. If a solid was unfolded and laid flat, finding the area of the unfolded area would be equivalent to the surface area. Therefore, the surface area of a closed box would be the sum of the areas of the sides of the box plus the area of the box top and bottom.

A **cylinder** is a solid with a circular top and bottom as shown. A dashed line indicates an outline that would be hidden from view if looking at an actual cylinder. You may use a cylinder to hold a drink.

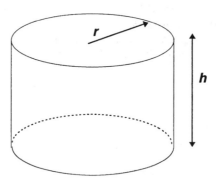

Below is a figure of the unfolded cylinder.

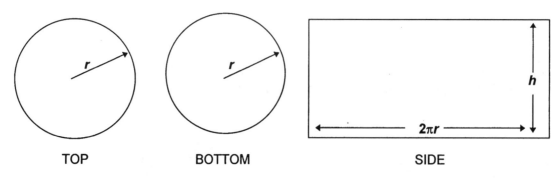

TOP   BOTTOM   SIDE

Based on the previous information given for circles, we can determine formulas for cylinders.

Cylinder Measurements

(r = cylinder radius)
(h = cylinder height)

Volume of Cylinder	$= \pi r^2 h$
Surface Area of Cylinder	= area of top + area of bottom + area of side
	$= \pi r^2 + \pi r^2 + 2\pi rh$
	$= 2\pi r^2 + 2\pi rh$

A circle may also be drawn in three dimensions. This 3-D circle is called a **sphere**. All points on the surface of the sphere are an equal distance from the center of the sphere. Two examples of a sphere are a beach ball and the earth. (Thankfully, the ball and earth are not drawn to scale.)

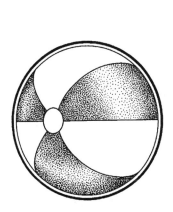 

Sphere Measurements

(r = sphere radius)

Volume of Sphere	$= \frac{4}{3}\pi r^3$
Surface Area of Sphere	$= 4\pi r^2$

16-5 Summary

Chapters 15 and 16 have provided an introduction to Geometry. You have been given the definitions and formulas required to move on to more advanced mathematics. The major topic of geometric proofs has not been demonstrated for reasons presented in the introduction of chapter 15. Proofs of most formulas such as the Pythagorean theorem and volumes of solids have also been omitted. The interested student will find such proofs common in most Geometry texts.

While many definitions and formulas have been presented, this information is used often in future mathematics. Math (especially Geometry) does require much memorization. However, you will find that your efforts will be well rewarded in the future.

The discussion of Geometry is complete. It is now necessary to combine some of the topics learned in Geometry with Algebra. This leads to the next subject -- Trigonometry. Do not be afraid of this topic because the name of the subject is a five syllable word. With a solid background in Algebra, and introductory knowledge of Geometry, you will find Trigonometry an understandable and useful subject.

Important Definitions

Pythagorean Theorem

Perimeter

Area

Circumference

Pi (π)

Circumscribed/Inscribed

Volume

Surface Area

You should be able to ...

1. Find the length of one side of a right triangle, if given the length of the other sides

2. Find the perimeter of any polygon

3. Find the area of a rectangle, parallelogram, triangle or circle

4. Find the volume of a cylinder or sphere

5. Find the surface area of a cylinder or sphere

6. Understand and work with different units of area and volume

Trigonometry

17-1   Introduction

Trigonometry is the study of the measurement of triangles. This subject is normally taught in high school at the junior or senior level. The fundamentals of Trigonometry are normally quickly presented and easily understood, assuming the student has a solid background in Algebra and knows basic Geometry. Therefore, Trigonometry (or 'Trig') is a topic usually taught at the end of a Geometry or Algebra II course. The course following Trigonometry is Calculus. Trigonometry is also used throughout Calculus, so a thorough understanding of the subject is required before continuing study of advanced math.

Today, Trigonometry is used in many areas including engineering, astronomy, and physics. Without Trigonometry, electricity, light, communications, and understanding the relationship of earth with the physical universe would all be impossible.

Before beginning the presentation of trigonometry in detail, we begin with a short story.

Assume that it is a sunny day outside, and you are eating lunch. While eating you notice a nearby flagpole. An annoying classmate named Gomez states that the flagpole is about 50 feet high. You believe the flag to be about 100 feet high. Gomez suggests wagering a candy bar on the height of the flagpole. But, how do you determine who is correct? First, you decide to make a simple drawing of the flagpole and its shadow.

Shadow

The flagpole and shadow are perpendicular and are actually two sides of a right triangle. Therefore, you complete the triangle drawing on a napkin. After remembering a little Algebra, and measuring the length of the flagpole shadow, you label the drawing with the one known constant and unknown. But, what good is this figure in helping to calculate the height of the flagpole?

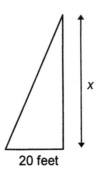

20 feet

While thinking about the problem, you look down and see your own shadow. Knowing that you are exactly 5 feet tall, and the shadow is only one foot long, you decide to draw another triangle.

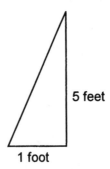

5 feet

1 foot

Suddenly you realize that these two drawings are of similar triangles. The sun hits both you and the flagpole at the same angle to create shadows. Chapter 15 explained that similar triangles have all of the same angles but are different sizes. Therefore, you setup two equal ratios.

$$\frac{1\,foot}{5\,feet} = \frac{20\,feet}{x\,feet}$$

Solving for x using Algebra shows that the flagpole indeed is exactly 100 feet high. It looks as though Gomez will be buying a candy bar for you.

17-2   Trigonometric Functions

The study of Trigonometry uses six popular ratios of right triangle sides and their included angles. Section **17-1** used one such ratio to determine the height of the flagpole. Each ratio is a function of (or "depends on") the length of the sides, so the ratios are called trigonometric functions.

Trigonometric Functions

Given any right triangle as shown, the following ratios are defined for any acute ∠A.

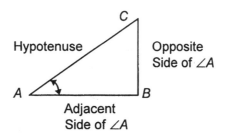

Function	Full Description (Calculation)	Abbreviation
tangent A	$\dfrac{\text{length of opposite side of angle } A}{\text{length of adjacent side of angle } A}$	$\tan A = \dfrac{\text{opp}}{\text{adj}}$
cosine A	$\dfrac{\text{length of adjacent side of angle } A}{\text{length of triangle hypotenuse}}$	$\cos A = \dfrac{\text{adj}}{\text{hyp}}$
sine A	$\dfrac{\text{length of opposite side of angle } A}{\text{length of triangle hypotenuse}}$	$\sin A = \dfrac{\text{opp}}{\text{hyp}}$
cotangent A	$\dfrac{\text{length of adjacent side of angle } A}{\text{length of opposite side of angle } A}$	$\cot A = \dfrac{\text{adj}}{\text{opp}}$
secant A	$\dfrac{\text{length of triangle hypotenuse}}{\text{length of adjacent side of angle } A}$	$\sec A = \dfrac{\text{hyp}}{\text{adj}}$
cosecant A	$\dfrac{\text{length of triangle hypotenuse}}{\text{length of opposite side of angle } A}$	$\csc A = \dfrac{\text{hyp}}{\text{opp}}$

TRIGONOMETRIC FUNCTIONS ARE JUST RATIOS OF TRIANGLE SIDE LENGTHS.

THAT ISN'T VERY COMPLICATED.

There are several things to note about trigonometric functions.

- The triangle must be a right triangle for the functions to be defined.

- The abbreviations shown for the trigonometric functions are standard abbreviations. (e.g. cos, sin, tan, etc., are standard abbreviations)

- Functions are only defined for either acute angle in a right triangle, not the right angle.

- The last three functions (cot, sec, and csc) are just reciprocals of the first three. (The first three functions tan, cos, and sin are the most often used.)

Let's clarify the use of a few trigonometric functions with an example.

Example - Using Trigonometric Functions

Given the following triangle, find tan, cos, and sin of $\angle C$ and $\angle A$.

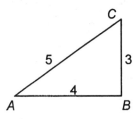

From the figure:

5 = the hypotenuse of the triangle
4 = side opposite angle *C*
3 = side adjacent to angle *C*

Answer:

$$\tan C = \frac{4}{3}$$

$$\cos C = \frac{3}{5}$$

$$\sin C = \frac{4}{5}$$

$$\tan A = \frac{3}{4}$$

$$\cos A = \frac{4}{5}$$

$$\sin A = \frac{3}{5}$$

Note that tan *B*, cos *B*, or sin *B* cannot be found since *B* is not acute. *B* is a right angle. Also note the relationships between the tangents of the two acute angles. (They are reciprocals.) Furthermore, sin *A* = cos *C*, and sin *C* = cos *A*. Do you see why this is true for the two acute angles in any right triangle?

Example - Understanding Trig. Functions.

May the value of the cosine or sine function ever be greater than one?

Answer: No. Both the cosine and sine of any acute angle divide a leg by the hypotenuse and the hypotenuse is always longer than either leg. However, the tangent may be greater than one as shown in the previous example.

So how are these trigonometric functions useful? By knowing the measure of either acute angle and the length of any side in a right triangle, the length of any side or the size of any angle may be found.

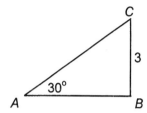

Assume that we would like to know the length of the hypotenuse, segment $\overline{AC}$. This may be easily accomplished by using the sine function. Let h = hypotenuse length. Then,

$$\sin 30° = \frac{3}{h} \quad \text{- or -} \quad h = \frac{3}{\sin 30°}$$

To determine h, we must first find the value of sin 30°. There are several methods.

Methods of finding sin 30°
1. Draw a right triangle with a 30° angle and measure the proper ratio of side lengths.
    * However, it is difficult to get an accurate measurement with a ruler.

2. Use Calculus.
    * This requires too much math. And, we haven't learned how yet!

3. Look up the answer in a table.
    * This is relatively easy. There is a table in Appendix B.

4. Use a calculator.
    * Almost every calculator has buttons for trigonometric functions. This is really easy!

Using a calculator or a table you will find that sin 30° = 0.5. Now, we can find h.

Answer: $h = (3) / (0.5) = 6$

I'M BECOMING A MATH CALCULATING FOOL.

I ACTUALLY ENJOY TRIGONOMETRY!

Assume you needed to find the value of angle A and length x given the following information.

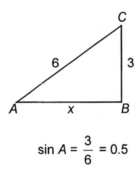

$$\sin A = \frac{3}{6} = 0.5$$

To find the value of $\angle A$, use a calculator or a table. However, this time you must find the angle whose sine equals 0.5. Finding the answer in a table is straightforward. However, the calculator requires using an inverse function.

We can isolate for the angle variable A by applying an inverse function to both sides of the equation. (Section **13-5** explained inverse functions.)

$$\sin A = 0.5$$

$$\sin^{-1}(\sin(A)) = \sin^{-1}(0.5)$$

$$A = \sin^{-1}(0.5)$$

Most calculators have buttons $\tan^{-1}$, $\cos^{-1}$, and $\sin^{-1}$ which are useful for finding angles. If the $\sin^{-1}(0.5)$ is correctly used on the calculator, 30° will result. (Note: Most calculators have a degree and radian mode. Make sure your calculator is in degree mode. Radians will be explained in section **17-7**.)

Another notation used with inverse trigonometric functions is the prefix **arc**. Therefore, some calculators have buttons atan, acos, and asin. This terminology or notation will not be used further in this text.

$$\arcsin(0.5) = \mathrm{asin}(0.5) = \sin^{-1}(0.5) = 30°$$

To find the value of x, we may use either the Pythagorean theorem or another trigonometric function. We'll arbitrarily choose the tangent function.

$$\tan 30° = \frac{3}{x} \quad \text{or} \quad x = \frac{3}{\tan 30°}$$

$$x = \frac{3}{0.577}$$

$$x = 5.196$$

Answer: $\angle A = 30°$
             $x = 5.196$

Verify the following problems using your knowledge of trigonometric functions. You will need a calculator.

Example - Using Trig Functions

Two runners jogging 3000 feet apart see an airplane. The first jogger sees the airplane directly over his head, but the other jogger sees the plane at an angle of 60°.
What is the altitude of the airplane?

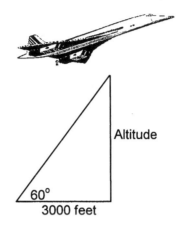

Answer: 5196 feet

Example - Using Trig. Functions

Find the lengths of all sides, and the values of all angles in the following triangle.

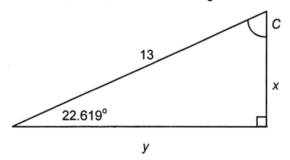

Answer: *x* = 5, *y* = 12, ∠C = 67.381°

Obtain the value of the two acute angles, and the length *y* of the following triangle.
Note that the answers obtained exactly match the triangle given above.

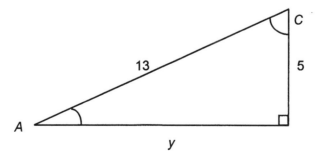

17-3 Commonly Used Triangles

There are two triangle shapes which are often encountered and commonly used on standardized tests. You should be familiar with the angles and relative side lengths of these popular triangles.

The first is the isosceles right triangle or the 45° - 45° - 90° triangle. The figure shows such a triangle, with legs having length x.

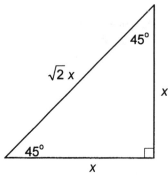

The length of the hypotenuse (h) of an isosceles right triangle with sides of length x may be found using the Pythagorean Theorem.

$$h^2 = x^2 + x^2$$
$$h^2 = 2x^2$$
$$h = \sqrt{2x^2}$$
$$h = x\sqrt{2} = \sqrt{2}x$$

Also,

$$\tan 45° = \frac{x}{x} = 1$$

$$\cot 45° = \frac{x}{x} = 1$$

$$\cos 45° = \sin 45° = \frac{x}{\sqrt{2}x} = \frac{1}{\sqrt{2}} \approx 0.7071$$

The second triangle commonly encountered is the 30° - 60° - 90° triangle. This triangle is formed by dividing an equilateral triangle in half.

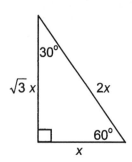

$$\sin 30° = \cos 60° = 0.5$$
$$\cos 30° = \sin 60° = \sqrt{3}/2 \approx 0.866$$

17-4   Oblique Triangle Relationships

An **oblique** triangle does not have a right angle. However, oblique triangle side lengths may be found by creating perpendicular segments to form right triangles. The trigonometric functions may then be applied.

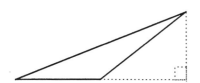   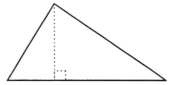

Rather than creating right triangles, known geometrical relationships may also be used to find side lengths. Section **15-4** stated that in any triangle the larger side is always opposite the larger angle. This is true, but more precisely a side is proportional to the sine of its opposite angle. This is formally stated in the **Law of Sines**. It is possible to prove this law by applying an altitude to an oblique triangle as shown above.

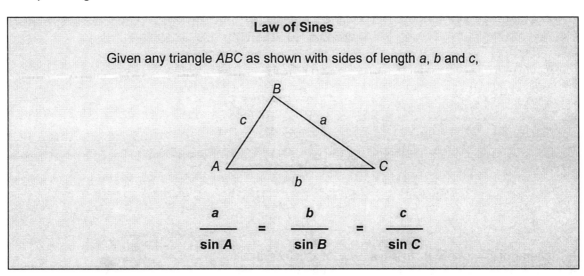

Law of Sines

Given any triangle *ABC* as shown with sides of length *a*, *b* and *c*,

$$\frac{a}{\sin A} = \frac{b}{\sin B} = \frac{c}{\sin C}$$

A **Law of Cosines** also exists for any triangle. This law is merely an extension of the Pythagorean theorem. Note that in a right triangle, the Law of Cosines reduces to the Pythagorean theorem since $\cos 90° = 0$.

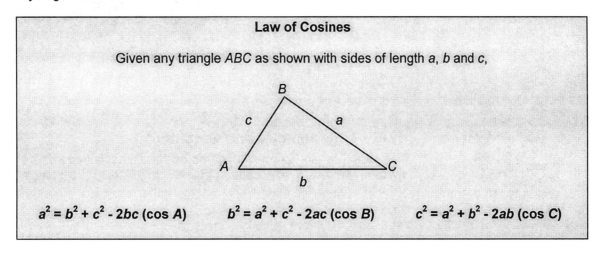

Law of Cosines

Given any triangle *ABC* as shown with sides of length *a*, *b* and *c*,

$$a^2 = b^2 + c^2 - 2bc\,(\cos A) \qquad b^2 = a^2 + c^2 - 2ac\,(\cos B) \qquad c^2 = a^2 + b^2 - 2ab\,(\cos C)$$

<u>Example - Using the Law of Cosines</u>

Find all of the angles in the following triangle.

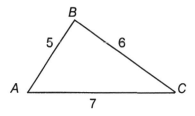

It is possible to use the Law of Cosines or the Law of Sines to solve the problem. However, in this case Law of Cosines is more simple to use, and is given below.

$$a^2 = b^2 + c^2 - 2bc \,(\cos A)$$
$$36 = 49 + 25 - 2(7)(5)(\cos A)$$

$$\cos A = 0.542857$$
$$A = \cos^{-1}(0.542857)$$

$$\angle A = 57.12°$$

$$c^2 = a^2 + b^2 - 2ab \,(\cos C)$$
$$25 = 36 + 49 - 2(6)(7)(\cos C)$$
$$\angle C = 44.41°$$

$$\angle B = 180° - 57.12° - 44.41° = 78.47°$$

Answer: $\angle A = 57.12°$ $\angle B = 78.47°$ $\angle C = 44.41°$

In general, it is easiest to use the Law of Cosines if all sides are given. However, it is easiest to use the Law of Sines if at least one angle is provided.

YOU MUST KNOW THE LAWS!

A VERY IMPORTANT SECTION.

17-5 Trigonometry and Graphing

It is useful to plot geometric figures on the Cartesian coordinate system which was introduced in chapter 14. A plot of a triangle inscribed in a circle with radius one is shown.

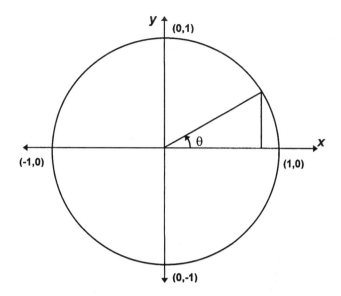

θ is the Greek letter *theta*, and is the symbol most often used to represent angles. In this section, θ is the angle from the positive portion of the *x*-axis to the hypotenuse.

Assume that the hypotenuse is rotated counterclockwise around the circumference of the circle, and the altitudo and base of the triangle are adjusted accordingly to make a right triangle.

- θ = 0°   the hypotenuse is directly on the *x*-axis at ordered pair (1,0).
- θ = 90°   the hypotenuse is on the *y*-axis at (0,1).
- θ = 180°   the hypotenuse is again on the *x*-axis at (-1,0).
- θ = 270°   the hypotenuse touches the circle at (0,-1).
- θ = 360°   the hypotenuse again is on the *x*-axis and touches the circle at (1,0).

There are 360° in one circle. Furthermore, negative angles may be used to represent clockwise rotations of the hypotenuse around the coordinate system.

- θ = -90° and θ = 270°   represent the same hypotenuse position.
- θ = -180° and θ = 180°   represent the same hypotenuse position.
- θ = -270° and θ = 90°   represent the same hypotenuse position.

Following is a graph of the first quadrant of the coordinate system, with a triangle of hypotenuse length equal to one, and a circle of radius equal to one. In the graph θ = 30°

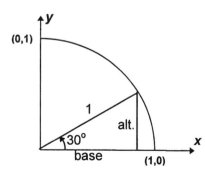

Using trigonometry, we can calculate the base and altitude of the right triangle.

cos 30° = base / 1 = base = 0.866   and   sin 30° = altitude / 1 = altitude = 0.5

After reviewing the drawing, you will see that the calculations have provided the ordered pair of the point of intersection between the hypotenuse and circle!

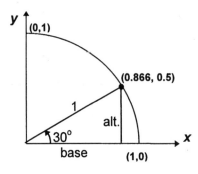

This may be repeated for any angle, and allows us to calculate trigonometric functions for angles that are not acute. *On a circle centered at the origin with radius one, the cosine of θ always equals the x coordinate, and the sine of the angle θ always equals the y coordinate.* We have combined a little Algebra and Geometry to provide us another tool for understanding.

By picturing θ and the coordinate system, you may quickly remember that

$\cos 0° = 1$	$\cos 90° = 0$	$\cos 180° = -1$	$\cos 270° = 0$
$\sin 0° = 0$	$\sin 90° = 1$	$\sin 180° = 0$	$\sin 270° = -1$

You may also easily picture the angles where the cos and sin functions will be positive, negative, and zero. You can also visualize where the cos and sin values increase or decrease for a changing θ. Since every circle has 360°, the cos or sin will be the same for angles which differ by 360°. For example,

$$\sin 32° = \sin (360 + 32)° = \sin (360 + 360 + 32)°$$

Combining the Pythagorean Theorem with the knowledge obtained in this section, we find that the cosine and sine of any angle θ are related by the following popular formula. Other popular formulas are provided in Appendix A.

$$\cos^2\theta + \sin^2\theta = 1$$

The figure also shows that the cosine and sine of any angle are related by the following formula.

$$\sin (\theta) = \cos (\theta - 90°)$$

Remember that the distributive law does not work for functions. You should clearly understand why.

$$f(x - 1) \neq f(x) - f(1)$$

$$\cos (\theta - 90°) \neq \cos (\theta) - \cos (90°)$$

Plotting triangles on a coordinate system is an extremely helpful tool. Plotting geometric figures is often used in advanced mathematics. It also should simplify your understanding of the values of sines and cosines.

Functions may also be used to create geometric figures. For example the following equation will produce a circle.

Equation of a Circle

A circle with center (*a*, *b*) and radius *r* is plotted with the equation:

$$(x - a)^2 + (y - b)^2 = r^2$$

Please review this section if necessary. It is very important to understand everything for further development.

17-6 Plotting Sine and Cosine Values

Observe the following functions which depend on an angle *x*.

$$y = f(x) = \cos(x)$$
$$y = f(x) = \sin(x)$$

These functions may be plotted on the Cartesian coordinate system using the methods established in chapter 14.

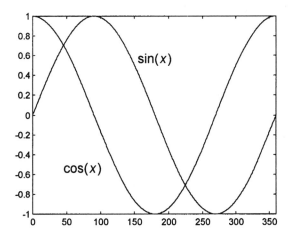

The graph shows another representation of the formulas presented earlier.

$$\sin(\theta) = \cos(\theta - 90°)$$

As shown, the cosine is merely the same value of the sine, with the angle shifted 90°. The plots of the repeating functions are often called a "sine wave" and "cosine wave", or in general a sinusoidal wave.

17-7 Using Radians

So far, all angles have been measured in degrees. However, there is one more popular unit of measure for angles, **radians**. A circle with a radius of one (or **unit circle**) has a circumference of 2π. Therefore, it is sometimes convenient to state that a circle which is composed of 360° is also composed of 2π radians.

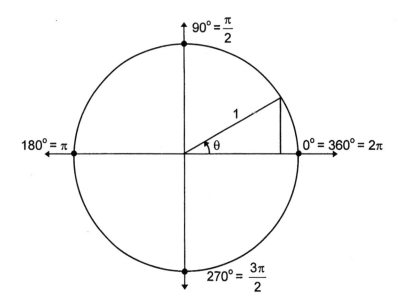

Since there are π radians in $180°$, it is simple to convert any number of degrees into radians, and vice-versa.

Converting between Degrees and Radians

$$x° \left(\frac{\pi}{180} \right) = y \text{ radians}$$

If an angle is referred to, and there is no $°$ to symbolize degrees, it is assumed that the measure is in radians. (Older texts may use a superscript [R] to denote radians.)

Examples - Using Radians

Convert $45°$ to radians.   Answer: $\pi / 4$

In radians, $\cos(3\pi/4) = ?$ Answer: -0.7071

17-8   Summary

This chapter has provided an overview of Trigonometry. This subject is usually taught in the last portion of a class in Geometry or Algebra II. The basics of the subject are not difficult, assuming that Geometry and Algebra are understood. However, the subject is also very powerful, and is often used in advanced mathematics as well as many of the sciences.

You should thoroughly understand the relationships that exist in right triangles, including all six trigonometric functions. Furthermore, you should understand how to combine ideas from Geometry and Algebra using the Cartesian coordinate system. Working with both degrees and radians also should be clearly understood.

In Part II of this text, Algebra has been covered thoroughly. The basics of Geometry and Trigonometry have also been explained. This chapter concludes Part II, and the mathematics normally taught at a high school level.

The final part of this text will first combine all of the mathematics explained in Parts I and II to create a few new and powerful relationships. After Algebra, Geometry, and Trigonometry have been fused, Calculus will be introduced. Although much math has been presented, you are just now beginning to understand the power of mathematics and the levels of math used by millions of people everyday.

If you've made it this far, congratulations. Amazing discoveries are ahead. The fundamentals of Geometry were established over 2200 years ago. However, Calculus is only about 300 years old. You've covered over 1900 years of mathematics. Only 300 more years to go!

Important Definitions

6 Trig. Functions

- Tangent
- Cosine
- Sine
- Cotangent
- Secant
- Cosecant

Inverse Trig. Functions

Oblique Triangle

Law of Sines

Law of Cosines

Equation of a Circle

Unit Circle

Radian

You should be able to ...

1. Remember and use all 6 trigonometric functions with right triangles

2. Find the trig. function for any angle using a table or calculator

3. Use the Law of Sines

4. Use the Law of Cosines

5. Write an equation for a circle, given the radius and center point

6. Understand that cosine and sine functions are sinusoidal

7. Convert from degrees to radians

8. Convert from radians to degrees

Logarithms

18-1   Introduction

Logarithms are usually taught in an Algebra II class after the student has learned how to use exponents. Therefore, this chapter is actually an extension of the discussion in chapter 8, since logarithms and exponents are inverse functions. Using logarithms is not difficult, and their basic properties could be summarized in about a page (section **18-3**).

However, a thorough understanding of logarithms is key to understanding mathematics from a broad perspective. Much of the material presented in this chapter is seldom taught in a classroom. However, it is so important conceptually that an entire chapter has been devoted to the subject. Not only will you be shown how to use logarithms, but you also will be shown the origin of the natural logarithm, which is commonly used in engineering, physics, and mathematics.

If necessary, review chapter 8 on exponents, section **10-4** on variable isolation, and the discussion of inverse functions in section **13-5**. This chapter assumes that all of the background information from these previous portions of the text is well understood.

18-2   Understanding Logarithms

An equation with one unknown is given below. Using previous knowledge of exponents and multiplication, you should be able to determine the answer simply by looking at the problem.

$$10^x = 1000 \qquad \text{Answer: } x = 3$$

However, the following equation is significantly more difficult since the value of x is not an integer but some decimal between 2 and 3 ($10^2 < 750 < 10^3$).

$$10^x = 750$$

We know from Algebra that it is necessary to isolate for the variable x in order to solve the above problem. However, the preceding chapters have not shown a method for isolating an unknown exponent. This chapter introduces a new mathematical function called a logarithm.

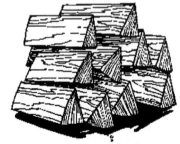

THESE ARE LOGS TOO.

A **logarithm** is a mathematical function which performs the inverse operation of a number written in exponential notation. A logarithm is written by the abbreviation, **log**. Remember that the inverse operation of addition was subtraction, and the inverse operation of multiplication was division. Now we have established that the inverse function of an exponential function is a logarithm.

Definition of a logarithm

If $\quad y = a^x$

then $\quad x = \log_a y$

The subscript of the logarithm function is called the **base** of the logarithm. You should read the following equation as "the base 10 logarithm of 750 equals *x*."

$$\log_{10} 750 = x$$

You must think of the problem as "10 raised to what power equals 750? " This is the exact same problem as the following equation.

$$10^x = 750$$

The following equations are also equivalent. As you can see, the base can be any number. You should realize the reason that the subscript of the logarithm is called the base. It is the same as the base of the number written in exponential form (see section **8-1**).

$$3^x = 27 \qquad \text{and} \qquad \log_3 27 = x$$

Verify the following examples of logarithms by using your knowledge of multiplication. Remember that $a^0 = 1$ for any positive or negative value of *a*. As the last example shows, the logarithm of a number may be negative. Does this make sense?

Examples - Calculating Logarithms

$$\log_2 1 = 0$$

$$\log_{1000} 1 = 0$$

$$\log_2 8 = 3$$

$$\log_6 36 = 2$$

$$\log_{14.65} 14.6500 = 1$$

$$\log_2 (0.5) = -1$$

By understanding exponents and the definition of the logarithm, we may generate some additional general properties of logarithms. The rule given below should make sense, since $\log_a a$ means "to what value must *a* be raised to equal *a* ?" Obviously the answer is 1, regardless of the value of *a*.

$$\log_a a = 1$$

Below is the rule obtained in chapter 8 for multiplying numbers with the same base and different exponents.

$$c^a \bullet c^b = c^{(a+b)}$$

This rule for exponents may be used to develop another rule for using logarithms. Remember that the logarithm of a number is actually the exponent that the base must be raised to equal that number.

$$\log_c (ab) = \log_c a + \log_c b$$

A numerical example may help clarify.

$$\log_2 (16) = \log_2 (2 \bullet 8) = \log_2 2 + \log_2 8 = 1 + 3 = 4$$

Equivalently,

$$2^1 \bullet 2^3 = 2^4 = 16$$

The rule for adding exponents was slightly modified in chapter 8 to yield the expression,

$$(a^b)^x = a^{bx}$$

This exponential rule produces the equation for logarithms given below. Note the similarity between this rule and the rule for adding logarithms given above. The argument of the logarithm is not *ab*, but is *b* multiplied a total of *x* times.

$$\log_a (b^x) = x \log_a b$$

An example may help clarify.

$$\log_{10} 100^2 = 2 \log_{10} 100 = 4$$

Using the two established rules, we find that,

$$\log_a a^x = x \log_a a = x (1) = x$$

Relationships may also be found for division. From section **8-5**,

$$c^a \div c^b = c^{(a-b)}$$

A slight modification produces the next rule regarding logarithms.

$$\log_c (a \div b) = \log_c a - \log_c b$$

Use the presented rules to verify the following examples.

Examples - Using Logarithms

$$\log_2(8 \bullet 16) = \log_2 (128) = 7$$

$$\log_2(8 \bullet 16) = \log_2 (8) + \log_2 (16) = 3 + 4 = 7$$

$$\log_{10} (1000/100) = \log_{10} (10) = 1$$

$$\log_{10} (1000/100) = \log_{10}(1000) - \log_{10} (100) = 3 - 2 = 1$$

$$\log_{10} (1000^5) = 5 \log_{10} (1000) = 5 \bullet 3 = 15$$

Don't forget that logarithms and exponentials are inverse functions. As section **13-5** stated,

$$\text{if} \quad g(x) \text{ and } f(x) \text{ are inverse functions}$$

$$\text{then} \quad g(f(x)) = x \quad \text{and} \quad f(g(x)) = x$$

We may write the functions $f(x)$ and $g(x)$ using logarithms to state,

$$\text{If } g(x) = \log_{10}(x) \quad \text{and} \quad f(x) = 10^x,$$

$$\text{then } \log_{10}(10^x) = x \quad \text{and} \quad 10^{\log_{10}(x)} = x$$

The function 10^x is often called the **anti-logarithm** to show that it is the inverse of the logarithm function. Many calculators have an **alog** button which represents the anti-log function.

$$\log_{10}(100) = 2 \quad \text{or} \quad \text{alog}(2) = 100 \quad \text{or} \quad 10^2 = 100$$

The following complicated looking expression is easily evaluated without even calculating the base 10 logarithm of 3.

$$10^{\log_{10}(3)} = 3$$

Let's look at just the exponent in the above example.

$$\log_{10}(3)$$

Again, this can be thought of as "10 raised to some power equals three." Whatever that value equals, after it is placed in the exponent of 10, the answer must equal 3.

To solve algebraic equations containing unknowns as arguments of a logarithm, make the base of the logarithm the base of the entire equation. For example,

$$\log_{10}(2x + 18) = 3$$

$$10^{\log_{10}(2x+18)} = 10^3$$

$$2x + 18 = 1000$$

$$x = 491$$

Another example follows.

$$\log_3(\log_3 x) = 1$$

$$3^{\log_3(\log_3 x)} = 3^1$$

$$\log_3(x) = 3$$

$$3^{\log_3(x)} = 3^3$$

$$x = 3^3 = 27$$

Verify the following examples.

Examples - Solving Equations Containing Logarithms

$$10^{\log_{10}(2x+7)} = 8 \qquad \text{Answer: } x = 0.5$$

$$\log_3(3^{3x}) = 6 \qquad \text{Answer: } x = 2$$

$$\log_{10}(\log_{10} x) = 1 \qquad \text{Answer: } x = 10^{10}$$

18-3   Calculating Logarithms

As section **8-6** stated, it is difficult to calculate bases with fractional exponents. Therefore, it is equally difficult to find fractional (or decimal) answers to problems containing logarithms. Note the difficulty of solving for x in the equivalent equations shown below, since x is not an integer. $(2 < x < 3)$

$$10^x = 750$$

- or -

$$\log_{10} 750 = x$$

There are two practical ways of solving such problems.

    1.   Use a table of logarithms
    2.   Use a calculator

A logarithm with base 10 is commonly used, and is therefore called a **common logarithm**. A logarithm of base 10 is so common, that if the word *log* is written down without a subscript, it is assumed that the base is 10. Base 10 logarithms may be solved using the *log* button on a calculator. Using a calculator, verify the following.

$$\log_{10}(750) = 2.875$$

The *log* button on a calculator assumes that the logarithm's base equals 10. A problem such as $\log_2(17)$ <u>may not</u> be directly solved on a calculator. Tables of already calculated logarithms also assume that the logarithm is a common logarithm. As you may guess, it is impossible to have a logarithm table for every base since the base could be any number (and would therefore require an infinite number of tables).

To solve this dilemma, it is necessary to find a method to convert a logarithm of any valued base into a common logarithm. The tables or calculators will then be useful. Let's try and find a conversion from base 2 to base 10. Then, we'll try and make a general rule for converting logarithm bases.

We know that,

$$\log_{10}(1000) = 3$$

But, what if the base were 2?

$$\log_2(1000) = x$$

Let's first rewrite the equation using exponents instead of logs.

$$2^x = 1000$$

We can relate the different bases with many equations. However, we find that it is convenient to use the following equation to relate bases. We know that n must be between 0 and 1 since $0 < 2 < 10$. Maybe the value of n will be proportional to some conversion factor for logarithms.

$$2 = 10^n$$

Using logarithms of base 10 the equation may be rewritten.

$$n = \log_{10} 2$$

By replacing n in the original relationship between the numbers 2 and 10, we can write another equation. This equation should also be clear by methods explained in section **18-2**.

$$2 = 10^n = 10^{\log_{10}(2)}$$

The original problem may be rewritten by substituting the newly developed expression (directly above) for the number 2.

Original Problem: $\qquad 2^x = 1000$

Substitution for the number 2: $\qquad (10^{\log_{10}(2)})^x = 1000$

Use of rule for exponents: $\qquad 10^{x \cdot \log_{10}(2)} = 1000$

Then, taking the base 10 logarithm of both sides of the equation yields,

$$x \cdot \log_{10}(2) = \log_{10}(1000) = 3$$

$$x = \frac{3}{\log_{10} 2}$$

Finally, x may be found by using the base 10 logarithm on the calculator.

$$\log_2(1000) = x = 9.9657$$

This is a long process to convert any logarithm to a common logarithm. However, variables may be used in the above procedure to prove that to convert any logarithm to a base 10 logarithm, a standard formula may be applied.

To find the logarithm of a number to any base, simply take the base 10 logarithm of the number, and then divide by a scale factor. The scale factor is the common logarithm of the new base.

$$\log_a x = \frac{\log_{10} x}{\log_{10} a}$$

A list of logarithmic laws developed in this chapter is provided on the next page.

Logarithmic Laws

$$\log_a a = 1$$

$$\log_c (ab) = \log_c a + \log_c b$$

$$\log_a (b^x) = x \log_a b$$

$$\log_c (a \div b) = \log_c a - \log_c b$$

$$\log_a x = \frac{\log_b x}{\log_b a}$$

18-4   Uses for Logarithms

Before the advent of calculators, slide rules were used. The slide rule contained a list of numbers of base 10 logarithms. Therefore, long multiplication or division problems could be solved by using logarithms and addition or subtraction as a shortcut calculation.

Example - Using Logarithms for Long Multiplication.

Use logarithms to find x.

$$x = 15,623 \bullet 124,651$$

$$\log_{10} (15,623) = 4.1937$$

$$\log_{10} (124,651) = 5.0957$$

$$\log_{10} (15,623 \bullet 124,651) = \log_{10} x = 4.1937 + 5.0957$$

$$\log_{10} x = 9.2894$$

Answer: $x = 1,947,422,573$

Adding (4.1937 + 5.0957) and using a chart is much quicker than multiplying (15,623 • 124,651) by hand. However, in this day of abundant computing machines using logarithms for shortcut calculations is seldom used. Before calculators were common, some people memorized entire tables of logarithms to quickly perform multiplication and division of multi-digit numbers mentally.

The hearing ability of humans is based on a logarithmic scale. If you hear a sound that you think is twice as loud as another sound, scientific instruments actually measure the intensity of the sounds to vary by a factor of ten. Therefore, sound is often measured in **decibels**. (A decibel is abbreviated dB. The suffix *bel* refers to the inventor of the telephone, Alexander Graham Bell.)

If the sound intensity is x, the sound intensity in dB is $10 \bullet \log_{10}(\frac{x}{x_o})$, where x_o is a reference value equal to 10^{-12}. Using this scale, the following measurements of various sounds have been made.

Source of Sound	Intensity (dB)
Close-by jet airplane	150
Jackhammer	130
Typical siren or rock concert	120
Lawn Mower	100
Vacuum cleaner	70
Typical conversation	50
Whisper	30

Measurements above 120 dB normally cause pain, and measurements below 0 dB few can hear. If you have an equalizer on your stereo at home, the scale is probably in dB. If you double the scale in dB, the stereo actually has to output ten times as much sound!

The **pH** is a measurement of the acidity in a chemical solution. This is also measured on a common log scale. Therefore, while orange juice may have a pH of 3.8 and taste sour, milk of magnesia has a pH of about 10.8 and taste bitter. In other words, milk of magnesia has $10^{(10.8-3.8)} = 10^7 = 10$ million times less hydrogen ion concentration than orange juice.

There are countless other uses of log scales in use today. Logarithms are also used in advanced mathematics for solving certain equations. The logarithm base most often used in advanced science is given in the next section.

18-5   Finding the Natural Logarithm

The common logarithm is a logarithm of base 10. There is one other logarithm base that is extremely useful, the **natural logarithm**. The base of the natural logarithm is a transcendental number, always represented by the letter e. A **transcendental number** is a number that cannot be written in the form a^b, where a and b are both rational numbers. Like an irrational number, a transcendental number has a never-ending, never-repeating decimal. Listed is the approximate value of e.

$$e \approx 2.7182818...$$

Instead of writing $log_e x$, the notation *ln x* is used (read aloud "the natural log of *x*" or "lawn of *x*").

$$log_e e = ln\ 2.7182818 = 1$$

The natural logarithm is used in many engineering and scientific studies. The value of e has amazing properties exhibited in Calculus. Properties of e are unique to any other number in existence. But, where does this value originate, and why is it the 'natural' logarithm?

These questions are seldom answered in math classes. The reason is that it is simple to press the *ln* button, rather than the *log* button on the calculator to find the natural logarithm of a number, so the solution to equations involving e is trivial. However, by learning the origin of e, you will obtain a glimpse of the beauty of mathematics. You will also gain further understanding in combining the disciplines of Algebra, Geometry, and Trigonometry. e is truly amazing.

We now will determine where the value of e originated. It is a number that naturally occurs by following already established mathematical rules.

Let's begin by assuming that the logarithm has simply been defined, and no calculator or tables of logarithms exist. That way, you'll get a good overall perspective.

At first, you may think that making a table to calculate the logarithm of any number would be an enormous effort. The number of calculations seem unimaginable. The following two examples are easy. (As stated, if the base it not shown the logarithm's base is assumed 10.)

$$\log 10 = 1$$
$$\log 100 = 2$$

But these are much more difficult,

$$\log x = 1.00001$$
$$\log y = 1.00002$$
$$\log z = 0.99999$$

To only calculate the logarithms of numbers 10 to 100 with six digits of accuracy requires 1 million calculations $\{(2-1) / 0.000001 = 10^6 \}$! Furthermore, the only way to calculate each number is by trial and error. (Actually, there is an exact procedure for finding roots, but it is very tedious. Yet another method is shown in **22-9, Newton's Method**)

After thinking a while, we remember that exponents add, so maybe we can make a limited table, and obtain some results by combining values in the table. First, we find the square root of 10.

$$10^{0.5} = 3.16228$$

Next, we find the fourth root, or the square root of the square root of 10.

$$10^{0.25} = 3.16228^{0.5} = 1.77828$$

We continue this process of finding square roots of the next root. Then, we can find 10 to any power. For example, $10^{1.875}$ may be found by adding the first four results of the table.

$$10^{1.875} = 10^1 + 10^{0.5} + 10^{0.25} + 10^{0.125}$$

With some effort, the following table of the first 10 roots is created.

a	10^a
1	10
1/2	3.16227766
1/4	1.77827941
1/8	1.33352143
1/16	1.15478198
1/32	1.07460783
1/64	1.03663293
1/128	1.01815172
1/256	1.00903504
1/512	1.00450736

By looking at the table, we realize that the values of 10^a, as a gets smaller, appear to be approaching a pattern. The decimal digits in the value of 10^a appear to be divided by 2, as the next value of a is reached.

Looking in the row $a = 1/128$ we see

$$0.01815172 / 2 = 0.00907586$$

This value is close to the decimal of the next number. Moving down a row,

$$0.00903504 / 2 = 0.00451752$$

We decide to add another column to see if the values really are changing by the same ratio as new roots are obtained. The formula for the added column was found with some experimenting. We'll also expand the number of roots with more tedious calculations. (Remember what we are trying to do here. We are trying to find where this amazing number e originates.)

a	10^a	$(10^a - 1) / a$
1	10	9
1/2	3.16227766	4.324555
1/4	1.77827941	3.113118
1/8	1.33352143	2.668171
1/16	1.15478198	2.476512
1/32	1.07460783	2.387451
1/64	1.03663293	2.344507
1/128	1.01815172	2.323420
1/256	1.00903504	2.312971
1/512	1.00450736	2.307770
1/1024	1.00225115	2.305176
1/2048	1.00112494	2.303880
1/4096	1.00056231	2.303232
1/8192	1.00028112	2.302909
1/16,384	1.00014055	2.302747
1/32,768	1.00007027	2.302666
1/65,536	1.00003514	2.302626
1/131,072	1.00001757	2.302605
1/262,144	1.00000878	2.302595
1/524,288	1.00000439	2.302590
1/1,048,576	1.00000220	2.302588
1/2,097,152	1.00000110	2.302586
1/4,194,304	1.00000055	2.302586
1/8,388,608	1.00000027	2.302585

After much calculation, we find that for some reason, the final column approaches the value of 2.302585. Therefore, we do not need to spend time calculating additional roots. We know that for small a, $10^a = 1 + 2.302585a$. For example since $(524,288)^{-1} = 1.907349E\text{-}6$

$$10^{1/524,288} \quad = 10^{\,1.907349E\text{-}6} = 1 + (2.302585)(1.907349E\text{-}6)$$

$$= 1 + 4.391832E\text{-}6$$

$$= 1.00000439 \text{ as in the table}$$

To repeat for very small *a*,

$$10^a = 1 + 2.302585a$$

However, *a* is simply a variable used to represent any small number. Let's replace *a* with the value *a*/2.302585 (which doesn't change anything, since *a* is still just a small number). With this substitution, the previous equation yields,

$$10^{a/2.302585} = 1 + a$$

Since *a* is a very small number (such as 1/524,288 and smaller),

$$1 + a \approx 1$$

The equation developed from the chart may then be rewritten,

$$10^{a/2.302585} = 1$$

Once again, remember the definition of a logarithm.

$$\log_{10} 1 = a \qquad \text{is the same as} \qquad 10^a = 1$$

Now look at the equation

$$10^{a/2.302585} = 1$$

Based on information in section **18-3**, you should realize that the factor of 2.302585 is simply a scaling factor of the base 10 logarithm. We now see that a natural scaling factor occurs. That scaling factor is:

$$10^{1/2.302585}$$

Using the table of base 10 logarithms developed by finding successive roots and multiplying the appropriate table entries, we can find this value

$$10^{1/2.302585} = 2.71828$$

This value of 2.71828 is a natural scaling factor of base 10 logarithms. The mysterious, yet ubiquitous value of *e*, the natural logarithm, has been found. Study of Calculus will show some of the amazing properties of the value of *e*.

18-6 Summary

This chapter has demonstrated the use and properties of logarithms. In the world today, computing values with logarithms is not difficult due to the widespread availability of the calculator and computer. However, you must understand logarithms, know the properties, and be able to manipulate algebraic equations containing logarithms and unknown exponents.

This chapter has also provided the origins of the value of the natural logarithm. Is it necessary that you remember every step to developing its value? No. However, having a basic idea of where the natural logarithm originates gives valuable insight. As your education progresses, you will be amazed at the occurrence and usefulness of *e*. Furthermore, ensuing chapters will use *e*, along with topics established in the next chapter to tie various mathematical disciplines together. The more one understands mathematics, the more astounded he becomes at its order and practicality.

Important Definitions

Logarithm

Base of a Logarithm

Anti-Logarithm

Common Logarithm

Natural Logarithm

Transcendental Number

You should be able to ...

1. Find the logarithm of any number with any base

2. Perform any of the four fundamental operations with logarithms

3. Memorize the value of the natural logarithm

4. Have a basic understanding of how the natural logarithm is found

Complex Numbers

19-1 Introduction

Complex Numbers are usually briefly introduced in an Algebra II class but will be given thorough explanation in this chapter. To begin, you will first learn why it is necessary to invent a new type of number which is called imaginary. After defining imaginary numbers, it will be necessary to understand how to perform all four fundamental operations with them. Finally, the close relationship between imaginary and complex numbers will be explained and complex numbers graphed.

Complex numbers are not required for most non-scientific disciplines. However, fields such as electrical engineering use complex numbers extensively.   Furthermore, understanding complex numbers is necessary to obtain a thorough math foundation.

THEY'RE NOT COMPLICATED. WE JUST CALL THEM COMPLEX.

This chapter is relatively short, since operating with complex numbers is actually not very complex if previous chapters are understood. However, the next chapter will use complex numbers and knowledge obtained from the development of logarithms to develop an amazing connection between Geometry and Algebra.

19-2 Defining Imaginary Numbers

Previous chapters have shown how to solve for an equation with one unknown using a variety of methods. At this point in our mathematical development, we can actually find the solutions to any unknown. However, what if the solution does not make sense? For example, let us solve for x in the following equation.

$$x^2 + 1 = 0$$

This seems like a simple equation. We will simply move 1 to the right hand side of the equals sign and take the square root of both sides of the equation to isolate for the variable.

$$x = \pm\sqrt{-1}$$

We now have an answer. However, what does the square root of (-1) equal?

$$1^2 \neq -1 \qquad \text{and} \qquad (-1)^2 \neq -1$$

There is no number multiplied by itself which equals (-1). This should be obvious since for any value x,

$$-x \bullet -x = x^2 \qquad \text{and} \qquad x \bullet x = x^2$$

Maybe it would help if we create a function from the equation $x^2 + 1 = 0$. We may then plot the function and determine where the function crosses the x-axis. Wherever the function crosses the x-axis will provide a solution for $f(x) = y = 0$, and thus determine the value of x.

$$y = f(x) = x^2 + 1$$

A plot, which was generated from making a table of x values, is given below.

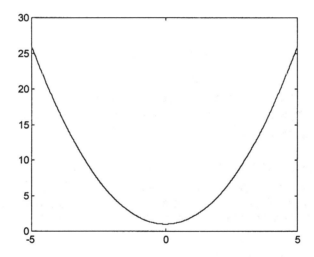

The function is a quadratic, and therefore has only one turn (which is shown). However, the function <u>never</u> crosses the x-axis, so $f(x) = 0$ appears to have no solution. It is clear that $f(x)$ is never zero. Hmmm ...

Let's return to isolating the variable using Algebra. We did find a solution for x, but the solution of $\sqrt{-1}$ does not make any sense based on our understanding of roots (section **8-6**). Without understanding what $\sqrt{-1}$ equals, we may at least still write the following mathematically correct statement.

$$x = \pm\sqrt{-1} \text{ is the solution to } x^2 + 1 = 0$$

From chapter 8 we know that for any number a,

$$\left(\sqrt{a}\right)^2 = a$$

Therefore, we may let $a = -1$, and write the equations given below. We may not understand what $\sqrt{-1}$ equals, but at least we can determine a value for $\left(\sqrt{-1}\right)^2$.

$$\left(\sqrt{-1}\right)^2 = -1$$

and

$$\left(-\sqrt{-1}\right)^2 = (-1)^2\left(\sqrt{-1}\right)^2 = (1)(-1) = -1$$

As shown, the solution may be either $+\sqrt{-1}$ or $-\sqrt{-1}$ since either one satisfies the original equation.

$$x^2 + 1 = 0$$

$$(\sqrt{-1})^2 + 1 = -1 + 1 = 0$$

$$(-\sqrt{-1})^2 + 1 = -1 + 1 = 0$$

Since $+\sqrt{-1}$ and $-\sqrt{-1}$ both satisfy the equation, we'll only concern ourselves with $+\sqrt{-1}$. We find that the negative solution, while equally valid, is never needed. Unfortunately, we still do not understand or know how to reduce $\sqrt{-1}$.

Remember from chapter 2 that numbers are simply symbols, and that it is not necessary to always have a physical interpretation for the symbol. Therefore, $\sqrt{-1}$ is the solution to the equation $x^2 + 1 = 0$. We don't understand the answer, but it is mathematically correct. However, this answer causes many new questions, which will be answered in the ensuing sections.

1. Where does $\sqrt{-1}$ fit on the number line?

2. Are there an entirely new set of mathematical rules for numbers that do not have physical significance?

3. What use is an answer that we do not even understand?

4. Can we always rely on plots to indicate solutions to equations?

5. How many other equations have answers that we don't understand?

As section **2-5** stated, a **real number** is any number that can be represented on the number line. We do not understand what $\sqrt{-1}$ equals, and one could never reach $\sqrt{-1}$ by counting. Therefore, it cannot be represented on the number line. Since it is not a real number, $\sqrt{-1}$ is defined as an **imaginary number**. In mathematics, $\sqrt{-1}$ is always represented by the letter i as a shortcut notation. (Although electrical engineers commonly use the letter j instead, since i is a symbol for electrical current.) This answers the first question.

Developing an entirely new set of mathematical rules for imaginary numbers seems like much trouble!   Fortunately, all mathematical rules developed for real numbers also apply to imaginary numbers. Remember that we used known rules to develop the answer of $\sqrt{-1}$ for the equation $x^2 + 1 = 0$ in the first place. This answers the second question. Now let's multiply and divide with imaginary numbers using rules that we already understand.

For any number b, the following formula may be written using known rules.

$$\sqrt{-b} = \sqrt{b} \bullet \sqrt{-1} = \sqrt{b} \bullet i$$

Verify the following examples.   Note that since i is always used to represent the imaginary number, the ($\bullet$) operator is not required.

Examples - Using the Imaginary Number

$$\sqrt{-64} = 8i$$
$$\sqrt{-100} = 10i$$
$$-\sqrt{-9} = -3i$$
$$\sqrt{-x^2} = xi$$

Since $\sqrt{-64}$ is imaginary just like $\sqrt{-1}$, and $\sqrt{-64} = 8i$, we state that any number multiplied by the imaginary number i is called an imaginary number. Therefore, $8i$, $10i$, $-3i$, and xi are all imaginary numbers.

Note the following values of i raised to integer powers. The answers repeat themselves in the pattern of 1, i, -1, $-i$ as powers increase. This is quite interesting, and is a pattern obtained with no real number. You should be able to obtain the value of i raised to any integer power.

$i^0 = 1$ $\qquad\qquad$ $i^1 = i$ $\qquad\qquad$ $i^2 = -1$ $\qquad\qquad$ $i^3 = i^2 \bullet i = -i$

$i^4 = i^2 \bullet i^2 = 1$ $\qquad$ $i^5 = i^3 \bullet i^2 = i$ $\qquad$ $i^6 = i^3 \bullet i^3 = (-i)^2 = -1$ $\quad$ $i^7 = -i$

$i^8 = 1$ $\qquad\qquad$ $i^9 = i$ $\qquad\qquad$ $i^{10} = -1$ $\qquad\qquad$ $i^{11} = -i$

We may also develop values for imaginary number raised to negative integers powers.

$$i^0 = 1 = i^1 \bullet i^{-1}$$

$$1 = i^1 \bullet (-i) = -i^2 = -(\sqrt{-1})^2 = -(-1) = 1$$

Therefore,

$$i^{-1} = -i$$

By writing the values of i as negative exponents increase, we see that the pattern continues. (Remember $i^x \bullet i^{-x} = i^0 = 1$)

$i^{-8} = 1$ $\qquad\qquad\qquad$ $i^{-7} = i$ $\qquad\qquad\qquad$ $i^{-6} = -1$ $\qquad\qquad\qquad$ $i^{-5} = -i$

$i^{-4} = i^{-2} \bullet i^{-2} = 1$ $\qquad$ $i^{-3} = i^{-2} \bullet i^{-1} = i$ $\qquad$ $i^{-2} = -1$ $\qquad\qquad\qquad$ $i^{-1} = -i$

Verify the examples given below. As shown above, the simplest form of an imaginary number will never have a power with a magnitude greater than one. Furthermore, an operation on two imaginary numbers may produce a result that is a real number!

Therefore, we often may obtain an imaginary number as an intermediate step in a long calculation. The use of imaginary numbers allows us to continue the mathematical calculations, instead of getting stuck. Then the final answer, if it represents something physical, will turn out real. So, the imaginary number allows the solution of problems that are not solvable using only real numbers. This answers the third question.

GET THE IDEA?

Examples - Using the Imaginary Number in Multiplication and Division

$$(15i^2) \div (5i) = 3i$$

$$100i \div 10i = 10$$

$$3i \bullet 4i \bullet 2i = 24i^3 = -24i$$

$$18i \div 6i^5 = 3i^{-4} = 3$$

19-3   Adding and Subtracting Imaginary Numbers

Remember that i is a symbol, just as any other number or variable. Therefore, all rules previously learned apply to imaginary numbers.

Examples - Adding and Subtracting with the Imaginary Number

$$i + i + i = 3i$$

$$3i + 2i = (3 + 2)i = 5i$$

$$14i - 3i = 11i$$

$$8i^6 + 3 = -8 + 3 = -5$$

$$6 + i = 6 + i$$

Note that the distributive law could not be applied in the final example. Therefore, we find that real numbers cannot be added to imaginary numbers. Just as *x* + *y* cannot be reduced since *x* and *y* are different variables, so *a* + *bi* cannot be reduced. We can treat *i* as if it were a variable when adding or subtracting. The same rules apply.

19-4   Complex = Real + Imaginary

When performing any math operation, we treat *i* as a variable. However, *i* certainly is not a variable. Rather, it is a known value equal to $\sqrt{-1}$. Therefore, the most general form of any number is:

$$a + bi$$

The above number is complex. A **complex number** is a number with a non-zero real part and a non-zero imaginary part. (The word *part* is an official mathematical term.) A complex number is usually written with the real part first and the imaginary part second.

Sometimes we only want the real part or only the imaginary part of a complex number. To obtain the real part, the notation *RE*, *Re*, or $\Re$ is used. The imaginary part uses the notation *IM* or *Im*.

COMPLEX NUMBER NOTATION

For any number

$$a + bi$$

$$RE\,(a + bi) = Re\,(a + bi) = \Re(a + bi) = a$$
$$IM\,(a + bi) = Im(a + bi) = b$$

Examples - Numbers

3 + 4*i*	Complex Number
4*i*	Imaginary Number
3	Real Number

$$\Re(3 + 4i) = 3$$
$$RE(20 + 2i) = 20$$

Performing operations with complex numbers is no different than that previously shown. The only difference is that both real and imaginary numbers exist in the same problem. Following are examples. Remember, treat *i* as a variable. However, if the power of *i* is anything other than 1 or -1, you may simplify the solution. That's all there is to it.

Examples - Using Complex Numbers

$$(3 + 2i) + (4 - 6i) = 7 - 4i$$

$$(15 + 10i) \div 5 = 3 + 2i$$

$$
\begin{aligned}
(3 + 2i)(4 - 6i) &= 12 - 18i + 8i - (2i)(6i) \\
&= 12 - 18i + 8i - 12i^2 \\
&= 12 - 10i - (12 \bullet -1) \\
&= 12 - 10i + 12 \\
&= 24 - 10i
\end{aligned}
$$

Note that $12i^2$ was reduced to -12 in the example above. Verify the following example.

Example - Using Complex Numbers

$$(2 + 3i)(4 + 5i) = -7 + 22i$$

Observe the following example which results in a real number.

$$(3 + 2i)(3 - 2i) = 9 - 6i + 6i + 4 = 13$$

The second term, $(3 - 2i)$, is the same as the first term but with the sign of the imaginary part changed. We see that in general,

$$(a + bi)(a - bi) = a^2 + b^2$$

This is an interesting and useful property. It is so interesting that mathematicians use an official definition, complex conjugate. A **complex conjugate** of a number is a number with its imaginary part multiplied by (-1).

Definition - Complex Conjugates

$a + bi$ and $a - bi$ are **complex conjugates**

Any number multiplied by its complex conjugate will result in a real number.

$$(a + bi)(a - bi) = a^2 + b^2$$

Please verify the following examples.

Examples - Using Complex Conjugates

Find the complex conjugates of the following numbers

3 - 6*i*	Answer:	3 + 6*i*
-8*i* + 4	Answer:	8*i* + 4 or 4 + 8*i*
5	Answer:	5
-5*i*	Answer:	5*i*
5 - *xi*	Answer:	5 + *xi*

19-5 Graphing Complex Numbers

As shown in chapter 14, displaying numbers and equations in graphical form is very helpful. In section **19-2**, we found that the graph of the expression $x^2 + 1$ showed no solution to the equation $x^2 + 1 = 0$. Algebraically the equation did have a solution which was an imaginary number. Therefore, we may use graphs to find real number solutions to equations. If an equation does not have a real solution, it must have an imaginary solution which may be found algebraically. So graphs are helpful after all. Not only do they show the characteristics of a function (or equation), but they also provide the answers to real solutions and show the existence of imaginary solutions. This answers the fourth question posed in section **19-2**. However, it would still be helpful to plot complex numbers on a graph to allow visual understanding.

There are two parts to any complex number, a real part and a complex part. Therefore, we may use the Cartesian coordinate system to plot a complex number. However, rather than calling the abscissa the *x*-axis, we will call it the **real axis**. Instead of calling the ordinate the *y*-axis, we will call it the **imaginary axis**. Finally, rather than calling the coordinate system the Cartesian coordinate system, we will call it the **complex plane**.

A plot of several complex numbers on the complex plane is given below.

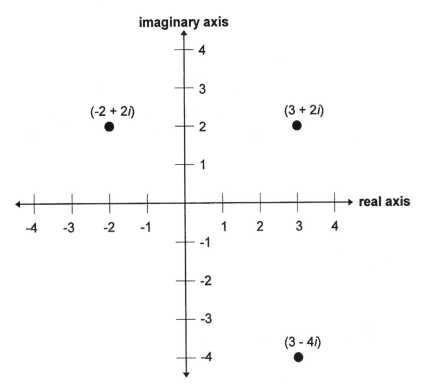

There is one more definition to complete our discussion of complex numbers. As shown in chapter 2, the magnitude (or absolute value) of a number is the distance the number is away from zero on the number line. The magnitude of a number must always be positive, since a negative distance does not make sense. As a review,

$$| 3 | = 3 \qquad | -14 | = 14$$

DISTANCE IS REAL

With the definition of the magnitude of a number, the help of a graph, and knowledge of the Pythagorean Theorem, we may find the magnitude of any complex number. The same absolute value sign used for real numbers is also used to find the magnitude of a complex number.

Note that the magnitude of a complex number must be a real number, since it represents the distance from 0 on the number line, or the distance from (0,0) on the complex plane. We can understand distance so it must be real.

$$| 3 - 4i | = | 3 + 4i | = | -3 - 4i | = | -3 + 4i | = 5$$

$$| 4 - 3i | = | 4 + 3i | = | -4 - 3i | = | -4 + 3i | = 5$$

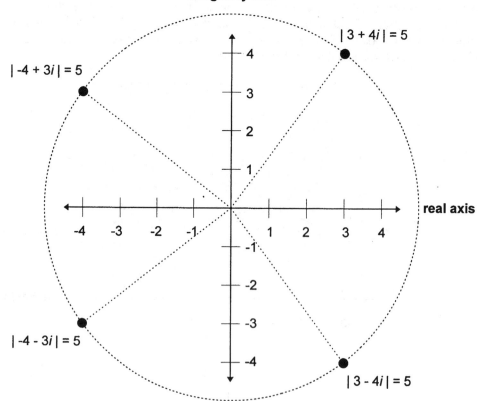

The length of every dashed line in the above figure is 5. In general, we may use the Pythagorean Theorem to state that for any complex number $a + bi$,

$$| a + bi | = \sqrt{a^2 + b^2}$$

Note that the sign of *a*, or *b* does not matter in determining the magnitude of the complex number, since both *a* and *b* are squared.

Furthermore, using trigonometry we find that the angle formed by plotting a complex number is as follows.

$$\theta = \tan^{-1}\left(\frac{b}{a}\right)$$

Therefore, any complex number may be represented by a magnitude and an angle.

$$|\,4 + 3i\,| = \sqrt{4^2 + 3^2} = 5$$

$$\theta = \tan^{-1}\left(\frac{3}{4}\right) \approx 36.87°$$

Using a different notation, 4 + 3*i* may also be represented as 5 ∠ 36.87°. This new notation is called **polar** notation, and is further explained in the next chapter. The angle is always measured from the positive portion of the real axis. You must be careful to ensure that the angle is correct, rather than merely relying on the answer provided by a calculator. Remember that $\tan^{-1}$ in the above equation gives the angle of a created triangle, not the angle from the positive *x*-axis.

Example - Graphing Complex Numbers

Verify that the following statements are true using calculations,
and plotting each complex number on the complex plane.

$$|\,12 + 5i\,| = 13 \angle 22.62°$$

$$|\,5 - 12i\,| = 13 \angle\text{-}67.38° \text{ or } 13 \angle 292.62°$$

$$|\,\text{-}5 - 12i\,| = 13 \angle 247.38°$$

$$|\,\text{-}12 + 5i\,| = 13 \angle 157.38°$$

Answer: (plot not shown)

19-6 Summary

This chapter has shown that it was necessary to invent imaginary numbers to solve some algebraic equations. Thankfully, there are no more new number inventions. **Every algebraic equation may be solved with the invention of the imaginary symbol *i*.** This statement answers question #5 from section **19-2**. The symbol *i* obeys all of the rules shown in previous chapters for real numbers and variables. You can now solve any quadratic equation by using the quadratic formula, even though the answer may contain an imaginary part in addition to the real part.

Complex numbers are often used in scientific and engineering fields, especially electrical engineering. The next chapter is exciting. We are only one step away from Calculus.

Important Definitions

Imaginary Number

Complex Number

Complex Conjugate

Complex Plane

Polar Notation

You should be able to...

1. Perform any math operation with complex numbers

2. Simplify i raised to any integer power

3. Find the complex conjugate of any number

4. Graph complex numbers on the complex plane

5. Find the magnitude of any complex number

6. Write any complex number using polar notation

7. Understand why imaginary numbers are necessary

Finding Geometry Using Algebra

20-1 Introduction

The information presented in section **20-2** is seldom presented at any educational level since its practical importance is easily summarized in one important equation, Euler's Identity. However, this section provides insights which not only allow you to appreciate some of the beauty of mathematics, but also allow a broader mathematical understanding. Section **20-3** uses Euler's Identity to simplify math operations using complex numbers.

It is assumed that the reader understands complex numbers as presented in chapter 19, and followed the development of the natural logarithm in section **18-3**. The development in the following section closely follows that given in Volume I of the *Feynman Lectures on Physics*.

20-2 Finding Geometry with Complex Exponents

What does it mean to raise a number to an imaginary exponent? We have no idea what the following value represents (or equals), even assuming *a* and *b* are known constants. 10 has been chosen since it is the base of the common logarithm, and it seems convenient.

$$10^{(a+ib)}$$

However, we do know that mathematical symbols must obey certain rules. Using the Law of Exponents (as given in chapter 8), we can rewrite the above equation.

$$10^{(a+ib)} = 10^a \bullet 10^{ib}$$

The value of *a* is a real number, so 10^a is not difficult to find for any value *a*. However, 10^{ib} is completely unknown, since we do not know the value of any number with an imaginary exponent. Since a complex number is the most general form of any number, we will assume that 10^{ib} equals some complex number with real part *x* and imaginary part *y*.

$$10^{ib} = x + iy$$

- or -

$$10^{-ib} = x - iy$$

Is it necessary to find the values of both x and y to find the value of 10^{ib} ? To answer this question, first rewrite the equation using the rule that any number raised to the zero power must equal 1. This will establish a relationship between x and y.

$$10^0 = 1 = (10^{ib})(10^{-ib}) = (x + iy)(x - iy) = x^2 + y^2 = 1$$

Therefore, if either variable (x or y) is known, the other variable can easily be found. Now we need to determine a value for one of the variables.

In section **18-3** we found that for very small a,

$$10^a = 1 + 2.302585a$$

We will now assume that this equation is true for both real and complex a. We do not have any proof of this assumption, but we'll see what happens. (Advanced mathematics may be used to prove that the equation is indeed true for very small real and complex numbers.)

$$10^{ia} = 1 + 2.302585 \bullet ia$$

With this formula, it is relatively simple to find values for 10^{ia} for a given value a. Remember, a must be a small number as shown in section **18-3**. Since the formula is valid for small a, we will choose $a = 1/524{,}288$. Any smaller value would be equally valid.

$$10^{i/524{,}288} = 1 + 2.302585 \bullet i / 524{,}288$$

$$= 1 + 0.00000439i$$

We now have a valid answer for the value of 10 raised to one unique complex exponent. Using rules of exponents, we may now find ensuing values of greater exponents. For example,

$$10^{i/262{,}144} = (10^{i/524{,}288})^2$$
$$10^{i/131{,}072} = (10^{i/262{,}144})^2$$
$$10^{i/65{,}536} = (10^{i/131{,}072})^2$$
$$10^{i/32{,}768} = (10^{i/65{,}536})^2$$
$$10^{i/16{,}384} = (10^{i/32{,}768})^2$$
$$10^{i/8{,}192} = (10^{i/16{,}384})^2$$

This process may be repeated by successively squaring values. A detailed chart is provided.

a	Real Part of 10^{ia} (x)	Imag. Part of 10^{ia} (y)
0.0	1.00000	0.00000
0.1	0.97361	0.22823
0.2	0.89582	0.44441
0.3	0.77075	0.63714
0.4	0.60500	0.79623
0.5	0.40731	0.91329
0.6	0.18812	0.98215
0.7	-0.04100	0.99916
0.8	-0.26796	0.96343
0.9	-0.48077	0.87685
1.0	-0.66820	0.74398
1.2	-0.92922	0.36952
1.4	-0.99664	-0.08193
1.6	-0.85640	-0.51632
1.8	-0.53772	-0.84312
2.0	-0.10701	-0.99426
2.2	0.34599	-0.93824
2.4	0.72691	-0.68673
2.6	0.95030	-0.29214
2.8	0.98657	0.16332
3.0	0.81121	0.58475
3.2	0.46684	0.88434
3.4	0.02519	0.99968
3.6	-0.42170	0.90673
3.8	-0.78074	0.62486
4.0	-0.97710	0.21280
4.2	-0.96987	-0.24360
4.4	-0.76058	-0.64925
4.6	-0.39281	-0.91962
4.8	0.05680	-0.99839
5.0	0.49458	-0.86913
5.2	0.82931	-0.55879
5.4	0.99125	-0.13202
5.6	0.94665	0.32225
5.8	0.70482	0.70938
6.0	0.31614	0.94871

The above table is interesting. Both real and imaginary parts alternate between positive and negative values. Furthermore, all values are less than or equal to 1.

It is insightful to plot both real and imaginary parts of 10^{ia} for the various values *a*. From the table and plot, we find that the real part of 10^{ia} first equals 0 at approximately *a* = 0.68. However, 10^{ia} also equals 0 for other values of *a*. A plot is given on the following page.

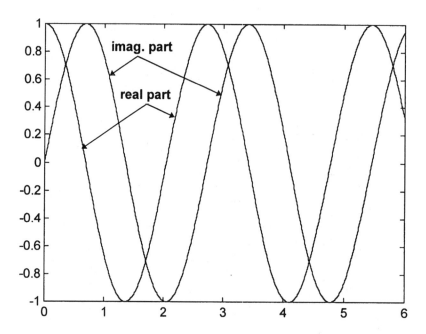

Does it makes sense that the plot repeats itself as *a* is increased? From the discussion of imaginary numbers in section **19-2**, we found that values of the imaginary number (*i*) repeat as its powers are increased or decreased by integers. Therefore, a repetitive (or **periodic**) plot should not be surprising.

You may want to plot the different values of 10^{ia} with the real part on the *x*-axis, and the imaginary part on the *y*-axis. The result will be a circle of radius one. Does this make sense?

The above plot also looks very similar to the sine and cosine plot given in section **17-6**. The only difference is the spacing of the *x*-axis. Now, a wonderful discovery is made. By changing the base from the common logarithm of 10 to the natural logarithm of *e* and measuring angles in radians, the plot (i.e. real and imaginary parts of e^{ia}) exactly matches that of the sine and cosine. We may then write an amazing but true equation which relates Algebra and Geometry, **Euler's Identity**. Leonhard Euler (1707-1783) is one of the greatest mathematicians who ever lived.

Euler's Identity

$$e^{i\theta} = \cos \theta + i \sin \theta$$

θ is in radians
e is the natural logarithm base ≈ 2.71828

A fact from Geometry (and Trigonometry), developed originally with the Pythagorean Theorem, has been verified independently with Algebra. This one equation is used extensively in scientific applications. This is because it is often necessary to use a sine and cosine to represent something physical that changes periodically (i.e. weather, electric current, stock market, etc.). However, it is also difficult to work algebraically with sine and cosine functions. Therefore, the form $e^{i\theta}$ may be used instead of the cosine and sine. Then, Algebra may be used to solve equations containing exponents without directly working with the cosine and sine functions. Complex equation solving becomes much more simple.

Examples - Working with Euler's Identity

$| e^{i\theta} | = (\cos^2 \theta + \sin^2 \theta)^{0.5} = 1$ for any value of θ

$e^{i\pi} = \cos \pi + i \sin \pi = -1$

$e^{i\pi/2} = \cos \pi/2 + i \sin \pi/2 = i$

Example - Plotting

Plot $5e^{i\pi/4}$.

Answer:
- The angle is $\pi/4$ which also equals $45°$
- $e^{i\theta}$ represents a complex number, and must be plotted on the complex plane
- The point must be a distance of 5 from the origin since $| 5e^{i\pi/4} | = | 5 | | 1 | = 5$
- Real coordinate $= 5 \bullet \cos (\pi / 4) = 3.5355$
- Imaginary coordinate $= 5 \bullet \sin (\pi / 4) = 3.5355$

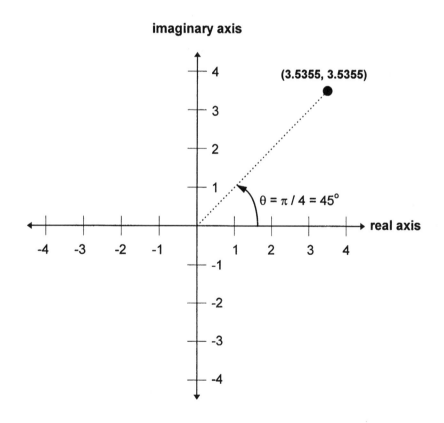

The previous example shows that any complex number may be written in an alternate form.

Representing a Complex Number with a Complex Exponent

$$x + yi = re^{i\theta}$$

where

$$r = \sqrt{x^2 + y^2} \quad \text{and} \quad \theta = \tan^{-1}(y/x)$$

$$x = r \bullet \cos\theta \qquad y = r \bullet \sin\theta$$

20-3   Using Complex Exponents

If it is necessary to add or subtract complex numbers, it is most simple to keep the numbers in the following form.

$$x + yi$$

Real parts and imaginary parts may then be separately added (or subtracted) to obtain the final complex number result. A complex number written as such is in **rectangular** form. It is called rectangular form since the number may be easily plotted on the complex plane.

However, if it is necessary to multiply or divide complex numbers, it is often most convenient to use the form $re^{i\theta}$ and apply the laws regarding exponents. This form is also called **polar** form. As stated in section **19-3**, polar form may also be written using a slightly different notation.

HELPFUL TIP!

$$re^{i\theta} = r \angle \theta$$

A number in polar form may be plotted on the complex plane by moving a distance r from the origin at an angle of θ from the real number axis. Therefore, in the previous example, it was not necessary to calculate x and y coordinates. Rather, the fact that $r = 5$, and $\theta = (\pi / 4)$ was sufficient for the plot. θ may be expressed in degrees or radians.

Verify the following examples. θ is in degrees in the first example box and radians in the second example. In general, if the exponent of e is in radians, the angle will be written using a coefficient for π. (e.g. written $e^{i\pi/2}$ rather than $e^{i(1.570795)}$)

Example - Adding Complex Numbers

$$10e^{i53.13} + 5e^{i(-135)} = ?$$

$$10e^{i53.13} = 6 + 8i$$

$$5e^{i(-135)} = -3.535 - 3.535i$$

$$6 + 8i + (-3.535 - 3.535i) = 2.465 + 4.465i$$

Answer: $2.465 + 4.465i = 5.10e^{i61.10}$

Example - Multiplying Complex Numbers

$(8 + 10i) (5 - 4i)$ = ?

$= 80 + 18i$ (rectangular form)

Answer: $= 82e^{i0.0704\pi}$ (polar form)

- or -

$8 + 10i$ = $12.806\, e^{i0.2852\pi}$

$5 - 4i$ = $6.403\, e^{-i0.2148\pi}$

so $(12.81\, e^{i0.2852\pi}) (6.4\, e^{-i0.2148\pi})$

$= 82e^{i0.0704\pi}$ (polar form)

Answer: $= 82 + 18i$ (rectangular form)

Verify that you can obtain the following answer by first converting the numbers to polar form. After the answer is in polar form, convert the number back into rectangular form.

Example - Dividing Complex Numbers

$(6 + 3i) / (3 - i)$ = ?

Answer: $1.5 + 1.5i$

First convert the number into polar form, and then use the laws of exponents to verify the following example.

Example - Raising a Complex Number to an Integer Power

$(3 + 4i)^4$ = ?

Answer: $-527 - 336i$

In general, the form of the answer should be in the same form as the question. If the question stated numbers in rectangular form, the answer should be in rectangular form. The same is true for polar form. The imaginary number i may be written before or after its coefficient.

Make sure than when converting a number from rectangular to polar form that the proper angle is obtained. For example, $(3 + 4i)$ and $(-3 - 4i)$ both have a magnitude of 5. Furthermore, $\tan^{-1}(4/3) = \tan^{-1}(-4/-3) = 53.13°$. However, the angle of $(3 + 4i)$ is $53.13°$, but the angle of $(-3 - 4i)$ is $233.13°$ or $-126.87°$. You must always determine in which quadrant the complex number lies to find the proper angle. $(3 + 4i)$ is in the first quadrant, so the angle must be between $0°$ and $90°$. However, $(-3 - 4i)$ is in the third quadrant, so the angle must be between $180°$ and $270°$.

20-4   Summary

This chapter has developed an amazing equation which relates Geometry (and Trigonometry) and Algebra. You do not need to know exactly how to perform this informal derivation. However, a basic understanding and an appreciation for the harmony in mathematics is very helpful. In advanced mathematics, complex exponents are usually always used with the base *e* because of its unique relation to the trigonometric functions.

This chapter also showed how and when to use complex exponents. Complex exponents make the solution to some algebraic and trigonometric problems much more simple. Rectangular and polar forms may be used as necessary.

Everything that we need to move on to Calculus has been explained. We now move to the final step in our mathematical development.

You should be able to ...

1. Have a basic understanding of the origin of Euler's Identity

2. Plot complex numbers given in rectangular or polar form

3. Convert numbers between rectangular and polar form

4. Know when to use rectangular or polar form for a given math operation

---

Introducing Calculus

21-1 What More is There to Learn?

Let's quickly review the lessons of mathematics already covered in this text.

- Part I thoroughly covered elementary math.

- Part II provided a complete introduction to Algebra, along with the essential topics in Geometry and Trigonometry.

- The advanced algebraic concepts of logarithms and complex numbers were developed in Part III.

- Part III also gave a glimpse at the harmony of mathematics. The equation $e^{i\theta} = \cos\theta + i\sin\theta$ found in chapter 20, is both incredible and remarkably useful.

The final subject of this text is Calculus. A typical engineering, physics, or math major takes three or four college level Calculus courses over the span of two years. An introductory college level Calculus text commonly exceeds over 1000 pages. Advanced Calculus texts also exist and typically consist of 1000 additional pages. Furthermore, the advanced foundation of Calculus is used in such advanced math courses as:

- Differential Equations
- Discrete Math
- Laplace Transforms

- Applied Numerical Analysis
- Vector Analysis
- Probability and Random Processes

Because of the vast amount of information contained in the subject, it is not practical for this book to thoroughly present Calculus Therefore, this book presents the essentials for increased learning. Often, students of Calculus memorize procedures for obtaining solutions, but do not understand why they are solving such problems in the first place. By removing extreme details, and explaining Calculus concepts in words, this book will provide you with a quick but important overview. This overview will help you tremendously as you move on to further study.

As Algebra was a first step, so Calculus is a first step to more advanced mathematics. Calculus is widely used in science and engineering. Elements of Calculus are also used in many areas of business. Do not think that Calculus is too difficult to learn or too impractical. Neither of these ideas is true.

21-2   An Essential Introduction to Calculus

Calculus was invented independently by the German Gottfried Leibniz and by the Englishman Isaac Newton in the late 1600s. Calculus extensively uses the concept of functions which was introduced in chapter 13 and plotted in chapter 14. Methods of Calculus can be used to determine two features of a function.

Two Features of a Function Found with Calculus
1.   The slope of a line tangent to a function at any one point
2.   The area between a section of the function and the *x*-axis

The figure below graphically shows each of the two unknown properties of a function which can be found using Calculus. Note that the slope of the tangent line is found *at one point*, P_1. However, the area of a section is found *between two points* on the function, P_2 and P_3.

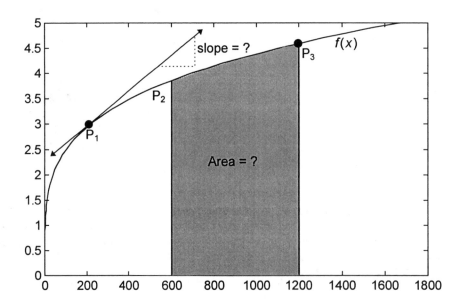

The concept of a tangent line may be a little confusing. As you remember from Geometry, a tangent to a circle touches a circle in only one point. To find the tangent line, imagine drawing a circle which touches the function at the point of interest. The tangent to the drawn circle will then be the tangent line of the function.

A function with three of many possible tangent lines is given in the following figure. No circles have been drawn, but you may draw them in if necessary to help you understand tangent lines. The function plotted is $f(x) = x^2 - 8x + 12$. Tangent lines are explained more fully in the next chapter.

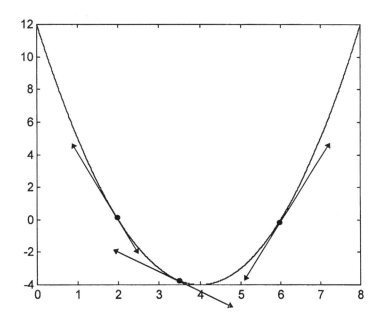

We previously stated that Calculus was a huge subject, whose thorough explanation requires thousands of pages of complicated mathematics. We then stated that all of Calculus is used to find two simple attributes of a function, namely the slope of a line tangent at a point and the area under a function between two points. Does this seem like a contradiction? It is not. Both statements are completely true.

The slope of a line that is tangent to a function at a point is called the **derivative** of the function. The derivative of a function is represented by the symbol ($'$) after the function. The process of finding a derivative is called **differentiation**. $f'(x)$ is read aloud "the derivative of $f(x)$" or "f prime of x."

function: $f(x)$

slope at a point x, or the derivative of function, $f(x)$: $f'(x)$

The area between a section of a function and the x-axis is called the **integral** of the function. The symbol $\int_a^b f(x)\,dx$ represents the integral of $f(x)$, and is read aloud "the integral of f of x". Remember that the area of a function lies between two points on the x-axis. Those points are labeled a and b.

The process of finding the answer to an integral is called **integration**. The points a and b, or the bounds of the area on the x-axis, are called the **limits of integration**. The upper limit is written above the integral sign (b), and lower limit is written below the integral sign (a).

If a and b are specified, the integral is called a **definite integral** since the area that needs to be found is completely defined. Sometimes $\int$ is shown without any values of a and b. This is called an **indefinite integral** since the area boundaries are not specified. As you may guess, it is impossible to find an exact number answer to an indefinite integral, but it will prove useful.

Note that dx follows $f(x)$ in the integral sign. The use of dx will be clarified in chapters 22 and 23.

The Derivative and Integral in Calculus

Function: $f(x)$

Derivative of function: $f'(x)$

Indefinite integral: $\int f(x)\,dx$

Definite integral: $\int_{a}^{b} f(x)\,dx$

The definite integral above is valid for any values of b and a. However, it is assumed that $b > a$ so that the area is found in moving from left to right on the x-axis. If $a > b$, then the integral still represents the area under the function, but the area is found by moving right to left on the x-axis. To make this distinction, the integral's sign is reversed. In general, we may state:

$$\int_{a}^{b} f(x)\,dx = -\int_{b}^{a} f(x)\,dx$$

A negative area does not make sense, but the negative sign is necessary to indicate the order of the limits. As expected, the magnitude of the integral remains the same.

The following examples will help clarify some of the preceding definitions.

<u>Example - Finding the Derivative</u>

What is the derivative at $x = 3$ of the following plotted function?

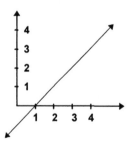

From the plot, we see that the function is a straight line. Therefore, a line tangent to any point on the function will plot directly on top of the function. Therefore, the derivative of the line at any point will be a constant equal to the slope of the function. (This is true for all linear functions.)

From the plot we may obtain the two ordered pairs (2,1) and (4,3). Using the equation for the slope of a line developed in section **14-3**, we may find the derivative.

$$\text{slope} \;=\; \text{derivative} \;=\; \frac{3-1}{4-2} \;=\; 1 = f'(x)$$

Answer: 1

Example - Finding the Derivative

What is $f'(4)$ if $f(x) = -2x - 1$?

In this example, we have another straight line. Furthermore, it is given in the slope-intercept form $y = mx + b$ as shown in chapter 14. Therefore, without even drawing a plot we see that the slope $= m = -2$ for any point on the line.

Answer: -2

Example - Finding an Integral

What is $\int\limits_{2}^{4} f(x)\,dx$ if $f(x) = x - 1$ as shown in the plot below?

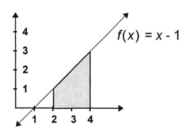

We may find the area using methods established in Geometry. By using the formula for the area of a trapezoid, or separating the area into a rectangle and triangle, we find that the area is $(2)(1) + 1/2\,(2)(2) = 4$. The area under the function is the answer to the integral.

Answer: 4

Example - Finding an Integral

What is $\int\limits_{4}^{2} f(x)\,dx$ if $f(x) = x - 1$?

This is the same function as the previous example. However, the limits of integration are reversed. (The lower limit of 4 is greater than the upper limit of 2.) Therefore, the answer is the negative area under the function.

Answer: -4

21-3 Summary of the Introduction

Remember the two fundamental questions that Calculus answers as given in **21-2**. The concept of what needs to be found is straightforward, but finding slopes and areas can become very complicated. Linear equations have been used exclusively in this chapter, since the slope of a linear function or the area under a linear function may be found using simple Algebra or Geometry. However, there is a need to develop procedures for finding slopes and areas of more complicated functions.

Recall that a function may be developed from any equation. Therefore, we must be able to find slopes and areas for multiple-order polynomials, functions of more than one variable, complex functions, trigonometric functions, and logarithmic functions. Calculus does get quite complicated as functions become more advanced, but everything is manageable assuming you have a firm math foundation, and patiently learn one step at a time.

Think of all of the different types of expressions and equations developed in the first 20 chapters of this book. Calculus can be used to find slopes and areas for all of them. Now the question is, "What good are finding slopes and areas?" The answer to this question is found in the following chapters.

Welcome to Calculus!

Important Definitions

Derivative

Integral

Indefinite Integral

Definite Integral

Limits of Integration

You should be able to ...

1. Understand the basic properties of a function that may be found using Calculus

2. Find the derivative of a linear function using Algebra

3. Find the integral of a simple function using Geometry

4. Realize that Calculus is an enormous, yet essential subject to learn

$$ $$

22

The Derivative

22-1   Introduction

This chapter will expand on the concept of the derivative which was introduced in chapter 21. Remember that this text provides an elementary introduction to Calculus. Therefore, this chapter will briefly describe some of the many sub-topics of Calculus. Each of these sub-topics would require an entirely separate chapter to be explained thoroughly with the necessary mathematical rigor. However, this chapter will provide a good introduction for using derivatives.

Calculus is often divided into the two tasks of working with derivatives and working with integrals. The terms **Differential Calculus** and **Integral Calculus** are even used to separate the two basic **areas**. Differential Calculus is the focus of this chapter, and Integral Calculus is the focus of the next chapter. You will learn that these topics are intimately related.

22-2   Development of the Derivative Using Limits

We first need to develop a better mathematical procedure for both describing and finding the slope of a line tangent to a function. A general function $f(x)$ is plotted below, and it is desired to find the slope of the tangent line at point z, or $f'(z_x)$

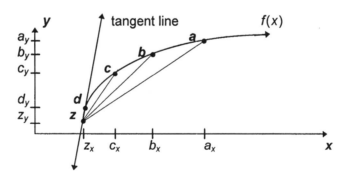

Several additional points have been plotted on the function, namely points a, b, c, and d. As shown in chapter 14, it is simple to find the slope of a line when two ordered pairs are known. For instance the slope m_{za} of the line extending from z to a is given by the following equation. Note that the coordinates of a are written (a_x, a_y) and the coordinates of z are written (z_x, z_y)

$$ m_{za} = \frac{a_y - z_y}{a_x - z_x} $$

Finding the slope of the line connecting points *zb*, *zc*, or *zd* is also simple. We see from the figure that as the points on the function become closer to the point *z*, the slope of the line created by connecting the points becomes closer to the slope of the tangent line at *z*. For example, the line connecting points *zd* is much closer in slope to the tangent line than the line connecting points *za*. Therefore, to find the tangent at any point, we simply have to find the slope of the line connecting the desired point and a very nearby point.

The problem is that we need to define 'very nearby'. In mathematics we want to describe everything with numbers rather than adjectives, so what number should we use to describe 'very nearby' ? We know that the closer the second ordered pair is to *z*, the better the estimate of the tangent line. However, point *z* itself cannot be used since a straight line is determined by two unique points. If we do use the ordered pair at point *z* twice in the calculation of the slope, we obtain 0/0. We have no idea how to calculate 0/0.

$$m_{zz} = \frac{z_y - z_y}{z_x - z_x} = \frac{0}{0} = ?$$

To solve this difficult problem, mathematicians have introduced a very powerful notation called a limit. The **limit** of a function is the value the function approaches, but never exactly reaches. Limits are not complicated, although the notation at first may look intimidating. Several examples are given below.

Examples - Using Limits

$$\lim_{x \to 5} x = 5$$

$$\lim_{x \to 1} 2x + 1 = 3$$

$$\lim_{x \to 5} \frac{1}{x} = \frac{1}{5}$$

$$\lim_{x \to 0^+} \frac{1}{x} = \infty$$

$$\lim_{x \to 0^-} \frac{1}{x} = -\infty$$

$$\lim_{x \to 0} \frac{1}{x} = \text{<does not exist>}$$

As you can see, the limit of an expression (or function) is abbreviated with the word **lim**. Below the word *lim* is the value that the variable approaches. The first example would be read aloud "the limit of *x* as *x* approaches 5 equals 5". This means that as *x* becomes as close as possible to 5, the answer will equal 5. The value of *x* may begin at 4.9, then 4.999, then 4.9999999, etc., always becoming closer to 5. The value of *x* may begin slightly higher than 5 such as 5.1, then 5.01, then 5.000001. In either circumstance, the value of 5 will be approached in the limit.

With this explanation, the second and third examples should be clear. However, at this point you may be thinking that limits are quite useless. All you seemingly must do is substitute the value that the variable approaches into the variable. For example,

$$(2x + 1) \text{ as } x \to 1 \text{ is } (2(1) + 1) = 3$$

Nevertheless, limits are very useful, as the third and fourth examples demonstrate. The final three examples all use a function in the form $1/x$ as $x \to 0$. But this statement alone is not entirely clear, since we do not know where to start approaching x. For example, if 0 is approached by starting with positive values, we obtain the following progression.

$$\frac{1}{1} = 1 \qquad \frac{1}{0.1} = 10 \qquad \frac{1}{0.01} = 100 \qquad \frac{1}{0.001} = 1000 \qquad \frac{1}{0.0001} = 10,000$$

Therefore, it appears that as x approaches 0, the answer is ∞. However, if 0 is approached from negative values, we obtain the progression given below.

$$-\frac{1}{1} = -1 \qquad -\frac{1}{0.1} = -10 \qquad -\frac{1}{0.01} = -100 \qquad -\frac{1}{0.001} = -1000 \qquad -\frac{1}{0.0001} = -10,000$$

Therefore, it appears that as x approaches 0, the answer is $-\infty$. However, this answer conflicts with our previous answer of positive infinity. So which answer is correct?

To distinguish which side 0 is approached from, a small + or - is written in the upper right-hand side of the number 0. This makes the answer clear. In the third example 0 is approached from positive numbers, and therefore the answer is positive infinity. In the fourth example 0 is approached from the negative side of the number line, and the answer is negative infinity.

In the last example, the problem does not specify on which side of the number line to approach 0. Since different answers are obtained if 0 is approached from the left or right side of the number line, the limit does not exist. If the same answers are obtained if the limit is approached from the left or right side of the number line, the limit does exist, and a $^+$ or $^-$ indicating direction of approach is not necessary.

You have been given a brief introduction into the powerful concept of limits. Limits allow symbols such as ∞ to be used in calculations.

STEP - BY - STEP

Calculating the limit of a function or expression

1. If possible, reduce the equation using factorization and cancellation.

2. Substitute the value the variable approaches into the equation.

3. If the obtained answer is legal (i.e. not divided by 0, or ∞ / ∞, etc.), then the final solution is obtained directly by the substitution from step #1.

4. If the obtained answer is in an illegal form, then substitute values which are close to the limit, and determine the answer that is approached. If necessary, approach the limit from the appropriate side of the number line.

Verify the following examples using your knowledge of limits.

<u>Examples - Using Limits</u>

$$\lim_{x \to 2} \frac{x^2 - 4}{x - 2} = 4$$

$$\lim_{x \to \infty} \frac{3x + 5}{6x - 8} = 0.5$$

$$\lim_{x \to 0^+} \frac{\sin x}{x} = 1 \quad (x \text{ is in radians})$$

Now let's return to our problem of finding the slope of the tangent line. The slope of the tangent line at a point is close to the slope of the line formed by connecting two points which are nearby. Using limits, we can allow the coordinates of one point to approach the coordinates of the original point. This method will then allow us to obtain the slope of the tangent line. Study the diagram below where z has coordinates (x_0, y_0) and a has coordinates (x_1, y_1) on the function $f(x)$.

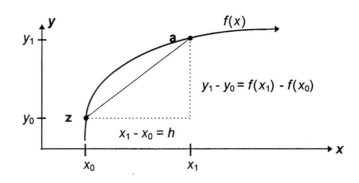

$$m_{za} = \frac{y_1 - y_0}{x_1 - x_0} = \frac{f(x_1) - f(x_0)}{h} = \frac{f(x_0 + h) - f(x_0)}{h}$$

Using this form of the equation for the slope of line extending from z to a, we may finally write the equation for the slope of the tangent line at a point.

Equation of Slope of Tangent Line to $f(x)$ at x_0

$$m_{\tan} = \lim_{h \to 0} \frac{f(x_0 + h) - f(x_0)}{h}$$

The slope of the tangent line has several popular notations. The following forms of this slope, or the derivative of the function $f(x)$, are equivalent. Remember that the slope is the change in y divided by the change in x. The final form is read aloud "the derivative of f of x with respect to x."

Equivalent Forms of the Derivative of *y* = *f*(*x*)

$$m_{\tan} = f'(x) = \lim_{\Delta x \to 0} \frac{\Delta y}{\Delta x} = \frac{dy}{dx} = \frac{d}{dx}[y] = \frac{d}{dx}[f(x)]$$

Much information has been developed in this section. To summarize, the derivative of a function at a point is the same as the slope of the line tangent at that point. The derivative is found by calculating the slope of the line as the change in *x* approaches zero. You should know the different ways of writing the derivative of a function as given in the box above.

Please do not worry about the apparent difficulty of finding slopes using limits. In later sections, we will develop shortcuts for calculating derivatives. However, first you need to understand why the derivative is so important.

22-3   Usefulness of the Derivative

IMPORTANT SECTION !

Let's review a little about what we have already learned. In Algebra we found that the slope of any horizontal line equals 0. Therefore, the derivative at any point on the horizontal line also equals 0.

A straight line in the general form *f*(*x*) = *y* = *mx* + *b* has a slope of *m*. Therefore, the derivative at any point on the straight line is a constant which also equals *m*. So, the derivative of any linear function is simply equal to the slope of the function.

However, a function, *f*(*x*), with a degree greater than one (i.e. a function that curves) does not have a constant slope. Therefore, we use limits to find the slope of a line that is tangent to *f*(*x*), and we call that slope the derivative of the function, *f'*(*x*). We can simplify the wording a bit, and also call *f'*(*x*) the slope of *f*(*x*) at any point *x*. Therefore, **the derivative of a function is the same as the instantaneous rate of change of that function**. But is knowing the rate of change of something useful in everyday life? Let's look at an example.

Assume that you plan on skydiving out of an airplane that is flying 5000 feet high. You read in a book that you need to pull the cord to open the parachute when your distance from the ground is between 1000 and 800 feet. Furthermore, your doctor told you to make sure that you do not fall at a speed of more than 700 feet per second, otherwise the tubes in your ears may erupt and cause pain. Would it be all right for you to skydive at 5000 feet? If you do, how will you know when to pull open the parachute?

By looking in any physics book, you will learn that for any object that is free-falling to earth:

$$\text{Position at any time } t = h(t) = -16t^2 + \text{initial height}$$

Therefore, since your initial height is 5000 feet, you may plot your height for any time *t*. This plot of *h*(*t*) = -16*t*^{2} + 5000 is given below.

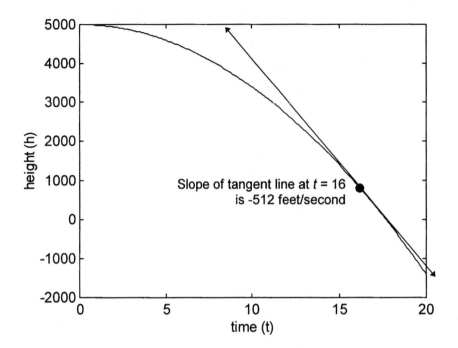

By looking at the plot, you can see that after jumping out of the plane, you should quickly count to about 16 seconds before opening your shoot since $h(16) = (-16)(16)^2 + 5000 = 904$ feet. Just don't count much past 17, otherwise you will hit the ground.

Ok, but will the tubes in your ears erupt? How can we find the speed of falling by only knowing $h(t)$? After thinking a little while, you may realize that speed is the rate of position change. If you move 55 miles in one hour, your speed is 55 miles per hour. You also know that the rate of change of any function is found by calculating the derivative.

Therefore, ***velocity is that derivative of the position function***. By using limits, or methods developed in the next section, we find that,

$$\text{velocity} = v(t) = h'(t) = -32t$$

Now we can calculate exactly how fast we will be falling after 16 seconds.

$$v(16) = -32(16) = -512 \text{ feet per second}$$

Since you will open the parachute to slow down after 16 seconds, the fastest that you fall is 512 feet per second. So, your ears should be safe. Jump away!

Acceleration is the rate of velocity change. Can you find the acceleration of anything due to the gravity of the earth using derivatives? (The answer is 32 feet per second per second.)

There are many, many more examples that could be shown. Derivatives are used to calculate rates of change in areas such as satellite orbits, population growth, chemical reactions, pricing, electric circuits, the flow of heat, movement of springs, tumor growth, childhood learning rates, and radioactive dating. The derivative is used to find the rate of change of a function that describes anything!

22-4 Finding the Derivative of a Function

With our previous knowledge, we can already establish two rules for finding derivatives. These rules are given below.

Derivative of Any Constant

$$\frac{d}{dx}[c] = 0$$

Derivative of Any Linear Function

$$\frac{d}{dx}[mx + b] = m$$

Limits are not needed to find the derivative of functions which are straight lines, because the derivative is a constant equal to the line's slope. However, finding derivatives of non-linear functions requires the use of limits. It would be helpful to find a convenient form of solution for the general problem given below.

$$\frac{d}{dx}[x^n] = ?$$

TIME-OUT TO LEARN FACTORIALS AND THE BINOMIAL THEOREM

A detailed development of the answer to the above problem is provided so you see that the solution is obtained by applying math rules, not magic. However, before developing the answer to the question, one important notation and one important formula from Algebra are required. Neither of these were presented in earlier sections of this text. Factorials are normally introduced when learning about probability, (which is not explained in this text).

A **factorial** is the multiplication of a sequence of positive consecutive integers. It is represented by an exclamation point (!) following the greatest integer to be multiplied. By definition 0! = 1.

Definition of a Factorial

For any positive integer *n*,

n! = n (n - 1) (n - 2) . . . (1)

Examples of Factorials

0! = 1

3! = 3 • 2 • 1 = 6

5! = 5 • 4 • 3 • 2 • 1 = 120

The **binomial theorem** is used to raise a binomial to any power. You already know how to calculate a binomial (e.g. $x + 1$) raised to any power by using the Distributive Law of Multiplication. However, when using the distributive law to multiply the same binomial factor many times, terms combine in a known sequence. The binomial theorem establishes this general sequence. This formula is often used in proofs. However, proof of the formula itself is omitted, since that is not the point of this discussion. Note that factorials exist in denominators.

Binomial Theorem

$$(x+h)^n = \frac{x^{n-0} h^0}{0!} + \frac{n\, x^{n-1} h^1}{1!} + \frac{n(n-1)\, x^{n-2} h^2}{2!} + \frac{n(n-1)(n-2)x^{n-3}h^3}{3!} + \dots + \frac{nxh^{n-1}}{1} + \frac{h^n}{1}$$

Finally, we may attempt to determine a general rule for $\frac{d}{dx}[x^n]$, which requires use of the binomial theorem.

First, substitute x^n for $f(x)$ in the limit equation for a derivative (developed in section **22-2**).

$$f'(x) = \lim_{h \to 0} \frac{f(x+h) - f(x)}{h} = \lim_{h \to 0} \frac{(x+h)^n - x^n}{h}$$

Then, expand $(x + h)^n$ using the binomial theorem.

$$f'(x) = \lim_{h \to 0} \frac{\left(x^n + nx^{n-1}h + \dots + nxh^{n-1} + h^n\right) - x^n}{h}$$

Note that x^n cancels with $-x^n$ in the numerator. A factor of h then exists in every term in the numerator and denominator, and therefore may be canceled.

$$f'(x) = \lim_{h \to 0} [nx^{n-1} + \dots + nxh^{n-2} + h^{n-1}]$$

Every term in brackets has an h except the first term. Furthermore, h approaches 0 in the limit. Amazingly, we have a simple answer to our question which is given in the following formula. Based on your knowledge of linear functions, you should verify that the formula is true for $n = 1$.

Power Rule: Derivative of $f(x) = x^n$

$$\frac{d}{dx}[x^n] = nx^{n-1}$$

Example - Finding the Derivative

$$\frac{d}{dx}[x^3] = 3x^2$$

Therefore, if the equation x^3 is plotted, the slope of the tangent line for any value of x is $3x^2$.

Example - Using the Derivative

What is the slope of the tangent line of x^4 at $x = 2$?

$$f(x) = x^4$$

$$\frac{d}{dx}(x^4) = f'(x) = 4x^3$$

$$f'(2) = 4(2)^3 = 4(8) = 32$$

Answer: 32

It is also possible to have derivatives of derivatives. This should not be surprising. A second derivative is represented by a ($''$) preceding the function's argument. $f''(x)$ is read aloud "*f* double prime of *x*", or "the second derivative of *f* of *x*".

$$f''(x) = \frac{d^2}{dx^2}[f(x)]$$

To find the second derivative, simply calculate the derivative once to obtain an intermediate answer. Then, calculate the derivative of the intermediate answer to obtain the final answer. It is also possible to find higher order derivatives following the same procedure. For example,

$$f(x) = x^3 \quad f'(x) = 3x^2 \quad f''(x) = 6x \quad f'''(x) = 6 \quad f''''(x) = 0$$

Below are some of the fundamental rules used for finding derivatives, followed by a few more examples. Note that the derivative of a quantity may be 'distributed' as shown in the second rule below. Verify that this is true for a linear function such as $f(x) = mx + b$.

Rules for Differentiation

$$\frac{d}{dx}[cf(x)] = c\,\frac{d}{dx}[f(x)]$$

$$\frac{d}{dx}[f(x) + g(x)] = \frac{d}{dx}[f(x)] + \frac{d}{dx}g[(x)]$$

$$\frac{d}{dx}[f(x) \bullet g(x)] = f(x)\,\frac{d}{dx}[g(x)] + g(x)\,\frac{d}{dx}[f(x)] \quad \textbf{(product rule)}$$

$$\frac{d}{dx}\left[\frac{f(x)}{g(x)}\right] = \frac{g(x)\dfrac{d}{dx}[f(x)] - f(x)\dfrac{d}{dx}[g(x)]}{[g(x)]^2} \quad \textbf{(quotient rule)}$$

Examples - Differentiation

$$\frac{d}{dx}[3x^2 - 4x + 1] = 6x - 4$$

$$\frac{d}{dx}[(4x^2 - 1)(7x^3 + x)] = (4x^2-1)\frac{d}{dx}[7x^3 + x] + (7x^3 + x)\frac{d}{dx}[4x^2 - 1]$$

$$= (4x^2 - 1)(21x^2 + 1) + (7x^3 + x)(8x)$$

$$= 140x^4 - 9x^2 - 1$$

- or -

$$\frac{d}{dx}[(4x^2 - 1)(7x^3 + x)] = \frac{d}{dx}[28x^5 - 3x^3 - x]$$

$$= 140x^4 - 9x^2 - 1$$

22-5   Derivatives of Special Functions

The following formulas may be proved by substituting $f(x)$ with the appropriate function and using the limit form of the derivative equation. Proofs are not provided here. Once again, remember that the derivative is the slope of the tangent line at a point. These formulas provide a general equation for the slope of a particular function at any point.

Derivatives of Trigonometric Functions

$$\frac{d}{dx}[\sin x] = \cos x \qquad \frac{d}{dx}[\cos x] = -\sin x \qquad \frac{d}{dx}[\tan x] = \sec^2 x$$

$$\frac{d}{dx}[\cot x] = -\csc^2 x \qquad \frac{d}{dx}[\sec x] = (\sec x)(\tan x) \qquad \frac{d}{dx}[\csc x] = (-\csc x)(\cot x)$$

Derivatives of the Natural Log and Exponential Functions

$$\frac{d}{dx}[\ln x] = \frac{1}{x}$$

$$\frac{d}{dx}[a^x] = a^x \ln a \quad (a \text{ is a constant})$$

$$\frac{d}{dx}[e^x] = e^x \quad (e \text{ is the base of the natural log})$$

Note a surprising property of the natural log base e. The derivative of e^x is simply e^x. (Think about what this means graphically.) This is a very useful property in advanced mathematics.

What happens as you find higher order derivatives of the function e^x?

22-6   The Chain Rule

So far, the derivative has only been found for single functions. However, it is possible to have a function of another function as shown in chapter 14. In this case, the chain rule is required to find the derivative.

An example is given below. The argument of the sine function is another function of x, specifically $3x$. Therefore, the derivative must be found using the chain rule.

$$f(x) = \sin 3x$$

The first step in using the chain rule is to find the derivative of the 'outside' function by itself. To help us ignore the 'inside' function, we'll replace the argument with the letter u. Note that the derivative is taken with respect to u, not with respect to x, because of the substitution.

$$\frac{d}{du}[\sin u] = \cos u$$

The second step is to find the derivative of the 'inside' function, or the argument by itself. This is the quantity that u replaced in the previous step.

$$\frac{d}{dx}[3x] = 3$$

Then multiply the two intermediate results to obtain the final answer. We also have to remember to replace u with the original argument, $3x$.

$$f'(x) = 3 \cos 3x$$

Note that by using a substitution of the letter u, we've actually factored the derivative into two separate derivatives.

$$\frac{dy}{dx} = \frac{dy}{du} \bullet \frac{du}{dx}$$

Following is another example. Since a function of x is raised to a power, the chain rule is again required.

$$f(x) = (x^2 + 1)^9$$

First, let $x^2 + 1 = u$. Then find the derivative of the outside function.

$$\frac{d}{du}[u^9] = 9u^8$$

Second, find the derivative of the inside function.

$$\frac{d}{dx}[(x^2 + 1)] = 2x$$

Third, multiply the two previous results to obtain the final result. Don't forget to replace *u*.

$$f'(x) = 9(x^2 + 1)^8 (2x) = 18x(x^2 + 1)^8$$

With practice, it will become easier to recognize functions that require the chain rule. Verify the following examples.

Example - Using the Chain Rule

$$\frac{d}{dx}[\cos(x^2 + 9)] = -\sin(x^2 + 9) \bullet 2x$$

$$\frac{d}{dx}[e^{2x}] = 2e^{2x}$$

22-7   L'Hopital's Rule

In previous sections of this chapter we learned that the derivative allows us to find the instantaneous rate of change of a function. We also learned how to calculate derivatives of many different types of functions. We now find that the derivative is useful in many more areas of mathematics. Some of these areas are described in the remainder of this chapter.

We first learned about limits in section **22-2**. As we found, sometimes the limit of a function's numerator and denominator approach zero, and the form $0 \div 0$ results.   Another form which causes difficulty is an expression in which the limit becomes $\frac{\infty}{\infty}$. To solve such problems we may use L'Hopital's Rule which states (informally):

L'Hopital's Rule

If $\lim f(x) \rightarrow 0$ and $\lim g(x) \rightarrow 0$
- or -
$\lim f(x) \rightarrow \infty$ and $\lim g(x) \rightarrow \infty$

$$\lim \frac{f(x)}{g(x)} = \lim \frac{f'(x)}{g'(x)}$$

In words, if the limit is such that the result of an expression is $\frac{0}{0}$ or $\frac{\infty}{\infty}$, take the derivative of the numerator and the derivative of the denominator separately; then find the limit of the new ratio.

Example - Using L'Hopital's Rule

$$\lim_{x \rightarrow 0} \frac{\sin x}{x} = ?$$

By substituting $x = 0$, we find that the equation results in $\frac{0}{0}$. Using, L'Hopital's rule,

$$\frac{d}{dx}[\sin x] = \cos x$$

$$\frac{d}{dx}[x] = 1$$

Therefore,

$$\lim_{x \to 0} \frac{\sin(x)}{x} = \lim_{x \to 0} \frac{\cos(x)}{1} = 1$$

Answer: 1

Example - Using L'Hopital's Rule

$$\lim_{x \to \infty} \frac{x}{e^x} = ?$$

By substituting $x = \infty$, we find that the equation results in $\frac{\infty}{\infty}$. Therefore, L'Hopital's rule may be applied.

$$\frac{d}{dx}[x] = 1$$

$$\frac{d}{dx}[e^x] = e^x$$

Therefore,

$$\lim_{x \to \infty} \frac{x}{e^x} = \lim_{x \to \infty} \frac{1}{e^x} = 0$$

Answer: 0

By slightly modifying an equation to obtain a form of $\frac{0}{0}$ or $\frac{\infty}{\infty}$, other equations such as $0 \bullet \infty$ may be solved using L'Hopital's Rule. This shows some of the mathematical significance of limits and a further use of derivatives.

22-8 Maxima and Minima

The derivative often assists in plotting a complicated function. Derivatives of a function may be used to indicate the x value where the function changes direction, or tendency to increase or decrease.

The derivative of a function is the slope of the tangent line. Therefore, wherever the derivative of a function equals zero, the tangent line is horizontal and the function must turn. Wherever a function turns, it must contain either a local (or 'relative') maximum or minimum value. We use the word *local*, since a function may have many maxima and minima, just like a roller coaster.

Wherever the derivative is positive, the slope of the tangent line is positive, and the function increases in value as x increases. However, when the derivative is negative, the slope of the tangent line is negative, and the function decreases in value as x increases. An example will help clarify this discussion.

<u>Example - Using Derivatives to Assist in Plotting a Function</u>

Let $f(x) = x^3 - 6x^2 + 9x - 2$

Find where the function turns, and thus has a local maximum or minimum value.

At $x = 2$ will the function be increasing or decreasing?

The function must turn where the derivative is zero. First, find the derivative of the function.

$$\frac{d}{dx}[f(x)] = f'(x) = 3x^2 - 12x + 9$$

Then determine the x value where the derivative equals zero.

$$3x^2 - 12x + 9 = 0$$

$$x^2 - 4x + 3 = 0$$

$$(x - 1)(x - 3) = 0$$

$$x = 1 \text{ or } 3$$

We can find the slope of the tangent line at $x = 2$ to determine if the function is increasing or decreasing at point $x = 2$.

$$f'(2) = 3(2^2) - 12(2) + 9 = -3 < 0$$

Since at $x = 2$ the slope of the tangent line is negative, the function must be decreasing.

Answer: The function turns where the tangent line is horizontal. This occurs at the local maximum $x = 1$ and the local minimum $x = 3$. The function is decreasing at $x = 2$, since $f'(2) < 0$. A plot is given below.

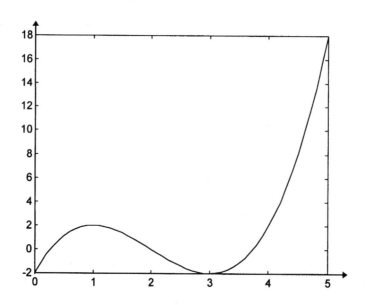

As you can see, derivatives are extremely helpful in plotting. Section **14-5** stated that a polynomial of degree (or order) n has at most $(n - 1)$ turns. You should now understand why this is true. An nth order polynomial has a derivative of order $(n - 1)$. The derivative has $(n - 1)$ solutions, indicating $(n - 1)$ turning points. Using the derivative you can immediately find the x values of the turns in any polynomial plot.

Assume the function reaches a minimum, such as at $x = 3$ in the previous example. Prior to $x = 3$ (and after $x = 1$) the derivatives are all negative since the function is decreasing. Therefore, at a minimum point the derivative increases in value (from negative to zero). So, the rate of change of the derivative, or the second derivative may be used to determine whether a turn occurs at a maximum or minimum point.

At any Maximum or Minimum ($f'(x) = 0$)

if $f''(x) > 0$ then a minimum exists.

if $f''(x) < 0$ then a maximum exists.

In the previous example,

$$f'(x) = 3x^2 - 12x + 9$$

$$f''(x) = 6x - 12$$

$$f''(1) = 6 - 12 = -6 < 0 \quad \text{Therefore, } x = 1 \text{ must be a maximum.}$$

$$f''(3) = 18 - 12 = 6 > 0 \quad \text{Therefore, } x = 3 \text{ must be a minimum.}$$

Verify the following example.

<u>Example - Using Derivatives in Plotting</u>

$$f(x) = -x^2 - x + 5$$

Plot the function and find the maximum and minimum values on the plot.

Answer: $f(x)$ is maximum at $x = -0.5$. There is no minimum (plot not shown).

A thorough explanation of plotting functions with the assistance of derivatives would require much more mathematical rigor (i.e. proofs, definitions, and rule exceptions) and practice. However, the methods presented here provide a very good start in using Calculus to assist in plotting algebraic functions.

The concept of finding maximum and minimum values may even be used in word problems which require the best way to perform a task. Such problems are called **optimization problems**. A sample optimization problem is given.

<u>Example - Optimization Problem</u>

Find the dimensions of a rectangle with perimeter 200 feet whose area is as large as possible.

Such a problem would be impossible to directly solve using only Algebra. However, by writing appropriate functions and utilizing Calculus, such problems may be directly solved. Solving optimization problems does require much practice. However, finding optimum sizes or determining methods to obtain maximum profit are very useful, and may be found using Calculus.

Optimization problems are not pursued further in this text, but are common in most Calculus texts. (Don't get too excited about finding maximum profits. Remember that you first must have a valid function. Obtaining the proper function is sometimes the most difficult task of all.)

22-9   Newton's Method

Calculus may be used to solve many algebraic equations in the form $f(x) = 0$. Remember that this is the point where the function crosses the x-axis, or x-intercept. Algebraic techniques for solving such equations required factorization as shown in the latter sections of chapter 10. However, now the ever-powerful derivative may be utilized.

Look at the function $f(x)$ plotted below. The goal is to find the value of x where the function crosses the x-axis. In other words $f(x) = 0$ for what value of x? To solve such a problem, we begin by choosing a value of x which is at least close to the true solution. This initial guess will be called x_1, and may be obtained from a rough (non-exact) plot of the function.

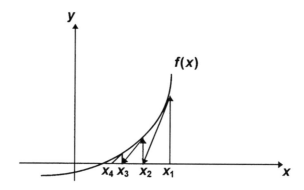

We then may find the tangent line at this point, where the tangent line has slope $f'(x_1)$. We may easily extend this tangent line until it crosses the x-axis. This new point (x_2) is closer to the real solution than the original guess. Therefore, we repeat the process of finding tangent lines and points of intersection, until the point of intersection is satisfactorily close to the desired answer. The figure above should provide clarity to this discussion.

As chapter 14 stated, an equation of a straight line is:

$$y - y_1 = m(x - x_1)$$

Using different notation, the same equation may be written:

$$y - f(x_1) = f'(x_1)(x - x_1)$$

This represents the equation of the tangent line.
The tangent line, $f'(x_1)$, crosses the x-axis at (x_2, 0).
So, we may rewrite the equation using these coordinates:

$$0 - f(x_1) = f'(x_1)(x_2 - x_1)$$

Solving for x_2 yields the result:

$$x_2 = x_1 - \frac{f(x_1)}{f'(x_1)}$$

Therefore, based on an initial guess of x_1, and knowing the function, we may find a closer approximation to the solution, namely x_2.

STEP - BY - STEP

Solving $f(x) = 0$ using Newton's Method

1. Make an initial guess to the answer of x_1.

2. Find the new approximation using the equation: $x_{n+1} = x_n - \dfrac{f(x_n)}{f'(x_n)}$ $n = 1, 2, 3, \ldots$

3. Repeat step #2 until the accuracy of x_{n+1} is satisfactory, or $| x_{n+1} - x_n | <$ the desired accuracy.

Note that it is possible that Newton's Method will not work if an improper guess of x_1 is made. For example, if the guess of x_1 is on the function's maximum or minimum the derivative will be zero. (Then the above expression requires division by zero.) Therefore, you must be careful with your initial guess. Furthermore, the better the guess, the fewer times step #2 must be performed.

Example - Using Newton's Method

Find the solutions to: $f(x) = x^3 - x - 1 = 0$

A plot of the function is given below:

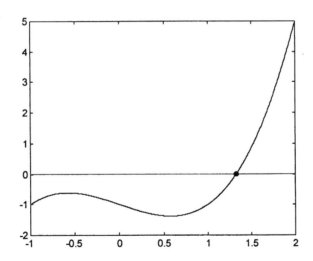

We'll make an initial guess of $x = 2.0$ (even though about 1.3 looks much closer)

Using the formula for Newton's Method:

$$f(x) = x^3 - x - 1$$

$$f'(x) = 3x^2 - 1$$

$$x_{n+1} = x_n - \frac{x_n^3 - x_n - 1}{3x_n^2 - 1}$$

We then make a table of values obtained using the equation developed with Newton's Method.

n	x_n	$f(x_n)$	$f'(x_n)$	x_{n+1}
1	2.000000	5.000000	11.000000	1.545455
2	1.545455	1.145755	6.165289	1.359615
3	1.359615	0.153705	4.545658	1.325801
4	1.325801	0.004625	4.273248	1.324719
5	1.324719	4.66E-06	4.264642	1.324718
6	1.324718	4.74E-12	4.264633	1.324718

We see that after repeating step #2 a total of six times (or six **iterations**), the value of $x = 1.324718$. Furthermore, using 6 decimal places of accuracy, $| x_6 - x_5 | = 0$.

$$\text{Answer:} \quad x = 1.324718$$

A slight modification to Newton's Method may be made to calculate the square root of any number.

STEP - BY - STEP

Solving Square Roots using Newton's Method

Let $\sqrt{a} \approx x_{n+1}$.

1. Make an initial guess of the answer of, x_1.

2. Find the new approximation using the equation $x_{n+1} = \dfrac{1}{2}\left(x_n + \dfrac{a}{x_n} \right)$

3. Repeat step #2 until the value of x_{n+1} is a satisfactory answer.

Verify the following example.

Example - Newton's Method

Use Newton's method to calculate $\sqrt{10}$.

(Hint: An initial guess of 3 is reasonable.)

Answer: ≈ 3.162

22-10 Summary of Derivatives

Much information has been explained in this chapter. The definition of the derivative was repeated on many occasions so that you do not forget the definition while you learn to find derivatives of various functions. You should understand that the derivative can be used to find the instantaneous rate of change of any function. Furthermore, the derivative can be used to solve problems containing limits, assist in plotting functions, and solve algebraic problems in the form $f(x) = 0$. You should clearly understand why the derivative of a function equals 0 wherever a local maximum or minimum value of the function occurs.

Proofs, countless examples, and mathematical rigor have been removed. However, by understanding the material presented in this chapter, you will have a solid foundation for more intense mathematical development. Calculus is a very powerful tool. You have been shown just a few problems that it alone can solve.

You should be able to ...

1. Realize a few of the practical uses for a derivative

2. Calculate problems containing limits

3. Find the derivative of a function in the form x^n (using the Power Rule)

4. Apply various rules to find the derivative of different functions

5. Use L'Hopital's Rule

6. Find the maxima and minima of a function

7. Use Newton's Method to solve an algebraic equation

8. Use Newton's Method to find the square roots of numbers

23

The Integral

23-1   Introduction

As stated in chapter 21, there are two features of a function which may be found with Calculus. The first is the slope of a line tangent to a function at any one point on the function. This slope provides an instantaneous rate of change of the function. Methods for finding the slope, or derivative, were explained in chapter 22.

The second feature that may be found is the area between a section of a function and the x-axis, also called the integral. The focus of this chapter is to determine a method for finding the integral of a function. In Calculus texts, hundreds of pages are usually devoted to finding integrals for specific types of functions. It is beyond the scope of this text to explain all of the different methods for finding integrals. Rather, the concept of an integral, an informal derivation, and its relationship with the derivative are emphasized.

23-2   Development of the Integral Using Limits

Again, the integral of a function is the area under the function. The goal of this section is to find a general method for finding the area under a function. Therefore, we first choose a specific function and find its area. Then, we can create a general method for finding the area under any function.

The chosen function is $f(x) = x^2$ since it is relatively easy to draw. A section of the function and its associated area are shown below.

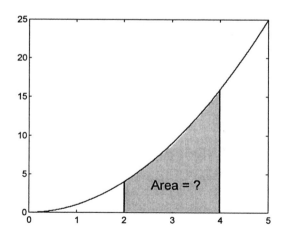

It is necessary to find the area under the function $f(x)$ between $x = 2$ and $x = 4$. Therefore, using notation established in chapter 21, the problem may be written as shown.

$$\int_{2}^{4} x^2 \, dx = ?$$

From Geometry we know how to find areas of circles, rectangles, triangles, and trapezoids. Therefore to find the integral above, it may be wise to split the area into many circles, rectangles, triangles, or trapezoids, and then add the areas of all of the objects together to find the integral. Which shape would be best?

The goal is to make a general rule for finding the area under any function. Circles seem difficult to use, so we won't use them. Every new function would require a newly shaped triangle to fit well under the function, so we won't use triangles. Trapezoids or rectangles seem the best. Rectangles are easier to work with, so we'll split the function into a series of rectangles.

The function has been split into a variety of different equal width rectangles. In the first figure, the function has been split into two rectangles of equal width.

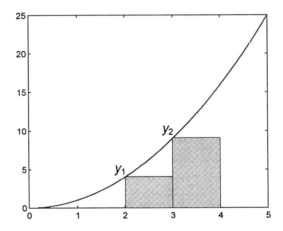

In the following figure, the function has been split into four rectangles of equal width.

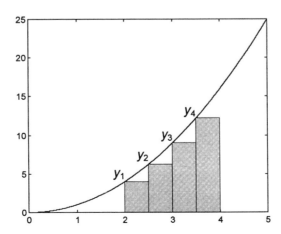

Below, the function has been split into eight rectangles of equal width.

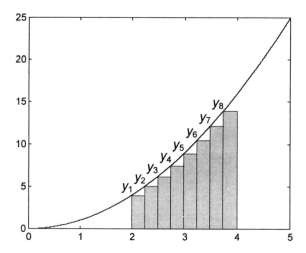

Observe that as the number of equal width rectangles increases, the sum of the areas of the rectangles becomes closer to the actual area under the function. Furthermore, this would be true regardless of the shape of the function.

Before continuing the effort to find a general form for the integral, another notation is introduced. The symbol Σ is used to indicate a **summation** (the sum of many numbers). Σ is the Greek letter "sigma", and therefore the notation may also be called **sigma** notation.

For example to add: $1^2 + 2^2 + 3^2 + 4^2 + 5^2$, the sigma symbol may be used as a shortcut notation.

$$\sum_{k=1}^{5} k^2 = 1^2 + 2^2 + 3^2 + 4^2 + 5^2 = 1 + 4 + 9 + 16 + 25 = 55$$

As shown in the example, the number below Σ indicates the starting value of the variable. The number above Σ indicates the final value of the variable. Values for each k are added.

Using sigma notation, we may represent the summation of the rectangles used to find the area under a function. We label the width of each rectangle Δx. Remember Δ is the Greek letter "delta" and mathematically represents "the change in."

The area of the first, or leftmost, rectangle in the above figure is $\Delta x \bullet y_1 = \Delta x \bullet f(x_1)$ and the area of the second rectangle is $\Delta x \bullet f(x_2)$. Therefore, by using delta notation and sigma notation we may write an expression for the area under the function.

An equation for the area under the function split into eight equal width rectangles is given below. We know that $\Delta x = (4 - 2) / 8 = 0.25$ in the following expression for the above figure.

Total area of 8 equal width rectangles under function $f(x) = x^2$ is $\displaystyle\sum_{k=1}^{8} f(x_k) \Delta x$

We have seen that as the width of each rectangle decreases (or equivalently, the number of total rectangles increases), the area obtained by summing rectangles becomes closer to the actual area under the curve. Therefore by using limits, we may say that as the limit of $\Delta x \to 0$, the sum of the rectangle areas equals the area under the function.

Finally, we may write an official definition for the integral of any function, assuming we have a total of n rectangles. (Note that $n \to \infty$ as $\Delta x \to 0$.)

Definition of the Definite Integral

$$\int_a^b f(x)dx = \lim_{\Delta x \to 0} \sum_{k=1}^n f(x_k)\Delta x_k$$

As stated in chapter 22,

$$\lim_{\Delta x \to 0} \Delta x = dx$$

Therefore, the $\int$ symbol is very similar to the Σ symbol. The only difference is that the symbol Σ indicates the summation of a finite number. However, $\int$ is an indication of the addition of an infinite number. We may say that Σ is used for a summation of a **discrete** (or countable) number of items, but $\int$ is used to indicate a **continuous** function.

Finding the integral by summing rectangles under the integral is a valid method for numerically calculating the integral and is often implemented with computers. This method is often called the **endpoint approximation** of an integral.

Separating the area using trapezoids is another valid method and is called the **trapezoidal approximation**. Finally, the area may be separated into shapes that look like the rectangles we've used for our derivation. However, instead of the top of the rectangle being flat, the top is replaced with a curve of a certain second order polynomial (e.g. $ax^2 + bx + c$). Constants are chosen such that they fit the polynomial best. This method of integral calculation is known as **Simpson's Rule**.

However, it is rather annoying to always plot the function and count rectangles until the area is close enough. It is necessary to find a mathematical method of exactly calculating the integral of a function. As with finding the derivative, we need a shortcut to calculating integrals.

23-3   Finding the Integral from the Derivative

In section **22-4**, we found a shortcut to finding the derivative of a function by using the binomial theorem. It would be very helpful if we could find a similar shortcut for calculating integrals. Unfortunately, the definition of an integral as given above contains a summation. Furthermore, it looks as though there is no shortcut that we can take to simplify the formula for the summation. Therefore, we need to take a different approach. An informal derivation follows.

Let's look at one of the rectangles that was used in section **23-2** to determine the integral.

Δx

The height of the given rectangle is y, and the base of the rectangle is Δx. Remember that we have previously defined dx as shown.

$$\lim_{\Delta x \to 0} \Delta x = dx$$

We may say that the area of the above rectangle is $A = y \cdot \Delta x$. However, the rectangles used in the integral actually had a width of dx, since the limit of the width approached zero. Therefore, we may use the symbol dA to represent the incremental portion of area of a rectangle with height y and width dx.

$$dA = y \cdot dx$$

or, using $f(x)$ rather than y,

$$dA = f(x) \, dx$$

The value dx is simply a number that approaches zero. Using simple Algebra, we may divide both sides of the above equation by dx. Then, we write A as a function of x. (This is valid, as shown in section **22-2**, since the area of a rectangle is a function of the width.) These equations are given in the box below.

Relating Differentiation to Integration

By definition, the total Area (A) under the function $f(x)$ is

$$A = \int f(x) \, dx$$

and as shown above,

$$\frac{dA}{dx} = f(x) \quad \text{or} \quad \frac{d}{dx}[A(x)] = f(x)$$

Combining the equations, as shown with the arrow, gives the result.

$$\frac{d}{dx}\left[\int f(x) \, dx\right] = f(x)$$

This development seems hard to believe but it is true.

OBSERVATION

Integration is the inverse (or complementary) process of differentiation.

In the third chapter of the book we found addition and subtraction to be inverse operations. In the fourth chapter we found multiplication and division to be inverse operations. Later, we found exponentials and logarithms to be inverse functions. Now, in Calculus, we have determined that differentiation and integration are inverses. Imagine the excitement of Newton and Leibniz as they independently discovered this fact. If they could have seen 300 years into the future, Newton and Leibniz would have been astounded at the incredible products that have been built with the help of their discovery (e.g. radios, TV, phones, and computers).

23-4 Solving Integrals

Let's solve an indefinite integral using the inverse process of differentiation, or **anti-differentiation**.

$$\int 5\,dx = ?$$

The function $f(x) = 5$ is a horizontal line at $y = 5$. To solve the above integral, we must find a function whose derivative equals 5. Using our knowledge of differentiation, we determine that the derivative of $5x$ equals 5.

$$\frac{d}{dx}[5x] = 5$$

So the answer must be $5x$, right? Well, after thinking a bit, we realize that any constant added to $5x$ also has a derivative of 5. Two such functions are given below.

$$\frac{d}{dx}[5x + 1] = \frac{d}{dx}[5x + 2] = 5$$

The problem is that the integral is indefinite. How can we find the exact answer of the area under a function when we don't know the limits of integration (or the bounds of the area)? The area under any given function will vary by some constant, depending on the limits of integration.

Therefore, we may state the answer by using a general constant C. (The letter C is normally used to represent the unknown constant that is always required when calculating an indefinite integral.)

Answer: $5x + C$

Remember that the derivative is the slope of a line tangent to a function. An equation for a straight line is given below.

$$y = mx + b$$

The slope (and derivative) of the above line will always be *m*, regardless of the value of *b*. Therefore, the answer to any indefinite integral must have a (+ *C*) term to represent an unknown constant value.

However, if the integral is definite, there is no need for an unknown constant, since the integral (or area) of any function may be exactly found. To find the definite integral, we may use the following formula which is an extension of the formula derived for an indefinite integral.

The Definite Integral

Let $F(x)$ be a function whose derivative equals $f(x)$. Then,

$$\int_a^b f(x)dx = F(b) - F(a)$$

We return to the prior example, except make the calculation of a definite integral.

$$\int_1^5 5\,dx = ?$$

As before,

$$\frac{d}{dx}[5x] = 5$$

Therefore, $F(x) = 5x$ and

$$\int_1^5 5\,dx = F(5) - F(1) = 5(5) - 5(1) = 20$$

Answer: 20

Is this correct? Using the following plot and the proper formula from Geometry, we verify that the area does equal 20.

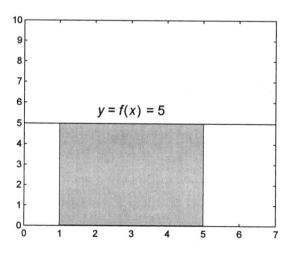

Using a single bracket, the question and answer may be written in an alternative mathematical notation.

$$\int_1^5 5\,dx = 5x\Big]_1^5 = 5(5) - 5(1) = 20$$

Example - Using the Definite Integral

Find the area under the function $f(x) = x^2$ between $x = 2$ and $x = 4$.

The problem may be rewritten.

$$\int_2^4 x^2\,dx$$

Using our knowledge of derivatives, we are able to find the answer,

$$\frac{d}{dx}\left[\frac{x^3}{3}\right] = x^2$$

$$\int_2^4 x^2\,dx = \frac{x^3}{3}\Bigg]_2^4 = \frac{4^3}{3} - \frac{2^3}{3} \approx 18.67$$

Answer: 18.67

Does this sound correct? Let's make a plot and use a single trapezoid to estimate the area. The darker shaded area indicates the amount of extra area measured by estimating the area with a single trapezoid. Therefore, the area of the trapezoid should be a slightly higher than 18.67.

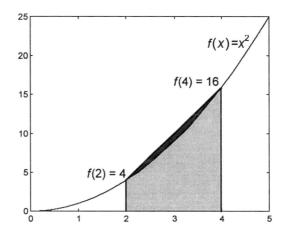

Area of trapezoid = 0.5(4 + 16) • 2 = 20 > 18.67

As you may guess, solving integrals of complicated functions can be quite difficult. Most Calculus texts present a set of techniques for solving integrals of different types of functions. However, even with these techniques, calculating integrals can be very challenging. There are basically three different methods to solving the integral of a function.

1.   Use known techniques from Calculus (i.e. Find the anti-derivative, if possible)

2.   Look up the answer in a table of integrals

3.   Calculate the integral using numerical analysis (with Geometry)

There are many books which consist of nothing but tables of integrals. Many of these integrals were found using math 'tricks', or techniques that are not straightforward. Some integrals are even impossible to solve without numerical analysis.

The goal of this book is not for you to become proficient at calculating integrals. Rather, the goal is for you to understand the definition of an integral, and how the definition was obtained. This information will allow you to concentrate on math techniques for solving integrals in the future.

Integrals are useful for many things. Following are just a few of the reasons for using integrals.

1.   Finding surface areas of shapes described by functions

2.   Finding volumes of shapes described by functions

3.   Solving equations containing derivatives, or equations that contain instantaneous rates of change

23-5   Summary of Integrals

This chapter has provided a very brief introduction to integrals. You should understand the definition of an integral, and the integral's relation to the derivative. The difference between definite and indefinite integrals should also be clear.

You should be able to ...

1.   Understand the definition of the integral

2.   Realize that integration is the inverse process of differentiation

3.   Find definite and indefinite integrals of certain functions using anti-differentiation

---

A Final Word on Mathematics

24-1   How Computers and Calculators Understand Math

From previous chapters, you may realize that many areas of mathematics take a considerable amount of thought to solve a problem. Furthermore, functions such as $\sin(x)$ or e^x are solved by humans using tables or calculators.   However, how does a calculator or computer solve a problem such as $\sin(x)$ for any angle x? Does every calculator have a huge table of the answers to special functions? How does the calculator know the difference between $\sin(30.0001°)$ and $\sin(30.0002°)$?

Functions and polynomials can often be written as summations, or as the sum of a series of numbers. This is possible by formulas developed hundreds of years ago by men such as Taylor, Maclaurin, and Lagrange. The series expansions are often known as either the Taylor or Maclaurin series, depending on the function.

The general formula and derivations are beyond the scope of this book. However, a few examples are given below. A calculator or computer actually uses the series form of the problem when finding a solution, since it can multiply and add very quickly. Therefore, the computer does not require memory to store tables. It only requires memory to store expansions for specific functions. A few expansions are given below.

$$e^x = \sum_{k=0}^{\infty} \frac{x^k}{k!} = 1 + x + \frac{x^2}{2!} + \frac{x^3}{3!} + \frac{x^4}{4!} + \dots$$

$$\cos(x) = \sum_{k=0}^{\infty} (-1)^k \frac{x^{2k}}{(2k)!} = 1 - \frac{x^2}{2!} + \frac{x^4}{4!} - \frac{x^6}{6!} + \dots$$

$$\ln(1+x) = \sum_{k=0}^{\infty} (-1)^k \frac{x^{k+1}}{k+1} = x - \frac{x^2}{2} + \frac{x^3}{3} - \frac{x^4}{4} + \dots \text{ (where } -1 < x \le 1)$$

Note that many of the summations have infinity as the upper limit, but a computer cannot add forever. Therefore, the computer adds a sufficient number of terms until the number is as accurate as the computer is able to store. Most calculators store approximately 8 or 16 decimal places of a number. Note that the magnitude of each term decreases as k becomes larger.

24-2   Continued Learning

As section **21-1** stated, there is much more math to learn. Only a brief introduction of Calculus has been provided. However, a thorough understanding of even introductory Calculus often requires two years of college study. At the conclusion of reading this text, you should be able to pick up any introductory Calculus text, and begin to understand it and work problems.

You know how to solve algebraic equations with variables. However, solving similar equations which contain derivatives is the study of the course differential equations. Differential equations are used extensively in most all scientific, engineering, and math disciplines.

Applied numerical analysis provides techniques for finding computer generated solutions to various math problems. Real world problems are often not as 'neat and orderly' as textbook problems, and therefore require numerical analysis.

Countless more courses could be described. It is impossible for anyone to know all areas thoroughly. However, it is your responsibility to choose an area to pursue, and then pursue it.

The seventh edition of the book *Advanced Engineering Mathematics* by Erwin Kreyszig is an excellent source for further study. As the title indicates, this book is advanced and rigorous. However, many techniques are discussed for solving mathematical problems commonly encountered in engineering and physics.

24-3   Now What?

First, you should understand all of the fundamentals presented in this text. Second, you should become proficient at solving all of the types of equations presented in the examples. This task alone will take much effort to accomplish. The material presented in this text explains and summarizes about 12 years of math education. However, do not despair. It is possible to obtain a thorough grasp of everything presented herein, and more.

If it is any word of encouragement, Richard Feynman, a renown scientist and Nobel Prize winner who passed away in 1988, first discovered the famous equation

$$e^{i\theta} = \cos\theta + i\sin\theta$$

for himself at the age of 15. Are you already scholastically ahead of the famous Mr. Feynman? (Although he did also have Trigonometry and Calculus mastered at this young age, and is commonly considered a genius.)

Math is a foundation. By understanding math, an entire world of information is open to you. After obtaining a firm grasp of mathematics, you may decide to pursue mathematics further, learn how to make useful products with engineering principles, or discover how the universe works using physics.

Trigonometric Identities

For any two angles Alpha (α) and Beta (β) the following relationships are true.

Angle Sum Relations

$$\sin(\alpha + \beta) = \sin\alpha \cos\beta + \cos\alpha \sin\beta$$

$$\sin(\alpha - \beta) = \sin\alpha \cos\beta - \cos\alpha \sin\beta$$

$$\cos(\alpha + \beta) = \cos\alpha \cos\beta - \sin\alpha \sin\beta$$

$$\cos(\alpha - \beta) = \cos\alpha \cos\beta + \sin\alpha \sin\beta$$

Function Sum and Function Difference Relations

$$\sin\alpha + \sin\beta = 2\sin\left(\frac{\alpha+\beta}{2}\right)\cos\left(\frac{\alpha+\beta}{2}\right)$$

$$\sin\alpha - \sin\beta = 2\cos\left(\frac{\alpha+\beta}{2}\right)\sin\left(\frac{\alpha-\beta}{2}\right)$$

$$\cos\alpha + \cos\beta = 2\cos\left(\frac{\alpha+\beta}{2}\right)\cos\left(\frac{\alpha-\beta}{2}\right)$$

$$\cos\alpha - \cos\beta = -2\sin\left(\frac{\alpha+\beta}{2}\right)\sin\left(\frac{\alpha-\beta}{2}\right)$$

Function Product Relations

$$2 \sin \alpha \sin \beta = \cos (\alpha - \beta) - \cos (\alpha + \beta)$$

$$2 \cos \alpha \cos \beta = \cos (\alpha - \beta) + \cos (\alpha + \beta)$$

$$2 \sin \alpha \cos \beta = \sin (\alpha - \beta) + \sin (\alpha + \beta)$$

Double-Angle Relations

$$\sin 2\alpha = 2 \sin \alpha \cos \alpha$$

$$\cos 2\alpha = 2 \cos^2 \alpha - 1$$

Power Relations

$$\cos^2 \alpha = \frac{1}{2} + \frac{1}{2} \cos 2\alpha$$

$$\sin^2 \alpha = \frac{1}{2} - \frac{1}{2} \cos 2\alpha$$

Pythagorean Relation

$$\cos^2 \alpha + \sin^2 \alpha = 1$$

Euler's Relations
(α in radians)

$$\sin \alpha = \frac{e^{i\alpha} - e^{-i\alpha}}{2i}$$

$$\cos \alpha = \frac{e^{i\alpha} + e^{-i\alpha}}{2}$$

Table of Trigonometric Functions

Angle θ (Deg)	COS θ	SIN θ	TAN θ
0	1.00000	.0000	.0000
1	.9998	.0175	.0175
2	.9994	.0349	.0349
3	.9986	.0523	.0524
4	.9976	.0698	.0699
5	.9962	.0872	.0875
6	.9945	.1045	.1051
7	.9925	.1219	.1228
8	.9903	.1392	.1405
9	.9877	.1564	.1584
10	.9848	.1736	.1763
11	.9816	.1908	.1944
12	.9781	.2079	.2126
13	.9744	.2250	.2309
14	.9703	.2419	.2493
15	.9659	.2588	.2679
16	.9613	.2756	.2867
17	.9563	.2924	.3057
18	.9511	.3090	.3249
19	.9455	.3256	.3443
20	.9397	.3420	.3640
21	.9336	.3584	.3839
22	.9272	.3746	.4040
23	.9205	.3907	.4245
24	.9135	.4067	.4452
25	.9063	.4226	.4663
26	.8988	.4384	.4877
27	.8910	.4540	.5095
28	.8829	.4695	.5317
29	.8746	.4848	.5543
30	.8660	.5000	.5774

Angle θ (Deg)	COS θ	SIN θ	TAN θ
31	.8572	.5150	.6009
32	.8480	.5299	.6249
33	.8387	.5446	.6494
34	.8290	.5592	.6745
35	.8192	.5736	.7002
36	.8090	.5878	.7265
37	.7986	.6018	.7536
38	.7880	.6157	.7813
39	.7771	.6293	.8098
40	.7660	.6428	.8391
41	.7547	.6561	.8693
42	.7431	.6691	.9004
43	.7314	.6820	.9325
44	.7193	.6947	.9657
45	.7071	.7071	1.0000
46	.6947	.7193	1.0355
47	.6820	.7314	1.0724
48	.6691	.7431	1.1106
49	.6561	.7547	1.1504
50	.6428	.7660	1.1918
51	.6293	.7771	1.2349
52	.6157	.7880	1.2799
53	.6018	.7986	1.3270
54	.5878	.8090	1.3764
55	.5736	.8192	1.4281
56	.5592	.8290	1.4826
57	.5446	.8387	1.5399
58	.5299	.8480	1.6003
59	.5150	.8572	1.6643
60	.5000	.8660	1.7321
61	.4848	.8746	1.8040
62	.4695	.8829	1.8807
63	.4540	.8910	1.9626
64	.4384	.8988	2.0503
65	.4226	.9063	2.1445
66	.4067	.9135	2.2460
67	.3907	.9205	2.3559
68	.3746	.9272	2.4751
69	.3584	.9336	2.6051
70	.3420	.9397	2.7475
71	.3256	.9455	2.9042
72	.3090	.9511	3.0777
73	.2924	.9563	3.2709
74	.2756	.9613	3.4874
75	.2588	.9659	3.7321

Angle θ (Deg)	COS θ	SIN θ	TAN θ
76	.2419	.9703	4.0108
77	.2250	.9744	4.3315
78	.2079	.9781	4.7046
79	.1908	.9816	5.1446
80	.1736	.9848	5.6713
81	.1564	.9877	6.3138
82	.1392	.9903	7.1154
83	.1219	.9925	8.1443
84	.1045	.9945	9.5144
85	.0872	.9962	11.4301
86	.0698	.9976	14.3007
87	.0523	.9986	19.0811
88	.0349	.9994	28.6363
89	.0175	.9998	57.2900
90	0.00000	1.00000	∞

Relationships Between Other Trigonometric Functions

$$\text{secant } \theta = \frac{1}{\cos \theta} \qquad \text{cosecant } \theta = \frac{1}{\sin \theta} \qquad \text{cotangent } \theta = \frac{1}{\tan \theta}$$

90° < θ ≤ 180°

$$\cos \theta = -\cos(180 - \theta) \qquad \sin \theta = \sin(180 - \theta) \qquad \tan \theta = -\tan(180 - \theta)$$

180° < θ ≤ 270°

$$\cos \theta = -\cos(270 - \theta) \qquad \sin \theta = -\sin(270 - \theta) \qquad \tan \theta = \tan(270 - \theta)$$

270° < θ ≤ 360°

$$\cos \theta = \cos(360 - \theta) \qquad \sin \theta = -\sin(360 - \theta) \qquad \tan \theta = -\tan(360 - \theta)$$

θ > 360°

$$\cos \theta = \cos(\theta - 360) \qquad \sin \theta = \sin(\theta - 360) \qquad \tan \theta = \tan(\theta - 360)$$

INDEX

Abscissa *208*
Absolute Value *22*
  Complex Numbers *284*
  Removing in Algebraic Expressions *169*
Acute Angle *228*
Acute Triangle *232*
Addition *15*
  Complex Numbers *282, 292*
  Decimals *28*
  Fractions *90*
  Matrices *182*
  Multi-Digit Integers *24*
  Negative Numbers *110*
  Percentages *101*
  Single-Digit Integers *15*
Adjacent Angles *228*
Algebraic Equation *134*
Algebraic Expression *134*
Altitude *234*
Angle
  Acute *228*
  Adjacent *228*
  Bisected *230*
  Complementary *229*
  Corresponding *230*
  Exterior *230*
  Interior *230*
  Obtuse *228*
  Supplementary *229*
Anti-Differentiation *325*
Anti-Logarithm *267*
Arc *254*
Area
  Circle *244*
  Rectangle *241*
  Parallelogram *242*
  Triangle *242*
Argument (of a Function) *203*
Arithmetic Equation *134*
Arithmetic Expression *134*
Associative Law
  of Addition *19*
  of Multiplication *39*
Augmented Matrix *180*
Average *107*
Axioms (of Multiplication) *37*

Base (of exponents) *116*
Base (of triangle) *242*
Binomial Theorem *308*
Binomial *142*
Bisector *230*
Borrow (for Subtraction) *30*

Calculators (uses of) *48, 129*
Cancellation *78*
Carot *117*
Carry (for Addition) *25*
Cartesian Coordinate System *208*
Center of Circle *238*
Chain Rule *311*
Chord *238*
Circle *238*
  Area *244*
  Circumference *244*
  Equation of *261*
Circumscribed *245*
Coefficient Matrix *180*
Coefficient *135*
Cofactor *187*
Cofactor Expansion *188*
Common Logarithm *268*
Commutative Law
  of Addition *16*
  of Multiplication *37*
Complementary Angles *229*
Completing the Square *158*
Complex Conjugate *282*
Complex Number *281*
Complex Plane *283*
Concentric Circle *238*
Congruent *233*
Constant *141*
Cosecant *251*
Cosine *251*
Cosines
  Law of *257*
Consistent System *172*
Counting *11*
Counting Numbers *7*
Cramer's Rule *189*
Cube *245*

Cubed Number   *117*
Cubed roots   *127*
Cylinder
   Surface Area   *246*
   Volume   *247*

Decibel   *270*
Decimal Point   *9*
Decimal System   *7*
Decimal   *9*
Degree (of angle)   *227*
Degree (of Polynomial)   *143*
Delta   *212*
Denominator   *72*
   Lowest Common Denominator (LCD)   *85*
Dependent Equations   *173*
Dependent Variable   *202*
Derivative   *297*
Derive   *19*
Determinant   *186*
Diameter   *238*
Differentiation   *297*
Digit   *7*
   Least Significant   *9*
   Most Significant   *9*
Dimension   *221, 245*
Discrete   *323*
Distributive Law of Multiplication   *39-41*
Dividend   *50*
Division   *49*
   Decimals   *66*
   Fractions   *97*
   Multi-Digit Integers   *52*
   Negative Numbers   *112*
   Percentages   *101*
   Synthetic   *163*
   with Remainders   *58*
Divisor   *50*

E, the number *e*   *271*
Element (of a Matrix)   *180*
Elimination Method   *177*
Ellipsis   *6*
Endpoint Approximation   *323*
Equal   *6, 13*
Equation   *134*
   Linear   *143*
   Quadratic   *143*
Equiangular   *235*
Equilateral   *231*
Euler's Identity   *290*
Even Number   *80*
Exponential Notation   *130*
Exponent   *116*
   Dividing with   *124*
   Fractional   *125*
   Multiplying with   *118*
   Negative   *121*
Expression   *134*

Factor   *77*
Factorial   *307*
Factoring
   Higher Order Polynomials   *161*
   Numbers   *77*
   Quadratics   *150*
Factorization Tree   *81*
Feynman, Richard   *3, 287, 330*
FOIL   *152*
Formula   *134*
Fractional Exponents   *125*
Fractions   *72*
   Adding   *90*
   Converting to Decimals   *74*
   Dividing   *96*
   Improper   *74*
   Multiplying   *76*
   Proper   *74*
   Reading   *73*
   Simplifying   *77*
   Subtracting   *90*
Function   *201*
   Inverse   *204*
Functional Notation   *201*

Gates, Bill   *3*
Geometry   *225*
   Plane / Solid   *245*
Graph   *207*
   Higher Order Polynomials   *220*
   Plotting Linear Equations   *210*
   Plotting Points   *208*
   Plotting Quadratic Equations   *218*
Greater   *6*
Greater than   *13*

Height (of triangles)   *234*
Highest Priority   *139*
Hippasus of Metapontum   *129*
Horizontal Line   *214*
Hypotenuse   *231*

Imaginary Axis   *283*
Imaginary Number   *278*
Improper Fractions   *74*
Inconsistent System   *172, 179, 217*
Independent Equation   *173*
Independent Variable   *202*
Infinity   *7*
Inscribed   *245*
Integer   *7*
Integral   *297*
Iteration   *318*
Intersection   *226*
Inverse Function   *204, 254*
Inverse Operation   *23*
Irrational Number   *128*
Isolating the Variable   *144*
Isosceles Triangle   *231*

L'Hopital's Rule *312*
Law
  of Cosines *257*
  of Exponents *119*
  of Sines *257*
Least Common Multiple (LCM) *87*
Least Significant Digit *9*
Legs of a Right Triangle *231*
Legs of a Trapezoid *237*
Leibniz, Gottfried *296*
Length *226*
Less *6*
Less than *13*
Like term *135*
Limit *302*
Limits of Integration *297*
Linear Equation *143*
Line *226*
  Slope of *211*
ln x *271*
Logarithm *264*
  Anti *267*
  Common *268*
  Natural *271*
Long Division *52*
Lowest Common Denominator (LCD) *85*

Maclurin Series *329*
Magnitude *22*
  Complex Number *284*
  Real Number *22*
Mathematics *5*
Matrix *180*
Maxima *313*
Mean *107*
Median *107*
Midpoint *226*
Minima *313*
Minor *187*
Mixed Number *74*
Mode *107*
Monomial *142*
Most Significant Digit *9*
Multinomial *142*
Multiplication *34*
  Decimals *63*
  Fractions *76*
  Matrices *182*
  Multi-Digit Integers *42*
  Negative Numbers *112*
  Percentages *101*
  Signed Numbers *112*
Multiplication table *36*

Natural Logarithm, *e* *271*
Negative Exponents *121*
Negative Numbers *7, 109*
Newton, Isaac *296*
Newton's Method *317*
No slope *215*

Number *5*
  Complex *281*
  Decimal *9*
  Even *80*
  Imaginary *278*
  Line *6*
  Mixed *74*
  Negative *7, 109*
  Odd *80*
  Positive *7*
  Prime *80*
  Real *7*
  Signed *109*
  Whole *7*
Numerator *72*
Numerical Analysis *161*
Numerical Place *8*

Oblique Triangle *257*
Obtuse Angle *228*
Obtuse Triangle *231*
Odd Number *80*
Operator *15*
  Multiplication *35*
  Division *49*
Optimization *315*
Order *143*
Order of Operations *136*
Ordered Pair *208*
Ordinate *208*
Origin *209*

Parallel Line *214, 217*
Parallelogram *237*
Parts (of a Triangle) *233*
Percentage *100*
Perfect square *158*
Perimeter *241*
Perpendicular lines *228*
Pi *243*
Place (Numerical) *8*
Placeholder *28*
Plane geometry *245*
Plotting
  High Order Polynomials *220*
  Linear Equations *210*
  Systems of Equations *216*
Point Slope Form *213*
Polar Form *285, 292*
Polygons *237*
Polynomial *142*
Positive Numbers *7*
Postulate *225*
Power *117*
Power Rule *308*
Prime factorization *81*
Prime Numbers *81*
Product *34*
Product Rule *309*
Proper Fractions *74*
Pythagorean Theorem *240*

Quadrant   *209*
Quadratic Equation   *143*
Quadratic Formula   *158*
Quadrilateral   *237*
Quantity   *137*
Quotient   *50*
Quotient Rule   *309*

Radian   *261*
Radical   *127*
Radius   *238*
Ratio   *74*
Rational Number   *62*
Ray   *226*
Reading
   Decimals   *10*
   Fractions   *73*
   Integers   *9*
Real Axis   *283*
Real Number   *12, 278*
Reciprocal   *95, 121*
Rectangle   *237*
   Area   *241*
Rectangular Form   *292*
Reduced Row-echelon Form   *183*
Reflexive Property   *225*
Remainder   *59*
Rhombus   *237*
Right Angle   *228*
Rise   *212*
Root   *126, 161*
Round   *70*
Row-echelon form   *183*
Run   *212*

Scalene triangle   *231*
Scientific Notation   *131*
Secant   *251*
Segment (line)   *226*
Sides (of an angle)   *227*
Sigma   *322*
Signed Numbers   *109*
Similar Triangles   *235*
Simpson's Rule   *323*
Simultaneous Equations   *172*
Sine   *251*
  Law of   *257*
Slope   *211*
   Negative   *212*
   Positive   *212*
Slope-Intercept Form   *213*
Solid Geometry   *245*
Sphere   *247*
Square Matrix   *180*
Square Root   *126*
Squared   *117*
Straight Angle   *228*
Substitution of Equations   *174*

Subtraction   *20*
   Decimals   *32*
   Fractions   *90*
   Imaginary Numbers   *280*
   Multi-Digit Integers   *29*
   Percentages   *101*
Summation   *322*
Supplementary Angles   *229*
Surface Area   *246*
Symbols (common math)   *13*
Symmetric Property   *225*
Synthetic Division   *163*
System of Equations   *172*

Tangent (function)   *251*
Tangent (line)   *238*
Taxes   *102*
Taylor Series   *329*
Term   *135*
Theorem   *225*
Times Table   *36*
Transcendental Number   *271*
Transitive Property   *225*
Transversal   *230*
Trapezoid   *237*
Trapezoidal Approximation   *323*
Triangle (types of)   *231*
Trigonometric Functions   *251*
Trigonometry   *249*
Trinomial   *142*
Truncate   *70*
Turn   *219*

Variables   *17*
   Dependent   *202*
   Independent   *202*
Vertex   *227*
Volume   *245*
   Cylinder   *247*
   Sphere   *247*

Whole Numbers   *7*
Word Problem   *192*

X-axis   *208*
x-intercept   *211*

Y-axis   *208*
y-intercept   *211*

Zero
   Exponent   *123*
   Slope   *214*

NOTES